The Open University

M249 P

Book 3

Multivariate analysis

About this course

M249 Practical Modern Statistics uses the software packages *SPSS for Windows* (SPSS Inc.) and *WinBUGS*, and other software. This software is provided as part of the course, and its use is covered in the *Introduction to statistical modelling* and in the four computer books associated with *Books 1* to *4*.

Cover image courtesy of NASA. This photograph, acquired by the ASTER instrument on NASA's Terra satellite, shows an aerial view of a large alluvial fan between the Kunlun and Altun mountains in China's Xinjiang province. For more information, see NASA's Earth Observatory website at http://earthobservatory.nasa.gov.

This publication forms part of an Open University course. Details of this and other Open University courses can be obtained from the Student Registration and Enquiry Service, The Open University, PO Box 197, Milton Keynes, MK7 6BJ, United Kingdom: tel. +44 (0)870 300 6090, e-mail general-enquiries@open.ac.uk

Alternatively, you may visit the Open University website at http://www.open.ac.uk where you can learn more about the wide range of courses and packs offered at all levels by The Open University.

To purchase a selection of Open University course materials, visit http://www.ouw.co.uk, or contact Open University Worldwide, Michael Young Building, Walton Hall, Milton Keynes, MK7 6AA, United Kingdom, for a brochure: tel. +44 (0)1908 858793, fax +44 (0)1908 858787, e-mail ouw-customer-services@open.ac.uk

The Open University, Walton Hall, Milton Keynes, MK7 6AA.

First published 2007.

Edited, designed and typeset by The Open University, using the Open University TEX System.

Printed and bound in the United Kingdom by Charlesworth Press, Wakefield.

ISBN 978 0 7492 1368 8

1.1

Contents

Study guide

You should schedule fifteen study sessions for this book. This includes time for working through *Computer Book 3*, answering the TMA questions and consolidating your work on this book. You should schedule four study sessions for Part I, five for Part II and six for Part III.

The sections vary in length. In Part I, Sections 1 and 4 are both shorter than average. In Part II, Sections 6 and 7 are both a little longer than average. In Part III, Section 10 is longer than average, and Sections 11 and 12 are a little shorter than average.

As you study this book, you will be asked to work through the six chapters of *Computer Book 3*. We recommend that you work through them at the points indicated in the text — Chapters 1 and 2 in Section 5, Chapters 3 and 4 in Section 9, and Chapters 5 and 6 in Section 14.

One possible study pattern is as follows.

Part I

Study session 1: Sections 1 and 2.
Study session 2: Sections 3 and 4.
Study session 3: Section 5. You will need access to your computer for this session, together with *Computer Book 3*.
Study session 4: TMA questions on Part I.

Part II

Study session 5: Section 6.
Study session 6: Section 7.
Study session 7: Section 8.
Study session 8: Section 9. You will need access to your computer for this session, together with *Computer Book 3*.
Study session 9: TMA questions on Part II.

Part III

Study session 10: Section 10.
Study session 11: Section 11.
Study session 12: Section 12.
Study session 13: Section 13.
Study session 14: Section 14. You will need access to your computer for this session, together with *Computer Book 3*.
Study session 15: TMA questions on Part III and consolidation of your work on this book.

If you follow this study pattern, then Study sessions 1 and 2 may be long ones.

Introduction

This book focuses on the analysis of data sets that contain two or more variables. At first sight, it might seem strange that the analysis of such data, which are called **multivariate data**, merits its own range of statistical techniques. However, as you will see, the mere presence of multiple variables brings its own particular difficulties. Seemingly straightforward tasks such as displaying data graphically in an appropriate way can sometimes be surprisingly difficult, particularly if the number of variables in the data set is not small.

Multivariate data arise in all areas of statistics. For example, the evaluation of quality of life after medical or surgical treatment requires measurements on several different variables. In social statistics, deprivation is best described by a range of economic and social indicators. In climate science, measurements of temperature, pressure and precipitation, from different areas and at different times, may be required for forecasting purposes. Multivariate statistics is not a new branch of statistics, having been used routinely for many decades in disciplines such as psychology and archaeology. However, more recently the need for novel multivariate analysis methods has arisen, in diverse areas such as pattern recognition and bioinformatics, as well as in more mundane applications such as the processing of data from supermarket loyalty cards. Thus multivariate analysis is an important part of modern applied statistics.

Graphical displays are often used to represent data, describe their key features, and suggest methods of analysis. However, visualizing and summarizing several variables at the same time, and in a useful way, is not an easy task. Visualization methods are thus an important aspect of multivariate analysis. In Part I, the focus is on summarizing multivariate data graphically and numerically. Basic techniques that are used with a single variable are extended to handle two or more variables. These techniques will enable you to get a feel for relationships between variables. The techniques also assist in the identification of points that do not follow the general pattern.

Dimension reduction is the subject of Part II — that is, transforming data in such a way that fewer variables need to be considered. An important technique called principal component analysis is described. The aim is to replace a multivariate data set with many variables by one with fewer variables, without losing too much information. The smaller data set will be easier to handle and to visualize than the larger one.

In Part III, methods for allocating observations to groups on the basis of the values of two or more variables are discussed. A technique called discrimination, which is used when the group membership is known for some observations, is described.

Part I Describing and displaying multivariate data

Introduction to Part I

In Part I, techniques for describing and displaying multivariate data are introduced. These techniques are used frequently in the initial analysis of a data set. The aim is to describe the location, the spread and the shape of the data. Using graphical techniques, observations, or even groups of observations, that follow a different pattern from the rest of the data can also be identified.

In Section 1, some examples that illustrate some of the contexts in which multivariate data arise are discussed. Methods for plotting multivariate data are described in Section 2. Numerical summaries of multivariate data are introduced in Section 3: the **mean vector** and the **covariance matrix** are defined.

In Section 4, a transformation that is often applied to multivariate data is described. This transformation, which is known as **standardization**, ensures that the analysis does not depend on the units in which the variables are measured. The **correlation matrix** is also discussed; this provides a way of describing the degree of association between the variables in a data set.

Many of the techniques of multivariate analysis are at best tedious, and often impossible, to do by hand. In Section 5, you will use SPSS to implement many of the techniques discussed in Sections 1 to 4.

1 Multivariate data

Multivariate data are data comprising two or more variables. Some examples which illustrate why it may be necessary to use multivariate data are given in Subsection 1.1. You will see that by considering a single variable, some interesting questions can be answered, but that other important questions can be answered only by considering two or more variables together — that is, by **multivariate analysis**.

In Subsection 1.2, some of the notation that is used with multivariate data, and some of the terminology used to describe them, are introduced.

1.1 Going beyond the one-dimensional world

Sometimes all that is required is to summarize data appropriately. For a small data set, this can be done by simply looking at numbers in a table, as Example 1.1 illustrates.

Example 1.1 *House affordability*

In a study of house affordability, researchers gathered data on the ratio of house price to household income. In order to focus on the affordability of houses for first-time buyers, the house price was taken to be the average price for a four-room or five-room dwelling between October and December 2002. The household income was taken to be the average income in 2002 for working households where one member was aged between 20 and 39 inclusive. Data for the nine regions of England are in Table 1.1.

Wilcox, S. (2003) *Can work — can't buy.* Joseph Rowntree Foundation, York.

Table 1.1 Ratio of house price to household income in nine English regions

Region	Ratio of house price to household income
London	4.79
South East	3.96
South West	4.20
Eastern	3.70
West Midlands	2.96
East Midlands	3.02
North East	2.27
North West	2.42
Yorkshire & Humber	2.41

Table 1.1 shows that the median ratio is 3.02, and that the ratios tend to be higher in the southern regions of England. Therefore houses are less affordable in the southern regions than in the northern regions. London and the South West have particularly high ratios. ♦

Example 1.2 *House price and household income*

From the data in Table 1.1, it is not possible to say whether houses are more affordable in some regions because house prices are low in those regions or because incomes are high. A better insight into affordability can be obtained by looking at house prices, at household income and at the relationship between them — that is, by considering the two variables jointly.

Table 1.2 contains the average house price and average household income (in thousands of pounds) for each of the nine English regions.

Table 1.2 House price and household income (in thousands of pounds) in nine English regions

Region	House price	Household income
London	221.537	46.288
South East	152.555	38.478
South West	124.508	29.626
Eastern	125.154	33.819
West Midlands	94.402	31.857
East Midlands	88.724	29.350
North East	62.089	27.405
North West	69.372	28.625
Yorkshire & Humber	66.958	27.832

Notice that the highest average house price is more than three times the lowest. The average household incomes seems to be slightly less variable, since the highest average household income is less than twice the lowest. A scatterplot of the data is shown in Figure 1.1.

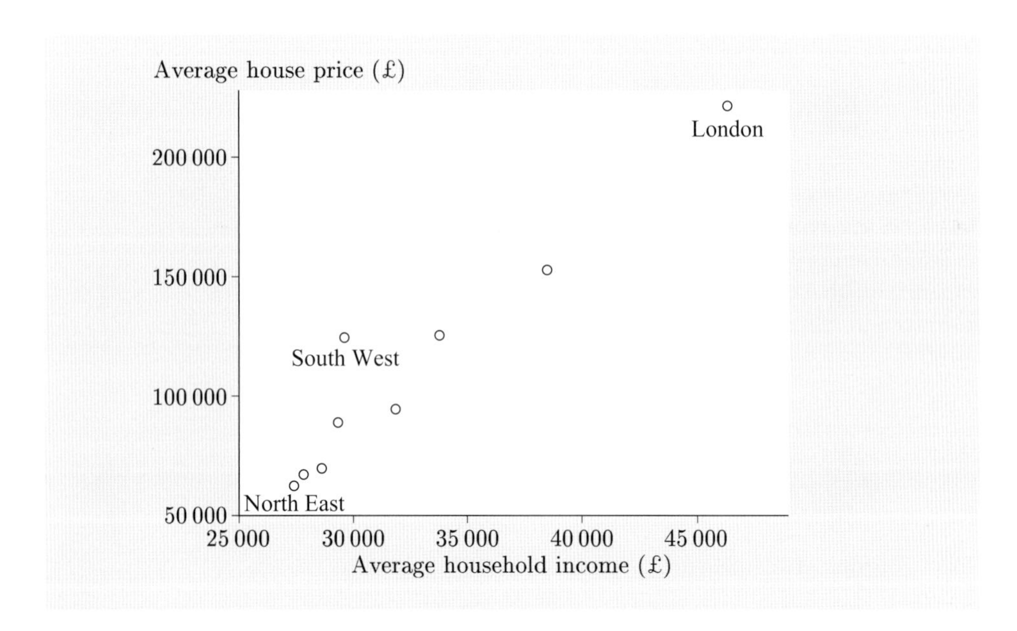

Figure 1.1 Scatterplot of average house price and average household income

From Figure 1.1 it is clear that the average household income and the average house price are higher in London than in the other regions. In contrast, the average household income and the average house price are lowest in the North East. There appears to be a strong positive linear relationship between the average household income and the average house price. Thus regions where household incomes are high tend to be those where house prices are high. However, there is one region, the South West, which does not fit this linear pattern. In this region, the average house price appears to be unusually high given the average household income. ♦

In Example 1.2, the dependence of both average house price and average household income on region was of interest. In Example 1.1, one variable, the ratio of average house price to average household income, was used in place of the two variables. Sometimes a single variable is used in place of three or more variables; this is illustrated in Example 1.3.

Example 1.3 Performance of local education authorities

On 4 December 2003, *The Times* published a primary school 'performance chart' for 150 English local education authorities (LEAs). The LEAs were ranked on the basis of a single total score which reflected the standards reached by eleven-year-old primary school students in the subject areas of English, Mathematics and Science. This enabled comparison of LEAs based on the performance of the primary schools in their areas.

The maximum possible total score for an LEA was 300. This score would be achieved if all the eleven-year-old primary school students in the LEA's area reached a particular standard in English, Mathematics and Science. The lowest possible total score, 0, would be achieved if none of the eleven-year-old primary school students reached this standard in any of these subjects. A histogram of the total scores achieved by the LEAs is shown in Figure 1.2.

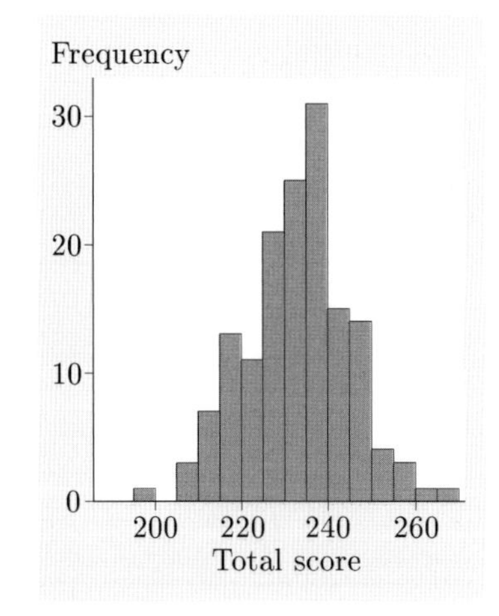

Figure 1.2 Histogram of total scores for English LEAs

This histogram shows that most LEAs scored between 210 and 250. The distribution of the scores is roughly symmetrical, with scores between 230 and 240 being the most common. Two LEAs had particularly high scores of more than 260. However, one LEA had a total score much lower than that achieved by any of the others. This indicates that the standard reached by eleven-year-old primary school students in that LEA area was noticeably worse than that reached by eleven-year-old primary school students elsewhere.

In fact, the total score is the sum of three separate scores: the percentages of eleven-year-old primary school students achieving at least level 4 standard (the level deemed essential to be successful at secondary school) in standardized tests of English, Mathematics and Science. Without consideration of these three separate scores jointly, important issues cannot be addressed. For example, to what extent is the relative performance of LEAs comparable across the three subjects? Is an LEA's poor performance in one subject masked by good performance in the other two subjects?

Table 1.3 gives the scores in English, Mathematics and Science for the ten LEAs with the highest total scores.

Table 1.3 English, Mathematics and Science scores for the top ten local education authorities

LEA	English	Mathematics	Science
City of London	96.6	79.3	93.1
Richmond upon Thames	86.9	82.5	94.0
Wokingham	84.9	81.2	91.8
Rutland	82.7	81.8	92.5
Kensington and Chelsea	84.2	78.8	92.4
Windsor and Maidenhead	82.5	79.0	91.7
Bracknell Forest	82.4	77.5	92.5
Bromley	83.4	78.2	90.5
Surrey	81.6	77.9	91.5
Havering	80.5	78.0	90.1

In this subset of the data, the performance was generally better in Science than in English or Mathematics. However, this was not the case for all these LEAs. For example, for the City of London LEA, the performance in English was particularly good compared to Science and Mathematics. This difference is hidden if only the total score is considered. ♦

Activity 1.1 Reactions to immunization

In a study investigating reactions to immunizations, 42 young adults were given a combined injection of diphtheria and typhoid toxoids. Four weeks later, the level of antibodies that each adult had to each of these toxoids was recorded.

One way of combining the two antibody measurements into a single combined score was given by Ipsen in a paper published in 1957. This score is a weighted sum of the two antibody measurements in which a greater weight is given to the tetanus antibody level.

Ipsen, J. (1957) Appropriate scores for reaction categories dependent on two variables. *Biometrics*, **13**, 177–182.

A histogram of the combined scores for the 42 adults is shown in Figure 1.3.

(a) Identify the two variables recorded in this study.

(b) Use the histogram in Figure 1.3 to describe the distribution of combined antibody scores.

(c) Why does the histogram in Figure 1.3 not necessarily reflect the distribution of levels of antibodies to tetanus?

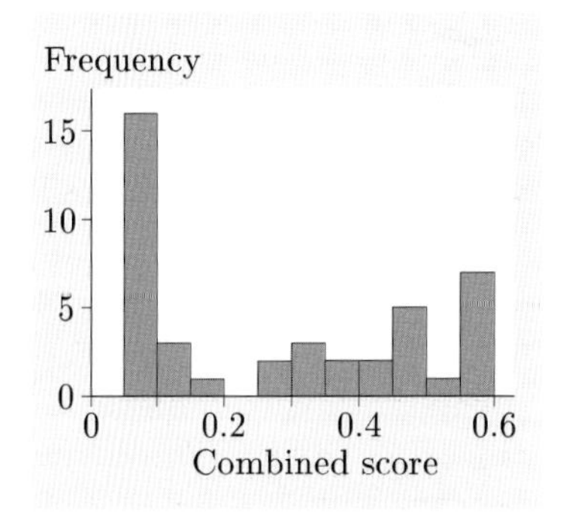

Figure 1.3 Histogram of combined antibody scores

In Example 1.3, the three subject scores were added together to produce a single variable. And in Activity 1.1, two antibody levels were combined using a weighted average to produce a single combined score. However, it is often not clear how to combine several variables into a single variable for analysis. This is illustrated in Example 1.4.

Example 1.4 Uptake of trace chemical elements

Scientists interested in the uptake of trace chemical elements by the plant *Echinacea purpurea* grew some specimens in controlled conditions. They took samples from different parts of the plants, some plants being harvested in the summer and some in the autumn. They then measured the amounts of nine chemical elements that were present in each of these samples. These elements were copper (Cu), iron (Fe), manganese (Mn), zinc (Zn), nickel (Ni), lithium (Li), strontium (Sr), magnesium (Mg) and calcium (Ca).

Razić, S., Onjia, A. and Potkonjak, B. (2003) Trace elements analysis of *Echinacea purpurea* — herbal medicinal. *Journal of Pharmaceutical and Biomedical Analysis*, **33**, 845–850.

Table 1.4 gives the concentrations of these chemicals measured in parts of autumn-harvested *Echinacea purpurea* plants.

Table 1.4 Concentrations of trace chemical elements found in different parts of autumn-harvested *Echinacea purpurea* plants

Plant part	Cu (μg/g)	Fe (μg/g)	Mn (μg/g)	Zn (μg/g)	Ni (μg/g)	Li (μg/g)	Sr (μg/g)	Mg (mg/g)	Ca (mg/g)
Root	11.5	170	13.1	4.5	0.5	2.8	7.6	3.24	4.97
Stem	9.4	101	18.9	6.4	3.7	0.9	4.4	3.39	8.98
Leaf	11.8	292	67.6	12.7	5.1	3.2	10.7	8.38	29.30
Flower	15.9	184	29.9	18.6	9.3	2.3	4.4	3.49	14.60
Herbs	10.2	220	42.0	12.6	4.3	2.8	6.8	6.30	23.50

Variation in the concentration of the trace elements in different parts of the plant is of interest because it provides information about the role the elements play in the health of the plant. Is the distribution of these elements the same in all parts of the plant? If not, are particular groupings of elements associated with particular parts of the plant? And do the concentrations of the chemical elements in the plants harvested in the summer differ from those found in plants harvested in the autumn? Note that the main interest is in comparing different parts of the plant and different harvesting times, rather than in comparing concentrations of different elements.

It is not at all clear that the variables (the concentrations) can usefully be combined into a single variable which could then be used to investigate some of the questions of interest. Methods for combining variables given data like these are described in Part II. ♦

1.2 What is a multivariate data set?

Examples of multivariate data sets are given in Tables 1.2, 1.3 and 1.4. What are the key features of these data sets?

First, and perhaps most obviously, multivariate data sets comprise observations on two or more random variables. When the data set has just two variables it is sometimes referred to as a **bivariate** data set. There is no upper limit to the number of variables a multivariate data set might have. In Table 1.4, there are nine variables. You may think this is quite a lot to deal with. However, some multivariate data sets consist of hundreds, thousands or even millions of variables!

A data set with only one variable is called **univariate**.

The **dimension** p of a multivariate data set is the number of variables in the data set. A high-dimensional data set has many variables; a low-dimensional data set has relatively few variables. In Table 1.2 there are two variables — average house price and average household income. The data set is therefore a two-dimensional, or bivariate, data set: $p = 2$. Three variables are listed in Table 1.3 — the scores for English LEAs in English, Mathematics and Science. So these data on LEA performance form a three-dimensional data set: $p = 3$. Similarly, the dimension of the data set in Table 1.4 is 9 ($p = 9$): each of the nine variables corresponds to a different trace chemical element measured in the *Echinacea purpurea* plants. Thus the house affordability and LEA performance data sets in Tables 1.2 and 1.3 are low-dimensional, whereas the *Echinacea purpurea* data set in Table 1.4 is relatively high-dimensional.

In a multivariate data set of p dimensions, the p measurements made on each sampled unit are referred to together as an **observation** on that unit. Thus each observation consists of p values, one value for each variable measured. For example, for the housing affordability data set in Table 1.2, each observation corresponds to an English region and has two values, the average house price and the average household income in that region. Similarly, for the LEA performance data in Table 1.3, each observation corresponds to an LEA and has three values — the scores for English, Mathematics and Science. For the data on *Echinacea purpurea* plants in Table 1.4, each observation corresponds to a part of the plant and has nine values associated with it, one for each chemical element measured.

Usually a single letter is used to denote all the variables, with the jth variable indexed by the subscript j. In Example 1.1, there are two variables: house price and household income. A sensible notation for the variables is X_1 to denote house price and X_2 to denote household income. The notation x_{ij} is used to denote the value of the variable X_j for observation i. The entire data set is normally given in the form of a matrix.

Mathematical Aside 1 Matrices

In mathematics, a **matrix** is a set of numbers arranged as a table, but without column or row headings, and often surrounded by brackets. In general, the number of rows of a matrix may be different from the number of columns. A matrix with n rows and p columns is referred to as an $n \times p$ matrix. Within a matrix, the number in the ith row and jth column is referred to as element (i, j), or as the (i, j)th element. A 4×3 matrix with the 2nd row, the 3rd column and element $(4, 1)$ labelled is shown in Figure 1.4.

The plural of matrix is matrices.

When referring to the size of a matrix, $n \times p$ is read as 'n by p'.

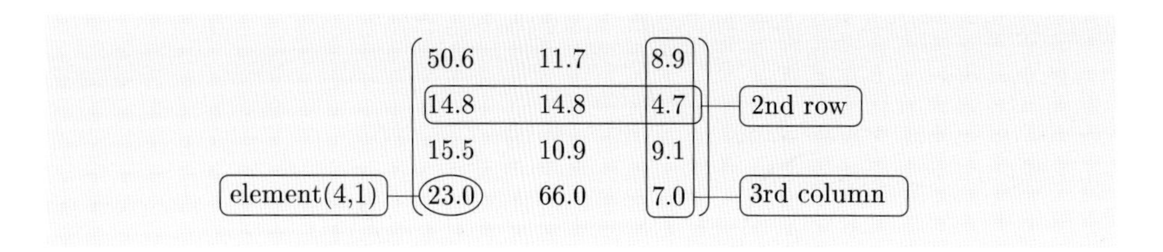

Figure 1.4 Parts of a matrix

A matrix representing a set of multivariate data is commonly referred to as a **data matrix**. The values for the jth variable are usually placed in the jth column. Similarly, the values for the ith observation are placed in the ith row. This means that element (i, j) corresponds to the value of variable j for observation i. When the variables are represented by $X_1, \ldots, X_p$, the corresponding data matrix is denoted $\mathbf{X}$. ♦

Bold capital letters are used to represent matrices.

Example 1.5 A data matrix for the LEA performance data

The percentages of eleven-year-old students reaching a particular standard in English, Mathematics and Science in the ten top performing LEAs were given in Table 1.3. Suppose that X_1 represents the percentage of students reaching the standard in English in each of the LEA areas. Similarly, suppose that X_2 and X_3 represent the percentages of students reaching the standard in Mathematics and Science, respectively. Then the data in Table 1.3 can be represented by the data matrix $\mathbf{X}$, where

$$\mathbf{X} = \begin{pmatrix} 96.6 & 79.3 & 93.1 \\ 86.9 & 82.5 & 94.0 \\ 84.9 & 81.2 & 91.8 \\ 82.7 & 81.8 & 92.5 \\ 84.2 & 78.8 & 92.4 \\ 82.5 & 79.0 & 91.7 \\ 82.4 & 77.5 & 92.5 \\ 83.4 & 78.2 & 90.5 \\ 81.6 & 77.9 & 91.5 \\ 80.5 & 78.0 & 90.1 \end{pmatrix}.$$

In data matrix $\mathbf{X}$, the values for the Mathematics score are given in the second column. The results for the fourth LEA, Rutland, are given in the fourth row. And, for example, element $(6, 3)$ corresponds to the percentage of eleven-year-old students in Windsor and Maidenhead LEA, the sixth LEA, who reached the standard in Science. ♦

Activity 1.2 Identifying parts of a multivariate data set

A multivariate data set consisting of measurements of trace chemical elements in parts of *Echinacea purpurea* plants was introduced in Example 1.4. The logarithms of the data for autumn-harvested plants in Table 1.4 are given in Table 1.5.

Table 1.5 Log concentrations of trace chemical elements found in different parts of autumn-harvested *Echinacea purpurea* plants

Sample	Cu	Fe	Mn	Zn	Ni	Li	Sr	Mg	Ca
Root	2.44	5.14	2.57	1.50	−0.69	1.03	2.03	8.08	8.51
Stem	2.24	4.62	2.94	1.86	1.31	−0.11	1.48	8.13	9.10
Leaf	2.47	5.68	4.21	2.54	1.63	1.16	2.37	9.03	10.29
Flower	2.77	5.21	3.40	2.93	2.23	0.83	1.48	8.16	9.59
Herbs	2.32	5.39	3.74	2.53	1.46	1.03	1.92	8.75	10.06

Suppose that the data matrix based on Table 1.5 is denoted by $\mathbf{X}$.

(a) The data for which chemical element is represented by X_1?

(b) The data for which chemical element is represented by X_6?

(c) Which part of the plant corresponds to observation 3?

(d) Write down the value of x_{48}.

(e) The log concentration of manganese (Mn) in the stem of the autumn-harvested *Echinacea purpurea* is 2.94. If this value is represented by x_{ij}, what are the values of i and j?

Summary of Section 1

In this section, some examples of situations where multivariate data sets are of interest have been described. The dimension of a multivariate data set has been defined, and the matrix representation of multivariate data has been introduced.

Exercise on Section 1

Exercise 1.1 The dimension of multivariate data

Descriptions of four multivariate data sets are given below. For each data set, state the dimension p and the number of observations n.

You will meet three of these data sets as you study this book.

(a) In a study on interest rates in different countries, data on ten countries were collected. For each country, two interest rates were recorded: the average three-month interest rate during 2004, and the average interest rate for ten-year government bonds in 2004.

(b) A study was conducted to investigate the effect of exercise on the bones of people with osteoporosis. Samples of bone tissue from thirteen patients were studied. The levels of each of five proteins in each sample were measured.

(c) In a study on the detection of counterfeit banknotes, 200 similar banknotes were measured. The length of each banknote was recorded, together with the widths at the left-hand and right-hand edges of the note, and three measurements relating to the positioning of the design on one side of the note.

(d) In a study investigating groundwater systems, 41 samples of water from wells in different localities were collected and chemically analysed. The concentration of each of 25 trace chemical elements in each sample was recorded.

2 Graphical displays

The first step in a statistical analysis is often to obtain graphical displays of the data. This is particularly true in multivariate analysis where it is very difficult to spot patterns in tables of data. One aim is to display data so that relationships between variables (or groups of variables) can be seen. Sometimes it is also important to depict the data in such a way that similarities between groups of observations are highlighted.

In this section, several graphical displays are discussed. In Subsection 2.1, the two-dimensional scatterplot is reviewed, and a generalization of the two-dimensional scatterplot which allows three variables to be plotted at once is described briefly. In Subsection 2.2, another generalization of the two-dimensional scatterplot, the **matrix scatterplot**, is discussed. An alternative to scatterplots, the **profile plot**, is introduced in Subsection 2.3; this is particularly useful when relationships between observations are of greater interest than relationships between variables.

2.1 Scatterplots

The two-dimensional scatterplot is used to investigate the relationship between two variables. On the plot, each observation is represented by a single point. The position of the point horizontally (that is, along the x-axis) represents the value of one variable for that observation, and the position vertically (that is, along the y-axis) represents the value of the other variable. Activity 2.1 will give you some practice at interpreting scatterplots.

Activity 2.1 House affordability

The average house price and the average household income (in thousands of pounds) for 353 local authorities in England are displayed in Figure 2.1.

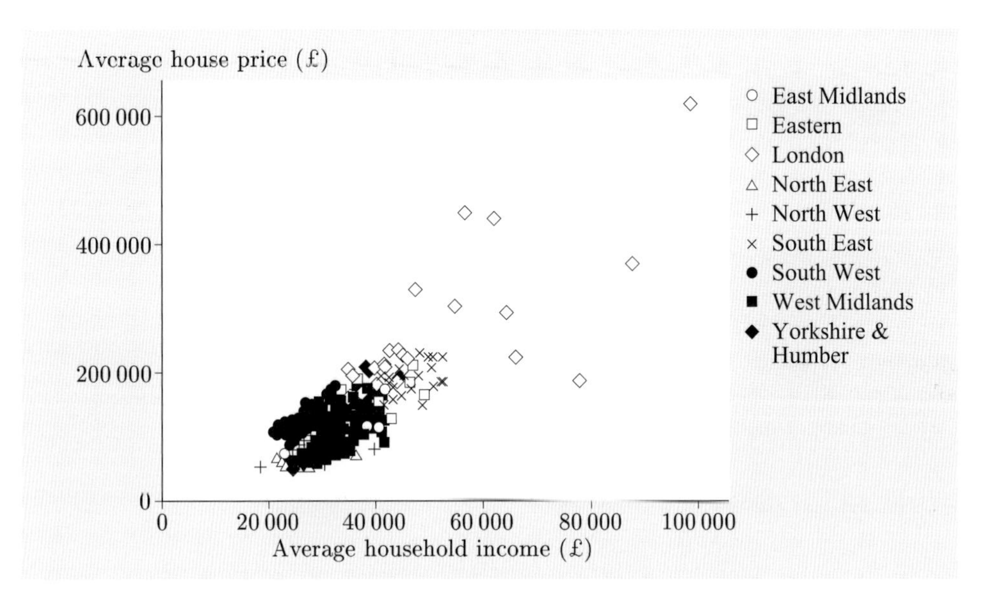

Figure 2.1 Scatterplot of average house price and average household income

In this scatterplot, authorities in different regions are represented by different plotting symbols.

(a) Do house price and household income appear to be related? If so, in what way?

(b) Describe any differences between London authorities and authorities in other regions. What can you say about differences between regions other than London?

(c) Do any of the points appear to be unusual? If so, in what way are they unusual?

A two-dimensional scatterplot can be an effective tool for displaying data when there are two variables. A generalization which allows three variables to be plotted is described in Example 2.1.

Example 2.1 LEA performance data

The LEA performance data introduced in Example 1.3 comprise three variables, the percentages of eleven-year-old primary school students reaching level 4 in standardized tests of English, Mathematics and Science. How can these data be represented on a scatterplot?

One option is to add an extra axis to the plot. This axis (a 'z-axis') needs to be at right angles to the other two axes. Unfortunately, on a flat piece of paper, it is not possible to draw a scatterplot with three axes all at right angles to each other. However, conceptually it is possible to manage this if the z-axis is considered to measure the distance above the paper. Thus the region in which the points are plotted forms a three-dimensional box. Points with a high value for the variable plotted along the z-axis would be far above the paper, whereas points with a value close to zero would be close to the paper. Such a plot is known as a **three-dimensional scatterplot** (or 3-d scatterplot for short). Figure 2.2 depicts a 3-d scatterplot for the LEA performance data.

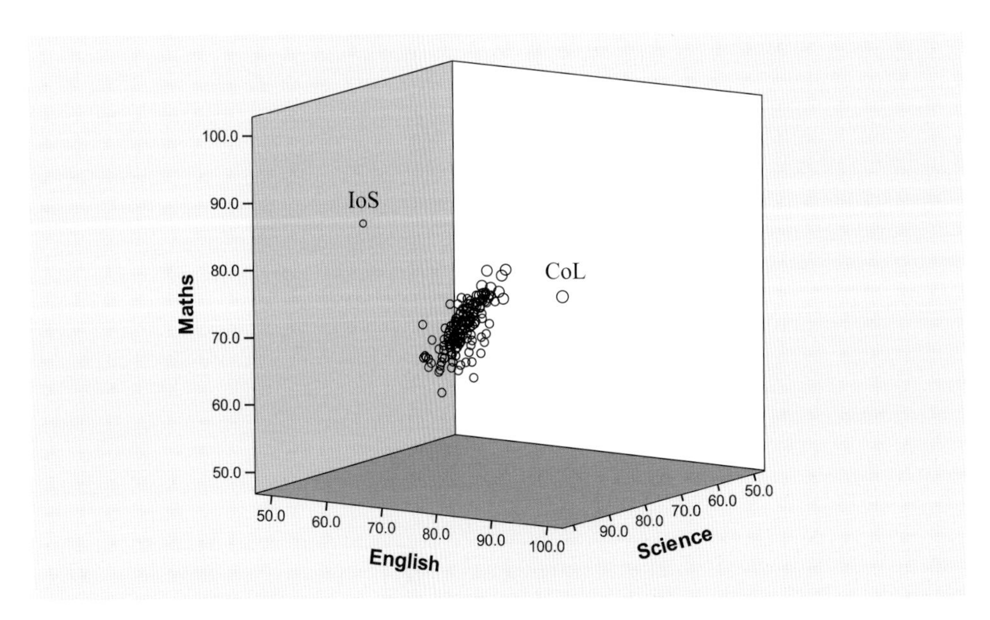

Figure 2.2 Three-dimensional scatterplot of the LEA performance data

Note that depicting what is essentially a three-dimensional plot on the page has required some use of perspective. The size of the plotting symbol used to represent each point decreases as the (notional) distance from the point to the eye of the observer increases. When interpreting this plot, imagine that the lines representing the axes correspond to the edges of a box from which the front, top and right-hand side panels have been cut away, so that you are looking inside the box.

On the plot, most of the points appear to form a group. However, there are two points representing local education authorities where the pattern of achievement in English, Mathematics and Science appears to be quite different from that in the other authorities. These two points are **outliers**. They correspond to the Isles of Scilly and the City of London, and have been labelled IoS and CoL, respectively. Within the main group, the local education authority areas where a higher percentage of students achieved level 4 in Mathematics also generally seem to be the areas where a higher percentage of students achieved the standard in English. However, owing to foreshortening it is less clear what the relationship is between achievement in Science and the other two subjects. This is a consequence of the difficulty of representing a three-dimensional plot on the page. ♦

Activity 2.2 Interpreting a 3-d scatterplot

Use the 3-d scatterplot in Figure 2.2 to answer the following questions.

(a) Which of the Isles of Scilly and the City of London achieved the higher score in Mathematics? Which of the two LEAs achieved the higher score in English?

(b) Can you tell whether the results in Science for the City of London were closer to 100% or to 50%?

(c) Can you tell whether the City of London obtained a better score in Science than the Isles of Scilly?

2.2 Matrix scatterplots

The three-dimensional scatterplot provides a means of displaying data comprising three variables on a single plot. However, as you saw in Example 2.1 and Activity 2.2, a 3-d scatterplot can be difficult to interpret. An alternative approach is to construct what is known as a **matrix scatterplot**; this is a series of two-dimensional scatterplots arranged in a grid. A 2-d scatterplot is produced for each combination of different variables, with one of the variables on the x-axis and the other variable on the y-axis. The scatterplots are arranged so that scatterplots which have the same variable along the x-axis are placed in the same column of the grid, and scatterplots which have the same variable along the y-axis are placed in the same row. This is illustrated in Example 2.2.

Example 2.2 A matrix scatterplot for the LEA performance data

Data on the performance of primary school students in English, Mathematics and Science in 150 local education authorities were described in Example 1.3. These data are displayed in a matrix scatterplot in Figure 2.3.

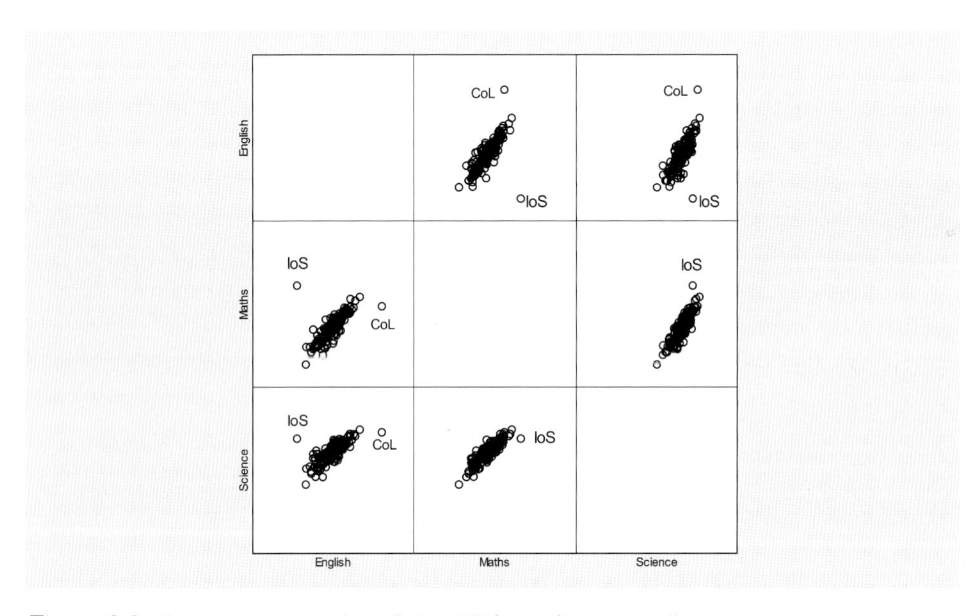

Figure 2.3 Matrix scatterplot of the LEA performance data

Notice that the plot is a combination of six 2-d scatterplots: English against Maths, English against Science, Maths against English, Maths against Science, Science against English, and Science against Maths. The two 2-d scatterplots with English on the y-axis are plotted in the top row. The 2-d scatterplots with Mathematics and Science on the y-axis are plotted in the middle and bottom rows, respectively. Similarly, the two 2-d scatterplots with English on the x-axis are plotted in the left-hand column, and the 2-d scatterplots with Mathematics and Science on the x-axis are plotted in the middle and right-hand columns, respectively.

In each individual 2-d scatterplot, the scales along the x-axis and the y-axis have been omitted to prevent the overall plot from becoming too cluttered. As the focus is usually on the relationship between variables, the omission of the scales does not really impact on the interpretation of the plot.

Note that there are no scatterplots in the diagonal positions. These positions correspond to scatterplots where the same variable would be used for the x-axis and the y-axis. Such plots would give no information about the relationship between different variables, so they are omitted. Furthermore, the plots above and to the right of the blank panels are essentially copies of the scatterplots below and to the left of the blank panels. The only difference between them is that the variables on the x-axis and the y-axis have been swapped. For example, the plot in the top right-hand corner of Figure 2.3 is essentially the same as the plot in the bottom left-hand corner; the only difference is that the variables on the axes (in this case, the results in English and Science) have been swapped.

Looking at the 2-d scatterplots contained within Figure 2.3 confirms the positive relationship between the performance in Mathematics and the performance in English that can be seen in the 3-d scatterplot (Figure 2.2). The other relationships are much clearer than in the 3-d scatterplot. Local education authorities with good results for Science also tend to have good results for Mathematics and English.

As in Figure 2.2, the points for the Isles of Scilly (IoS) and the City of London (CoL) appear to be unusual. In the City of London, the results for English were particularly high, even given its good results for Mathematics and Science. The Isles of Scilly, on the other hand, achieved a poor result for English even though its Science results were not unusual and its Mathematics results were very good.

Interestingly, these two outlying authorities are also by far the smallest. In both LEAs, the scores are based on fewer than 30 students, whereas the scores for each of the other authorities are based on at least ten times as many students. ♦

As a matrix scatterplot is simply a collection of 2-d scatterplots arranged in a grid, matrix scatterplots can also be used to display multivariate data sets that consist of four or more variables. The matrix scatterplot for a data set of dimension 4 is the subject of Activity 2.3.

Activity 2.3 Mathematical ability

In the early 1900s, a researcher interested in the theory of reasoning investigated the mathematical ability of boys at an English public school. The boys sat three mathematics exams set by the researcher. One exam focused on geometry, one on arithmetic and the other on algebra. When marking the exams, the researcher focused on 'the intellectual processes involved in answering the questions'. Exam scores for 83 boys, aged between 13 and 18, were obtained. Figure 2.4 shows a matrix scatterplot of the scores of the boys for geometry, arithmetic and algebra, and the ages of the boys.

Brown, W. (1910) An objective study of mathematical intelligence. *Biometrika*, **7**, 352–367.

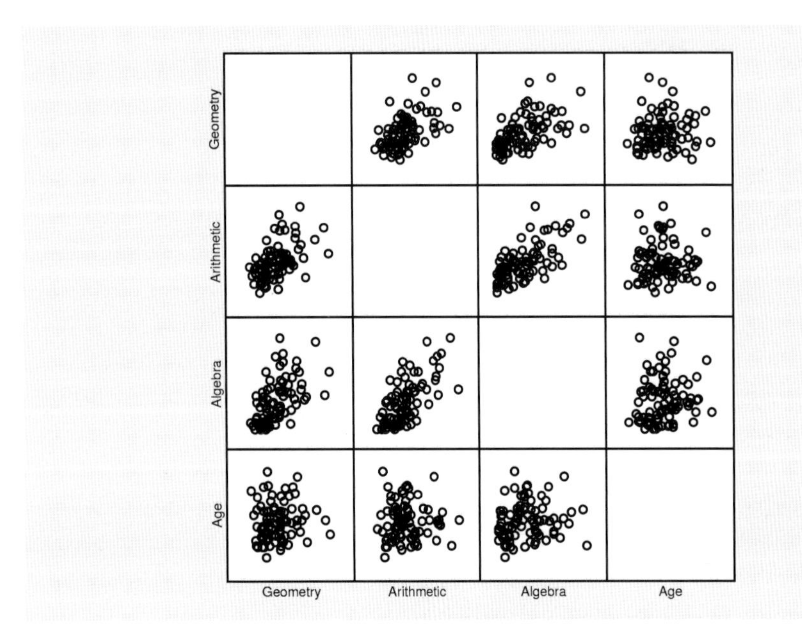

Figure 2.4 Matrix scatterplot of scores for geometry, arithmetic and algebra, and age

(a) Describe the relationships between the three mathematics variables. For which two variables is the relationship strongest? Explain your answer.

(b) How is age related to the other three variables?

When there are p variables, a matrix scatterplot comprises a grid of 2-d scatterplots that has p columns and p rows — one column and one row for each variable — with p blank panels in diagonal positions. So a total of $p(p-1)$ scatterplots form the matrix scatterplot. When the dimension p is small, the matrix scatterplot is made up of only a few individual 2-d scatterplots. For example, the matrix scatterplot of LEA performance data in Figure 2.3 consists of six individual scatterplots; and the matrix scatterplot of mathematical ability data in Figure 2.4 consists of twelve scatterplots. Thus for data sets of low dimension there are just a few plots to look at and, when plotted on a page (or computer screen), each individual plot is of reasonable size. However, as the dimension of the plotted data increases, the number of subplots on a matrix scatterplot quickly becomes large. As you will see in Example 2.3, this can make a matrix scatterplot difficult to interpret.

Example 2.3 Mathematical ability revisited

In the study described in Activity 2.3, the mathematical ability of the schoolboys was actually studied in greater detail: nine subscores were recorded for each boy. Four different aspects of geometrical ability (labelled A, B, C and D) were recorded, together with three different aspects of arithmetical ability (labelled E, F and G) and two aspects of algebraical ability (labelled H and I).

A matrix scatterplot of these nine subscores is shown in Figure 2.5.

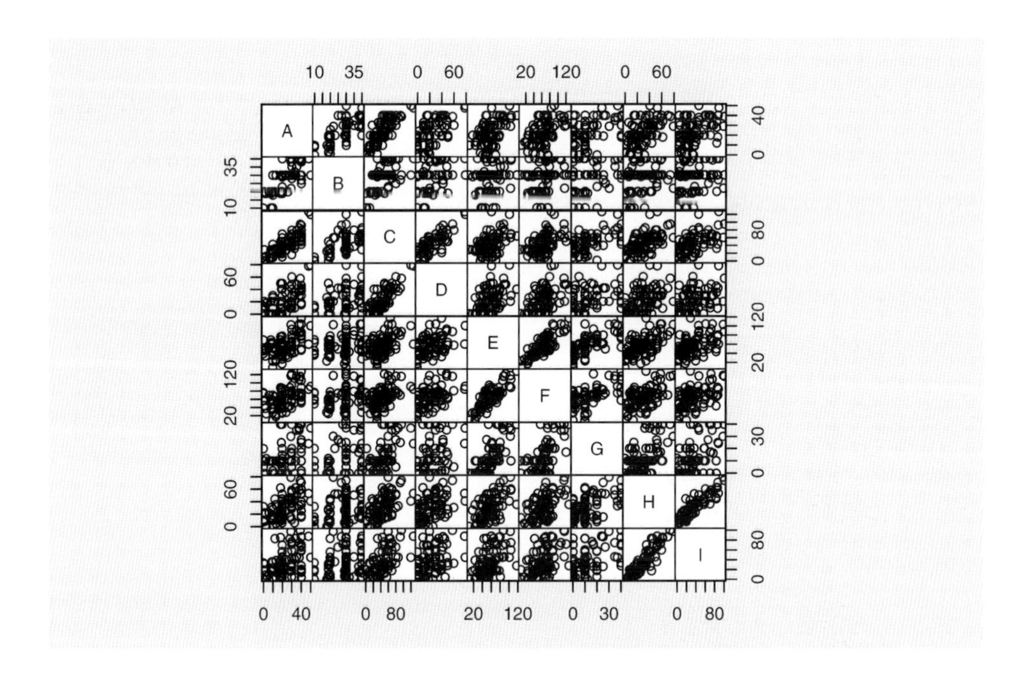

Figure 2.5 Scores on nine aspects of mathematical ability

Each variable is identified by a label in the diagonal position corresponding to its row and column. For example, subscore B is plotted in the second row and second column.

The dimension of the data set is 9, so the matrix scatterplot consists of $9 \times 8 = 72$ individual subplots. There are many more subplots than in either Figure 2.3 or Figure 2.4, and each subplot has to be smaller in order to fit the matrix scatterplot on the page. Thus it is much harder to take in all the information presented in Figure 2.5 than in Figure 2.4. ♦

Activity 2.4 Interpreting a larger matrix scatterplot

The large number of subplots in Figure 2.5 makes it a daunting task to interpret the scatterplot. Nevertheless, it is possible to spot some important relationships. Use the matrix scatterplot to answer the following questions about the mathematical ability data set.

(a) Comment in general terms (that is, without mentioning any specific variables) on the direction of the relationships between the subscores.

(b) Identify four pairs of subscores which have strong positive relationships.

(c) Identify one subscore variable that appears to be only weakly related to most of the other subscores.

In Activity 2.4, you saw that it is possible to pick out only the most striking patterns from a matrix scatterplot of a 9-dimensional data set. However, as multivariate data sets go, a dimension of 9 is by no means large. A data set with a much higher dimension is described in Example 2.4.

Example 2.4 Trace elements in water from wells

When storing nuclear waste long-term, information on the groundwater system of the surrounding geographic area is important in case there should be an accidental leaching of radioactive material. One method for investigating the groundwater system is by comparing the chemical composition of water drawn from wells drilled in that area. The composition of water drawn from different wells should be more similar if the groundwater for the two wells is linked than if it is not.

One such study of groundwater systems was carried out in Nevada, USA. Researchers collected 41 samples of water from a total of fourteen wells. For each sample, the concentration of each of 57 trace chemical elements was measured. So this multivariate data set consists of 41 observations on 57 variables.

Farnham, I.M., Johannesson, K.H., Singh, A.K., Hodge, V.F. and Stetzenbach, K.J. (2003) Factor analytical approaches for evaluating groundwater trace element chemistry data. *Analytica Chimica Acta*, **490**, 123–138.

A matrix scatterplot of these data would consist of $57 \times 56 = 3192$ subplots — far too many to plot in one go! One way around this problem is to omit some of the variables from the analysis. The researchers decided to ignore data relating to 32 of the 57 trace chemical elements. A trace chemical element that was ignored was chosen for one of two reasons. Either the researchers felt that there was insufficient variation in the concentration of the element between samples to make its inclusion worthwhile, or the concentration of the element in the samples tended to be so low that it could not be reliably measured. Nevertheless, the researchers' analysis was still based on the concentrations of 25 trace chemical elements.

A matrix scatterplot of the remaining 25 variables is given in Figure 2.6.

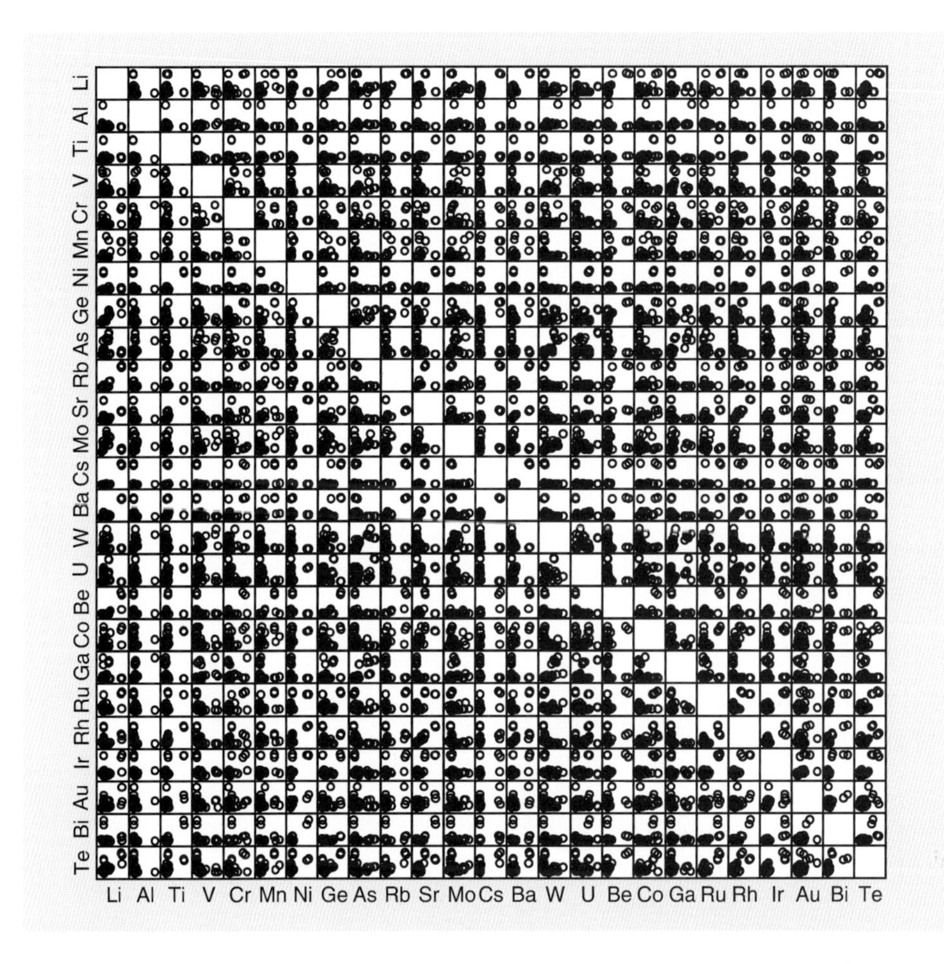

Figure 2.6 Matrix scatterplot of the concentration of 25 trace elements in samples of well water

The overall impression from this plot is of a confusing array of small panels. It is difficult to pick out important detail, or even to form a general impression about the relationships between variables; and it is not possible to identify points which do not seem to follow the same pattern as the rest of the data. ♦

When a multivariate data set consists of a small number of variables, the matrix scatterplot is usually an effective way to explore relationships between variables. However, as you have seen, when the dimension of a data set is large, the matrix scatterplot is rather unwieldy and difficult to interpret. So if the dimension of the data is such that the usefulness of techniques such as the matrix scatterplot is compromised, what is to be done? One solution is to replace the data set by a data set of lower dimension, and apply techniques such as the matrix scatterplot to this smaller data set. A technique for constructing a data set of lower dimension that can be thought of as being as good an approximation as possible to the original data set is the subject of Part II of this book.

2.3 Profile plots

Scatterplots are good for examining relationships between variables. However, sometimes it is more important to bring out relationships between observations. For instance, in Example 1.4, interest focused on comparing different parts of the plant *Echinacea purpurea* with respect to concentrations of the trace elements found within them. In such situations, other types of plot, which are not based around the scatterplot, are often used. One such plot is the **profile plot**.

In a profile plot, each variable in the multivariate data set is represented by a category along the x-axis. The values for each of the variables are then plotted along the y-axis. Finally, the points corresponding to the same observation are joined by a line. This is illustrated in Example 2.5.

Example 2.5 *Profile plot for the Echinacea data*

In Example 1.4, data on the uptake of chemicals in different parts of the *Echinacea purpurea* plant were described. A profile plot of the log concentrations of trace chemical elements found in the different plant parts in the autumn-harvested plants is shown in Figure 2.7.

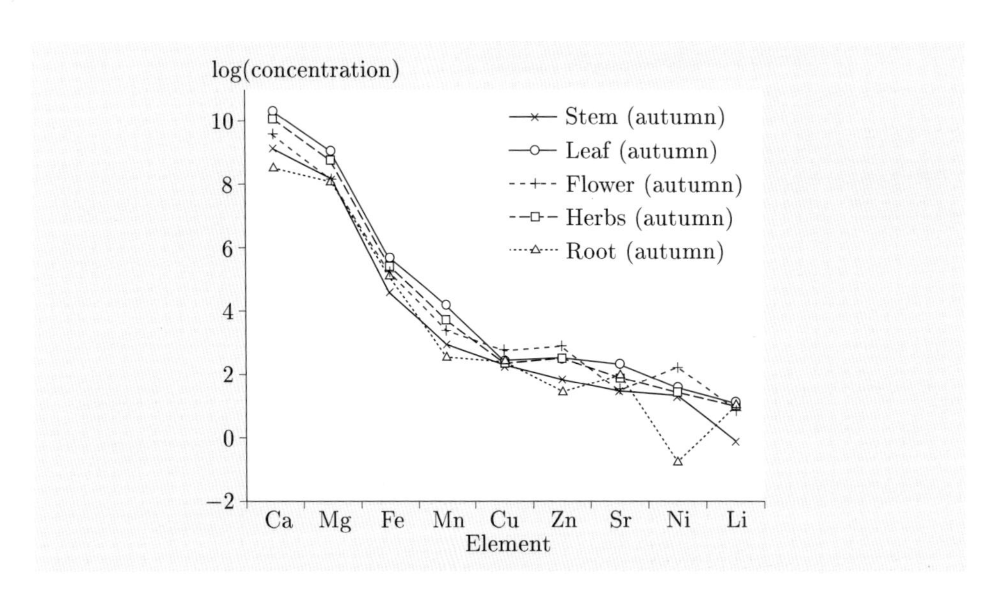

Figure 2.7 Profile plot of the *Echinacea purpurea* data

Five different parts of the autumn-harvested plants were isolated and analysed: stem, leaf, flower, herbs and root. Thus there are five lines in this plot, each line representing a different part of the plant. Marked along the x-axis are the variables — in this case, the nine trace chemical elements for which concentrations were obtained. Note that the data along the x-axis are categorical, so the spacing (and the ordering) along the x-axis is arbitrary. The y-axis represents the concentration of the trace chemical elements. For this plot, the logarithms of concentrations were obtained prior to plotting so that all the points fit conveniently on the scale.

In Figure 2.7, the categories have been ordered to give generally downward sloping graphs. This makes it easier to identify patterns in the data.

A number of things can be seen from Figure 2.7. First, the similar shapes of the lines suggest that the pattern of the concentrations of the trace elements is generally very similar across the parts of the plant. The highest concentrations tend to be in the leaves, and the lowest concentrations in the stems and roots. Secondly, the elements on the left-hand side of the graph (calcium and magnesium) were found in much higher concentrations than the other elements. Finally, the relative concentrations of zinc (Zn) and nickel (Ni) in the plant parts appear to be different from the relative concentrations of the other elements in the plant parts. The concentration of nickel is particularly low in the roots, and the concentrations of zinc and nickel are highest in the flowers. The scientists who conducted this study attributed the relatively high concentrations of zinc and nickel in the flowers to the high mobility of these trace elements within the plant. ♦

Activity 2.5 will give you some practice with interpreting profile plots.

Activity 2.5 Gene profiling

Insights into the roles different genes play can be gained by studying the extent to which each gene is used ('expressed'). One particular study focused on the changes in gene expression that occur whilst recovering from cerebral ischemia (blockage of arteries in the brain). The researchers measured the relative expression of a range of genes in five groups of mice. Measurements were taken at a time point for each group of mice. The first group consisted of mice for whom no ischemia had occurred (0 hours). For the other four groups, measurements were taken 2, 6, 12 and 24 hours after the ischemia. So in this data set, each gene corresponds to one observation, and the five variables are the measurements at each of the five time points.

Nagata, T., Takahashi, Y., Sugahara, M. *et al.* (2004) Profiling of genes associated with transcriptional responses in mouse hippocampus after transient forebrain ischemia using high-density oligonucleotide DNA array. *Molecular Brain Research*, **121**, 1–11.

The data were transformed so that, for each gene, the median relative expression over the time points was 1. Initially the relative expression of over 6000 genes was considered. However, the analysis focused on 25 genes where a change in expression as a result of the ischemia was most definite. A profile plot of the data for these 25 genes is shown in Figure 2.8.

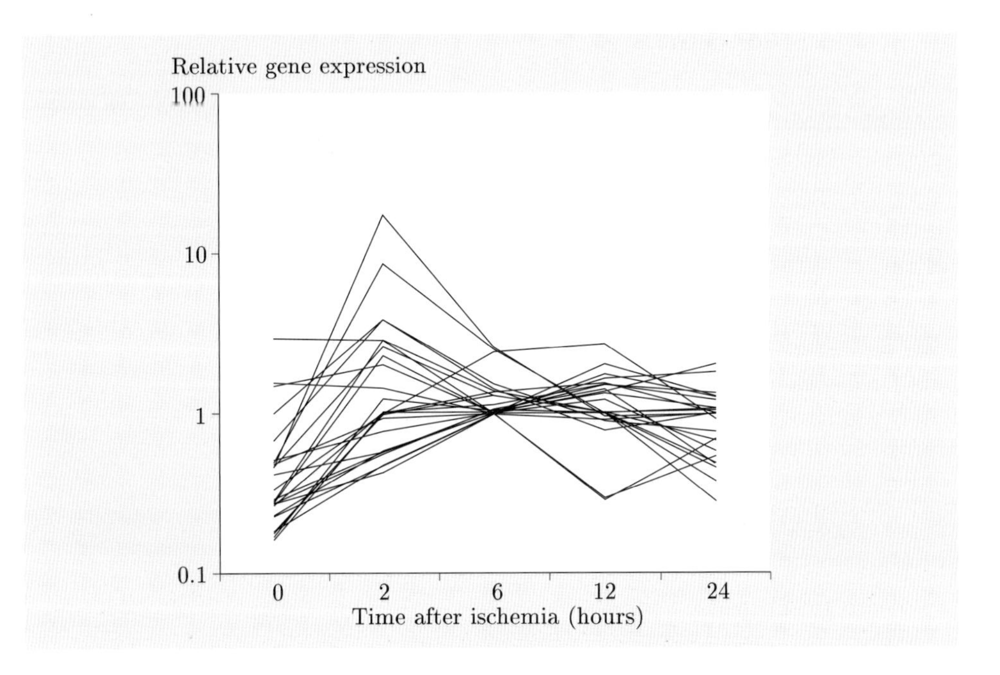

Figure 2.8 Profile plot of the relative expression of genes in response to cerebral ischemia

In this plot, the five time points are placed in order along the x-axis, so each line represents the relative expression over time for a single gene. However, note that the distances between neighbouring points along the x-axis are equal even though successive gaps correspond to increasing lengths of time.

(a) Describe how, on average, gene expression varied over time.

(b) On the basis of some additional statistical analysis of the relative expressions, the investigators felt that the 25 genes split into four groups. Profile plots for the four groups are shown in Figure 2.9. Briefly describe the features that distinguish the four groups.

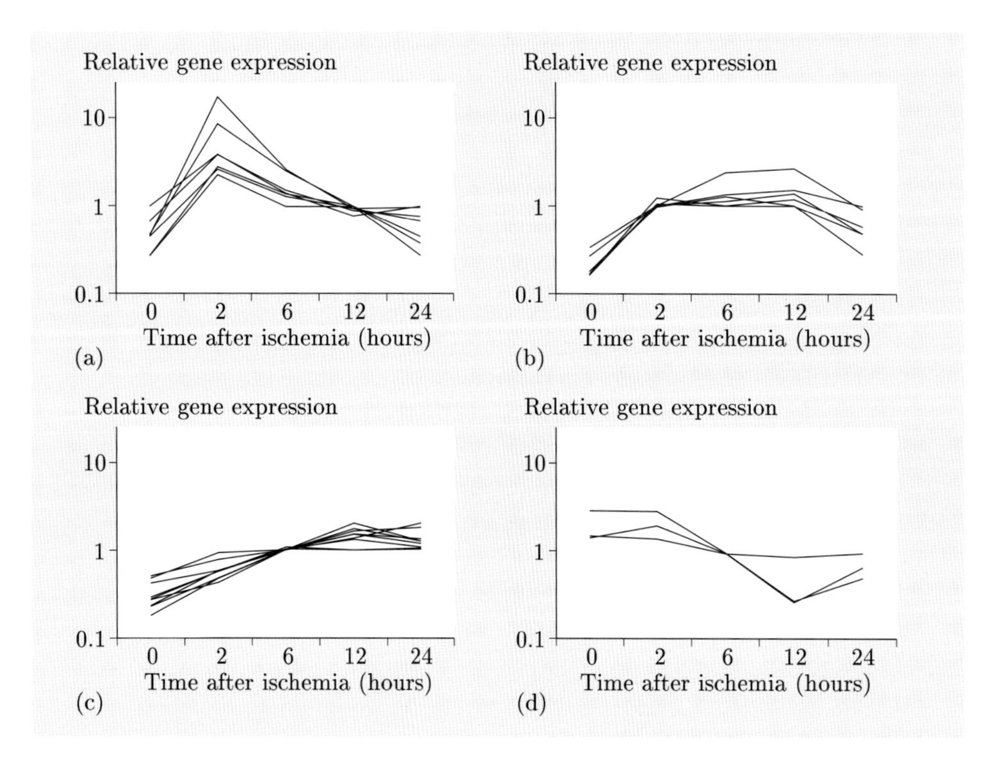

Figure 2.9 Profile plots of the four groups

Summary of Section 2

In this section, techniques for the graphical display of multivariate data have been described. The two-dimensional scatterplot, the three-dimensional scatterplot and the matrix scatterplot can be useful for displaying relationships between variables and for identifying outliers. However, you have seen that when the dimension of a data set is large, the matrix scatterplot is rather unwieldy and difficult to interpret. The other method described, the profile plot, is useful for exploring relationships between observations.

Exercises on Section 2

Exercise 2.1 *Costs of crime and expenditure on police*

In a study to determine an optimal expenditure on policing, researchers estimated the cost of crime and expenditure on policing per capita in each state in the US and for the District of Columbia. The cost of crime, given in US dollars, was given separately for crimes against property and crimes against the person. The expenditure on policing, also in US dollars, was split into expenditure at state level and expenditure at local level.

Correa, H. (2005) Optimal expenditures on police protection, *Socio-Economic Planning Sciences*, **39**, 215–228.

A matrix scatterplot of the data is shown in Figure 2.10.

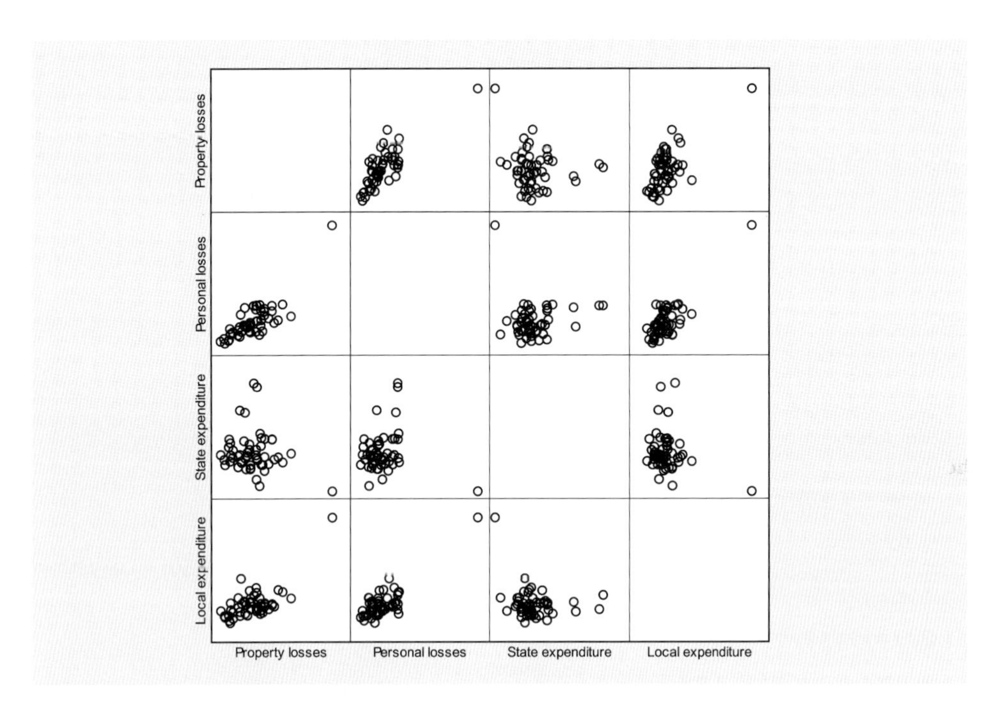

Figure 2.10 Per capita cost of crime and expenditure on policing

(a) Describe the relationship between the cost of crimes against property (represented by the variable Property losses) and the cost of crimes against the person (Personal losses).

(b) Describe the relationship between state expenditure and local expenditure on policing.

(c) 'Higher spending on policing is associated with lower losses from crime.' Do the data appear to support this statement? Justify your answer.

(d) Identify any outliers, and explain in what way these points do not follow the general pattern.

Exercise 2.2 *Trace chemical elements in summer-harvested Echinacea*

In Example 2.5, the interpretation of a profile plot of data relating to autumn-harvested *Echinacea purpurea* was discussed. Some *Echinacea purpurea* plants were also harvested in the summer. The concentrations of various trace chemical elements in four parts of the plants were measured. The logarithms of these measurements are displayed in the profile plot in Figure 2.11 (overleaf).

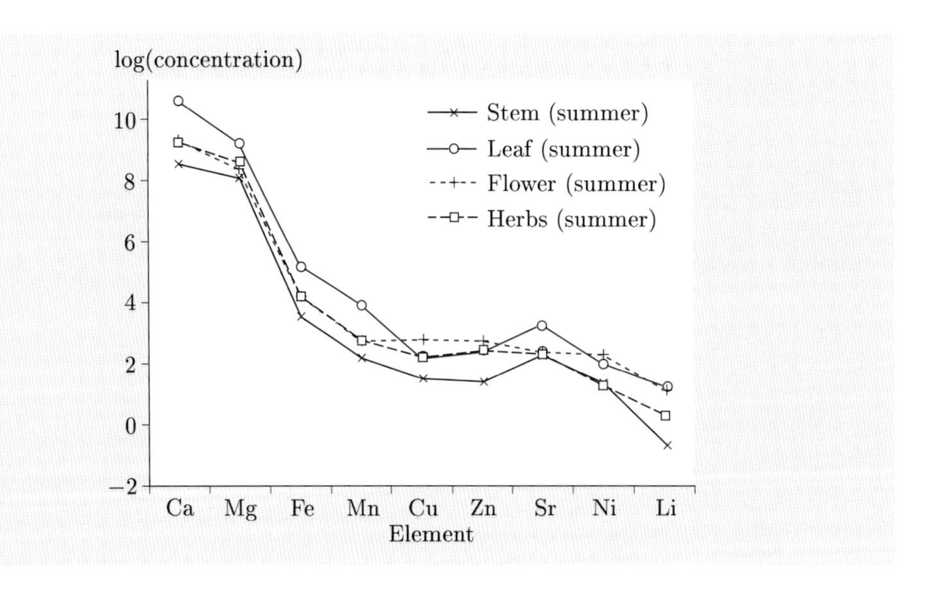

Figure 2.11 Log concentrations of trace chemical elements in summer-harvested plants

(a) Briefly describe the main features of this profile plot.

(b) For which chemical elements does the pattern of the relative concentrations in the parts of the plant appear to differ from the pattern for all the other chemical elements? Explain your answer.

3 Numerical summaries

To describe a data set, it is common to include some indication of what value a typical or average observation takes and also of the spread of values across observations. In this section, numerical summaries suitable for multivariate data are introduced. In Subsection 3.1, the **mean vector** is defined; this is used to describe an average observation. The **covariance matrix**, which is used to describe the spread of values across observations, is discussed in Subsection 3.2; it also carries information about relationships between variables.

3.1 Mean vectors

When there is only one variable to be summarized, the mode, the median or the mean might be used as the 'average' depending on the type of data. With multivariate data, it no longer makes sense to think of a single number representing the average for a given data set. The variables are often measured in different units, rendering any averaging of different variables meaningless; for example, age might be in years and exam score as a percentage. Even when the variables are all measured on the same scale (such as the percentage of pupils achieving level 4 or above in a standard exam), a single number may not help the process of comparing and contrasting variables. Instead, averages are calculated separately for each variable. These averages are then presented together in a *vector*.

Mathematical Aside 2 Vectors

In mathematics, a **vector** is an ordered list of p numbers $y_1, y_2, \ldots, y_p$. The numbers can be written either as a **row vector** or as a **column vector**; that is,

$$\mathbf{y} = (y_1, y_2, \ldots, y_p), \quad \text{or} \quad \mathbf{y} = \begin{pmatrix} y_1 \\ y_2 \\ \vdots \\ y_p \end{pmatrix}.$$

The row vector is said to be the **transpose** of the column vector, and vice versa. When a vector (or a matrix) is transposed, rows become columns, and columns become rows. In this book, row vectors and column vectors are used interchangeably. However, note that the order of the numbers within a vector matters. For example, in general, (y_1, y_2) is a different vector from (y_2, y_1).

The jth number in this collection of numbers, y_j, is known as the **jth element** of the vector. ♦

Generally, the average calculated for each variable is the mean. The vector containing the mean for each of the variables in a data set is referred to as the **mean vector**. For a data set with n observations on p variables $X_1, X_2, \ldots, X_p$, the (sample) mean vector, which is denoted $\overline{\mathbf{x}}$, is defined as

$$\overline{\mathbf{x}} = (\overline{x}_1, \overline{x}_2, \ldots, \overline{x}_p),$$

where $\overline{x}_j$ is the sample mean for the variable X_j. The sample mean $\overline{x}_j$ is found by summing all the values for variable X_j and dividing by the sample size n:

$$\overline{x}_j = \frac{1}{n}(x_{1j} + x_{2j} + \cdots + x_{nj}) = \frac{1}{n}\sum_{i=1}^{n} x_{ij}.$$

Example 3.1 Calculating a mean vector

In Example 1.2, when discussing house affordability, the two variables house price (X_1) and household income (X_2) were of interest. The values of these variables for each of nine English regions were given in Table 1.2. The data are reproduced in Table 3.1.

Table 3.1 House price and household income (in thousands of pounds) in nine English regions

Region	House price	Household income
London	221.537	46.288
South East	152.555	38.478
South West	124.508	29.626
Eastern	125.154	33.819
West Midlands	94.402	31.857
East Midlands	88.724	29.350
North East	62.089	27.405
North West	69.372	28.625
Yorkshire & Humber	66.958	27.832

Based on these data, the mean house price, $\overline{x}_1$, is

$$\overline{x}_1 = \frac{1}{9}\sum_{i=1}^{9} x_{i1} = \frac{221.537 + 152.555 + \cdots + 66.958}{9} = \frac{1005.299}{9} \simeq 111.700.$$

Similarly, the mean household income, $\overline{x}_2$, is

$$\overline{x}_2 = \frac{1}{9}\sum_{i=1}^{9} x_{i2} = \frac{46.288 + 38.478 + \cdots + 27.832}{9} = \frac{293.280}{9} \simeq 32.587.$$

Thus the mean vector (in thousands of pounds) for these data is

$$\overline{\mathbf{x}} = (\overline{x}_1, \overline{x}_2) \simeq (111.700, 32.587).$$ ♦

Activity 3.1 Interpreting a mean vector

A study in which the concentrations of nine trace elements were measured in various parts of the plant *Echinacea purpurea* was described in Example 1.4. In this activity, the variables of interest are the log concentrations at all locations and at all times. The variables are labelled as follows:

$$\begin{array}{ll} X_1 = \log(\text{concentration of Cu}), & X_2 = \log(\text{concentration of Fe}), \\ X_3 = \log(\text{concentration of Mn}), & X_4 = \log(\text{concentration of Zn}), \\ X_5 = \log(\text{concentration of Ni}), & X_6 = \log(\text{concentration of Li}), \\ X_7 = \log(\text{concentration of Sr}), & X_8 = \log(\text{concentration of Mg}), \\ X_9 = \log(\text{concentration of Ca}). & \end{array}$$

In the analysis of the resulting multivariate data, the mean vector was calculated:

$$\overline{\mathbf{x}} = (2.31, 4.81, 3.41, 2.47, 1.52, 0.77, 2.08, 8.49, 9.48).$$

(a) What was the mean log concentration of copper (Cu)?

(b) What was the mean log concentration of nickel (Ni)?

(c) For which chemical element was the mean log concentration the greatest?

Activity 3.2 Calculating average LEA performance

In Example 1.3, the performance of local education authorities in England was discussed. For the local education authorities that were deemed to be in the top ten in 2003, the percentages of eleven-year-old primary school students passing standardized tests were given in Table 1.3. The data are reproduced in Table 3.2.

Table 3.2 English, Mathematics and Science scores (%) for the top ten local education authorities

LEA	English (X_1)	Mathematics (X_2)	Science (X_3)
City of London	96.6	79.3	93.1
Richmond upon Thames	86.9	82.5	94.0
Wokingham	84.9	81.2	91.8
Rutland	82.7	81.8	92.5
Kensington and Chelsea	84.2	78.8	92.4
Windsor and Maidenhead	82.5	79.0	91.7
Bracknell Forest	82.4	77.5	92.5
Bromley	83.4	78.2	90.5
Surrey	81.6	77.9	91.5
Havering	80.5	78.0	90.1

(a) Calculate the mean performance in English for these ten local education authorities.

(b) The mean performance in Mathematics was 79.42%, and the mean performance in Science was 92.01%. Using your answer to part (a), write down the mean vector.

3.2 The covariance matrix

When summarizing the degree of spread in a multivariate data set, values are given for each variable separately. In principle, these values could be any summary statistic that measures the degree of spread for a single variable. However, for mathematical convenience, the (sample) variance is generally used. The spread for variable X_j is denoted s_j^2 and is calculated using the following formula:

$$s_j^2 = \frac{1}{n-1} \sum_{i=1}^{n} (x_{ij} - \overline{x}_j)^2. \tag{3.1}$$

Example 3.2 Calculating variances

In Example 3.1, the mean vector for the house affordability data in Table 3.2 was calculated. The sample variances of the two variables, average house price (X_1) and average household income (X_2), can be calculated using (3.1), as follows.

From Example 3.1, $\overline{x}_1 \simeq 111.700$. Thus the variance of X_1 is

$$\begin{aligned} s_1^2 &= \tfrac{1}{8}\sum_{i=1}^{9}(x_{i1} - \overline{x}_1)^2 \\ &\simeq \frac{(221.537 - 111.700)^2 + \cdots + (66.958 - 111.700)^2}{8} \\ &\simeq \frac{12064 + \cdots + 2002}{8} \simeq 2645. \end{aligned}$$

Similarly, $\overline{x}_2 \simeq 32.587$, so the variance of X_2 is

$$\begin{aligned} s_2^2 &= \tfrac{1}{8}\sum_{i=1}^{9}(x_{i2} - \overline{x}_2)^2 \\ &\simeq \frac{(46.288 - 32.587)^2 + \cdots + (27.832 - 32.587)^2}{8} \\ &\simeq \frac{187.7 + \cdots + 22.6}{8} \simeq 38.6. \end{aligned}$$

The units for both these variances is $(£000\text{s})^2$. Thus the spread in average house prices between the regions is greater than the spread in average household income. ♦

The sample variances for the variables could be given in a variance vector. However, just giving the variances misses important information about the spread of points in a multivariate data set. This is illustrated in Activity 3.3.

Activity 3.3 Comparing bivariate distributions

Figure 3.1 shows scatterplots of three bivariate data sets, each consisting of 100 observations on two variables, X_1 and X_2. In each data set, the sample mean vector is $(0, 0)$, and the sample variances s_1^2 and s_2^2 are both 1.

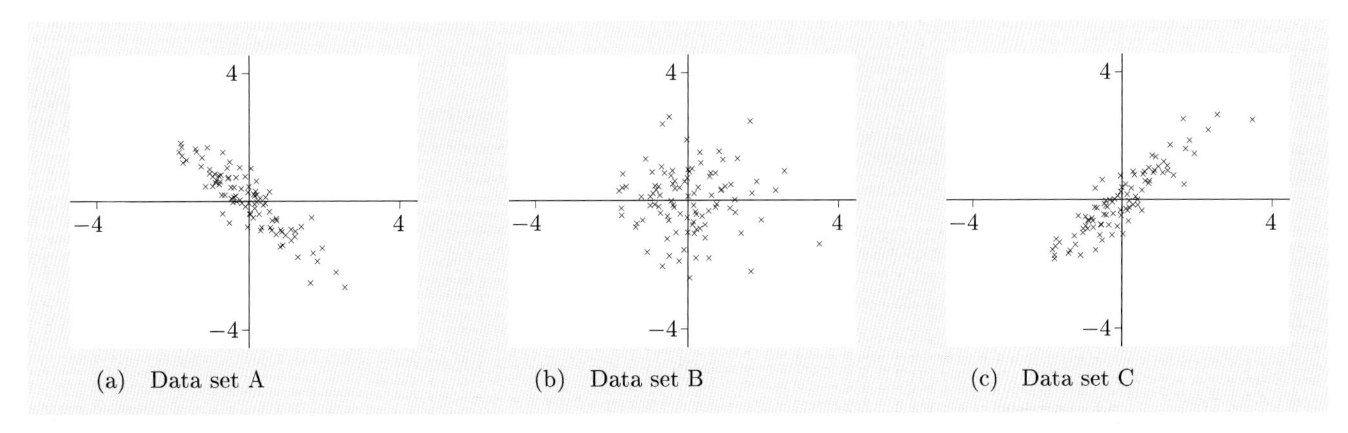

Figure 3.1 Scatterplots of observations from three bivariate distributions

Compare the distributions of observations in these three data sets. In what ways are they different?

In Activity 3.3, you saw that data sets can have the same sample mean vector and the same sample variances and yet show quite different relationships between variables. So, to distinguish such data sets, some means of summarizing numerically the relationship between variables is needed. One such measure is the **covariance**.

The **sample covariance** between two variables X_j and X_k is denoted s_{jk} and is defined as follows:

$$s_{jk} = \frac{1}{n-1}\sum_{i=1}^{n}(x_{ij} - \overline{x}_j)(x_{ik} - \overline{x}_k). \qquad (3.2)$$

If X_j and X_k are positively related, then the covariance will tend to be positive. If they are negatively related, then the covariance will tend to be negative. If X_j and X_k are unrelated, then the covariance will tend to be close to zero. Note also the following facts about covariances.

These properties of covariances were discussed in Subsection 5.1 of the *Introduction to statistical modelling*.

- ◇ In Formula (3.2), the roles of X_j and X_k can be swapped without changing the value of the expression on the right-hand side. Thus $s_{kj} = s_{jk}$.
- ◇ When $k = j$, Formula (3.2) is equivalent to Formula (3.1). So the covariance between a variable X_j and itself is just the variance of X_j: $s_{jj} = s_j^2$.
- ◇ The units associated with the value of s_{jk} is the product of the units in which X_j and X_k are measured. For example, if X_j represents length, measured in metres (m), and X_k represents time, measured in hours (h), then s_{jk} is measured in metre hours (m h).

Example 3.3 Calculating a covariance

The sample covariance, s_{12}, between house price (X_1) and household income (X_2) is calculated using the data in Example 3.1, as follows:

$$\begin{aligned} s_{12} &= \frac{1}{8}\sum_{i=1}^{9}(x_{i1} - \overline{x}_1)(x_{i2} - \overline{x}_2) \\ &\simeq \frac{(221.537 - 111.700)(46.288 - 32.587) + \cdots + (66.958 - 111.700)(27.832 - 32.587)}{8} \\ &\simeq \frac{1504.9 + \cdots + 212.7}{8} \simeq 306. \end{aligned}$$

The values for both X_1 and X_2 are given in thousands of pounds, so the covariance is given in $(£000s)^2$. Since the covariance s_{12} is positive, there is a positive relationship between house price and household income. In particular, regions where household incomes are high tend to be regions with high average house prices. ♦

Activity 3.4 Calculating variability in LEA performance

Data on the performance in English, Mathematics and Science for the top ten local education authorities are in Table 3.2. The mean vector is $(84.57, 79.42, 92.01)$.

You found the mean vector in Activity 3.2.

(a) Calculate the variance of the performance in English for the top ten LEAs.

(b) Calculate the covariance between the performance in Mathematics and the performance in Science.

When there are three or more variables in a data set, it is customary to quote the covariance between each pair of distinct variables. For example, if there are four variables, X_1, X_2, X_3 and X_4 (as in the case of the mathematical ability data set described in Activity 2.3), the following six covariances would be given: s_{12}, s_{13}, s_{14}, s_{23}, s_{24} and s_{34}. Note that the six covariances s_{21}, s_{31}, s_{41}, s_{32}, s_{42} and s_{43} can be deduced from these six covariances, because $s_{jk} = s_{kj}$ for all j and k.

The variances and covariances for a given data set are usually written as a matrix, called a **variance-covariance matrix**, or **covariance matrix** for short. When the data set has p variables, $X_1, X_2, \ldots, X_p$, the covariance matrix has p rows and p columns. Element (j, j) of the covariance matrix is s_j^2, the sample variance for the variable X_j. Element (j, k) is s_{jk}, the sample covariance between variables X_j and X_k.

Mathematical Aside 3 Square matrices

Matrices which have the same number of rows and columns are known as **square matrices**. (Covariance matrices are square matrices.) In a square matrix with p rows and p columns, the elements (i, i), $i = 1, \ldots, p$, are said to lie on the **main diagonal**. The elements (i, j) where $i > j$ are said to lie in the **lower triangle**. The elements (i, j) where $i < j$ are said to lie in the **upper triangle**. Collectively, the elements in the lower and upper triangles are known as the **off-diagonal** elements. The main diagonal, the lower triangle and the upper triangle for a 4×4 square matrix are labelled in Figure 3.2.

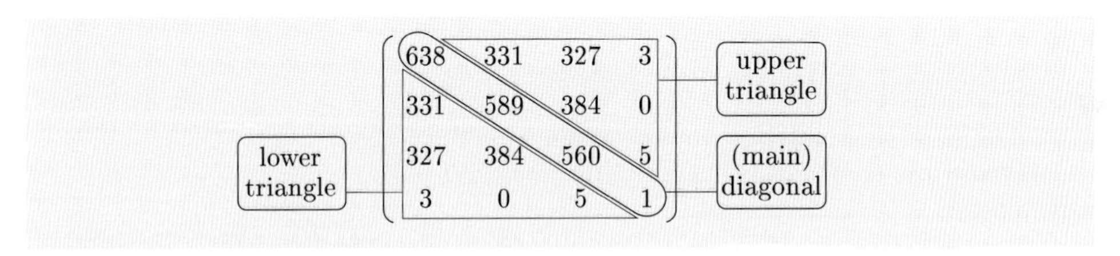

Figure 3.2 Parts of a square matrix ♦

Example 3.4 Writing down a covariance matrix

In Examples 3.2 and 3.3, the sample variances and covariances of the regional average house prices (X_1) and average household incomes (X_2) were calculated: $s_1^2 = 2645$, $s_2^2 = 38.6$ and $s_{12} = 306 (= s_{21})$. Thus $\mathbf{S}$, the covariance matrix for these data, is

$$\mathbf{S} = \begin{pmatrix} 2645 & 306 \\ 306 & 38.6 \end{pmatrix}.$$ ♦

Activity 3.5 Covariance matrix for the LEA data

In Activity 3.4, you calculated the variance of the performance in English (X_1) for the top ten LEAs using the data in Table 3.2: $s_1^2 \simeq 21.071$. You also found that the covariance between the performances in Mathematics (X_2) and Science (X_3) is 1.230. For the top ten LEAs, the variance of the performance in Mathematics is 3.155, and the variance of the performance in Science is 1.345. The covariance between the performances in English and Mathematics is 2.095, and the covariance between the performances in English and Science is 3.028. Write down the covariance matrix for the data.

Activity 3.6 Interpreting a covariance matrix

The mean vector for the log concentrations of trace elements found in parts of the plant *Echinacea purpurea* was given in Activity 3.1. The covariance matrix for these data is

$$\begin{pmatrix} 0.141 & 0.398 & 0.196 & 0.064 & -0.026 & 0.202 & -0.034 & -0.088 & 0.001 \\ 0.398 & 2.939 & 1.397 & -0.336 & -0.655 & 0.766 & 0.046 & -0.745 & -0.340 \\ 0.196 & 1.397 & 1.129 & 0.271 & 0.060 & 0.587 & -0.010 & -0.145 & 0.127 \\ 0.064 & -0.336 & 0.271 & 0.585 & 0.517 & 0.230 & -0.088 & 0.281 & 0.357 \\ -0.026 & -0.655 & 0.060 & 0.517 & 0.844 & -0.015 & 0.011 & 0.343 & 0.466 \\ 0.202 & 0.766 & 0.587 & 0.230 & -0.015 & 0.515 & 0.047 & -0.021 & 0.136 \\ -0.034 & 0.046 & -0.010 & -0.088 & 0.011 & 0.047 & 0.283 & 0.114 & 0.138 \\ -0.088 & -0.745 & -0.145 & 0.281 & 0.343 & -0.021 & 0.114 & 0.472 & 0.457 \\ 0.001 & -0.340 & 0.127 & 0.357 & 0.466 & 0.136 & 0.138 & 0.457 & 0.586 \end{pmatrix}.$$

(a) Write down the variance of the log concentration for manganese (variable X_3).

(b) Write down the variance of the log concentration for strontium (X_7).

(c) What is the covariance between the log concentration of copper (X_1) and the log concentration of lithium (X_6)?

(d) What is the covariance between the log concentration of zinc (X_4) and the log concentration of iron (X_2)?

(e) Is the log concentration of nickel (X_5) positively related to the log concentration of calcium (X_9)? Justify your answer.

(f) Compare the upper and lower triangles of this matrix. In what way are they similar? Why must all covariance matrices have this property?

Summary of Section 3

In this section, the mean vector and the covariance matrix have been introduced; they are frequently used to summarize multivariate data sets numerically. The mean vector gives the means of the individual variables. The diagonal elements of the covariance matrix are the variances of the variables; the off-diagonal elements are the covariances between pairs of variables.

Exercises on Section 3

Exercise 3.1 Reactions to immunization

A data set giving the antibody levels after a combined injection of diphtheria and typhoid toxoids was introduced in Activity 1.1. There were 42 participants in the study concerned. Unfortunately, three of the participants had both local and systemic adverse reactions to the injection. In other words, they had both redness or soreness near the injection site and more general symptoms such as a malaise or fever. The recorded antibody levels to both diphtheria and typhoid for these three participants are given in Table 3.3.

(a) Calculate the mean vector for participants who had both a local and a systemic adverse reaction to the injection.

(b) Of the remaining 39 participants in the study, nineteen had no adverse reaction, thirteen had a local adverse reaction only, and seven had a systemic reaction only. The mean vector for those who had no reaction is $(1.52, 0.67)$. For those who had a local reaction only, the mean vector is $(1.92, 0.94)$, and for those who had a systemic reaction only, the mean vector is $(2.84, 0.68)$.

Table 3.3 Antibody levels in three participants

Tetanus (X_1)	Diphtheria (X_2)
2.8	1.3
3.4	1.1
3.4	2.5

Assuming that systemic reactions are more serious than local reactions, and that having both a systemic and a local reaction is worse than having a systemic reaction only, does there appear to be a relationship between mean antibody levels and strength of adverse reaction? If so, is the relationship linked with antibodies to both of the toxoids, or to just one? Justify your answer.

Exercise 3.2 Quantifying the relationship between the cost of crime and expenditure on police

Data on the cost of crime and expenditure on police in the 50 US states and the District of Columbia were introduced in Exercise 2.1. In this data set, there are four variables: per capita cost of crimes against property (X_1), per capita cost of crimes against the person (X_2), per capita state expenditure on policing (X_3), and per capita local expenditure on policing (X_4). The pattern of expenditure on policing in the District of Columbia is markedly different to that in the states, so in this exercise only the data from the 50 states will be used. The covariance matrix for these data is

$$\mathbf{S} = \begin{pmatrix} 224 & 1803 & -2 & 269 \\ 1803 & 30204 & 971 & 3441 \\ -2 & 971 & 229 & -10 \\ 269 & 3441 & -10 & 1774 \end{pmatrix}.$$

(a) Which variable had the largest variance?

(b) Between which pair of variables was there the greatest covariance (in absolute value)?

(c) In the solution to Exercise 2.1, the following two assertions were made.

◇ There is a positive relationship between the cost of property crime and the cost of crimes against the person.

◇ There does not seem to be a relationship between local and state expenditure on policing.

Does the covariance matrix support these assertions? Explain your answers.

4 Variable standardization

The covariance matrix for a multivariate data set was introduced in Subsection 3.2 to describe the spread of values across observations. The covariances in the matrix provide information about relationships between variables. However, as you will see in Subsection 4.1, their absolute values depend on the units in which the variables are measured. In Subsection 4.2, a transformation that is commonly applied to variables that form part of a multivariate data set is introduced. This transformation is known as **standardization**. The transformation is designed so that the standardized variable has mean 0 and variance 1, and the values of the standardized variables are scale-free. The covariance matrix of a data set based on standardized variables is called the **correlation matrix**. This matrix, which is discussed in Subsection 4.3, is used to describe the strength of relationships between variables in a multivariate data set.

4.1 Why standardize?

In some of the data sets discussed in this book, the variables are all measured on the same scale. For instance, in Example 1.3 the performance of local education authorities is given for three subjects: English, Mathematics and Science. For each subject, the results represent the percentage of eleven-year-old primary school students who reached level 4 in national tests. However, in other data sets, the variables to be compared are measured in different units. For example, Activity 2.3 featured a four-dimensional data set representing the ability of some schoolboys in different aspects of mathematics. For each boy, the variables recorded are age, exam score in geometry, exam score in arithmetic and exam score in algebra.

The age of each boy is recorded in years and months. However, it could just as easily have been given in months (only), days or even seconds. None of these units (years, months, days and seconds) is suitable for the measurement of exam scores. But even with the exam scores, there is room for some arbitrariness. The amount of knowledge represented by '1 mark' is not defined. The scores could be multiplied by 2 or by 10 and they would still identify the boys who were showing more ability in these aspects of mathematics than the others.

Does it matter whether the variables are measured in different units? Yes, sometimes it does, especially when comparing variables or investigating relationships between different variables, because the relative sizes of variances and covariances depend on the units used. This is illustrated in Example 4.1.

Example 4.1 *A covariance matrix for the mathematical ability data*

Data representing the mathematical ability of schoolboys were introduced in Activity 2.3. Let X_1 represent the geometry score, X_2 the arithmetic score, X_3 the algebra score, and X_4 age.

With age measured in years, the covariance matrix for the data is given by

$$\mathbf{S}_1 = \begin{pmatrix} 638 & 331 & 327 & 3.03 \\ 331 & 589 & 384 & 0.0492 \\ 327 & 384 & 560 & 4.81 \\ 3.03 & 0.0492 & 4.81 & 1.46 \end{pmatrix}.$$

The entries in the covariance matrices in this example have been rounded to three significant figures.

If age is measured in months, the covariance matrix becomes

$$\mathbf{S}_2 = \begin{pmatrix} 638 & 331 & 327 & 36.4 \\ 331 & 589 & 384 & 0.591 \\ 327 & 384 & 560 & 57.7 \\ 36.4 & 0.591 & 57.7 & 210 \end{pmatrix}.$$

And if age is measured in days, the covariance matrix is given by

$$\mathbf{S}_3 = \begin{pmatrix} 638 & 331 & 327 & 1110 \\ 331 & 589 & 384 & 18.0 \\ 327 & 384 & 560 & 1760 \\ 1110 & 18.0 & 1760 & 194\,000 \end{pmatrix}.$$

In each of the three matrices, $\mathbf{S}_1$, $\mathbf{S}_2$ and $\mathbf{S}_3$, the elements that refer only to exam scores are unchanged. For example, the covariance between arithmetic and algebra scores, element $(2,3)$ (or, equivalently, element $(3,2)$) is 384 whichever matrix is used.

However, the numbers in the fourth row and the fourth column are different in $\mathbf{S}_1$, $\mathbf{S}_2$ and $\mathbf{S}_3$. The variance of the ages increases as smaller units are used to measure time. Looking at the main diagonal of $\mathbf{S}_1$, the spread in ages appears to be much smaller than the spread in the exam scores for any of the subjects. But when age is measured in months, the spread in ages is not very different from the spread in exam scores (look at the main diagonal of $\mathbf{S}_2$). And when age is measured in units as small as days, the spread in ages appears much larger than the spread in the exam scores.

The covariances between age and the other variables are also influenced by the change in units. These covariances are larger when age is measured in months than when age is measured in years, and larger still when age is measured in days. Thus the largest covariance appears to be between the arithmetic and algebra scores when age is measured in years (384), but between age and algebra score when age is measured in days (1760). ♦

Activity 4.1 Would the covariance matrix be helpful?

Details of four hypothetical data sets are given below. Each data set comprises observations on 1000 individuals and has three variables. In each case, explain whether or not it would make sense to attempt to interpret a covariance matrix calculated from the unstandardized variables.

(a) The three variables correspond to the weights of the individuals on three successive occasions.

(b) The three variables correspond to the weekly income of an individual, the age of an individual, and the number of years the individual has had in full-time education.

(c) The three variables correspond to the number of trips to the cinema an individual made last year, the distance from the individual's home to the nearest cinema, and the estimated amount spent on entertainment by the individual in the past year.

4.2 The standardization transformation

The covariance between positively related variables tends to be positive, the covariance between negatively related variables tends to be negative, and variables that are unrelated tend to have a covariance close to zero. However, since the absolute values of covariances depend on the units of measurement, how do we know whether a covariance is large because there is a strong relationship between the variables, or because of the choice of measurement units? And if a covariance is close to zero, is this because the variables are unrelated, or because of the choice of measurement units? Standardization removes this ambiguity by providing a common scale on which to compare and assess covariances.

In standardization, each variable is transformed separately and in such a way that it has mean 0 and variance 1. For variable X_j, the transformation is applied to each value x_{ij} of X_j to obtain values of a new variable Z_j. For observation i, the value x_{ij} of X_j is transformed to obtain the value z_{ij} of Z_j as follows:

$$z_{ij} = \frac{x_{ij} - \overline{x}_j}{s_j},$$

where $\overline{x}_j$ is the (sample) mean and s_j is the (sample) standard deviation for variable X_j. Subtracting $\overline{x}_j$ from each x_{ij} ensures that $\overline{z}_j$, the sample mean of the standardized variable Z_j, is 0. Dividing $(x_{ij} - \overline{x}_j)$ by the standard deviation s_j ensures that the sample variance of Z_j is 1. Note that the values z_{ij} are just numbers, they do not have any units associated with them. Thus each standardized variable Z_j is **scale-free**, whatever the measurement units of the original variable X_j.

Example 4.2 Standardizing a variable

In Example 3.1, the mean vector of house price (X_1) and household income (X_2), in thousands of pounds, across nine regions in England was calculated to be $(111.700, 32.587)$. The variances of these two variables, s_1^2 and s_2^2, were found in Example 3.2: they were 2645 and 38.6, respectively.

If Z_1 is the standardized house price, then z_{i1}, the value of Z_1 for observation i, is obtained by applying the standardization transformation to x_{i1}, the value of X_1 for observation i. Since $\overline{x}_1 = 111.700$ and $s_1^2 = 2645$,

$$z_{i1} = \frac{x_{i1} - \overline{x}_1}{s_1} = \frac{x_{i1} - 111.700}{\sqrt{2645}}.$$

For the first observation, $x_{11} = 221.537$ (relating to London),

$$z_{11} = \frac{221.537 - 111.700}{\sqrt{2645}} \simeq 2.14.$$

Similarly, for the second observation, $x_{21} = 152.555$ (relating to the South East),

$$z_{21} = \frac{152.555 - 111.700}{\sqrt{2645}} \simeq 0.79.$$

These two values and the other seven values of Z_1 are given in Table 4.1.

You will be asked to complete the final column of Table 4.1 in Activity 4.3.

Table 4.1 House price and household income (in thousands of pounds), and standardized house price, in nine English regions

Region	House price (£000s)	Household income (£000s)	Standardized house price	Standardized household income
London	221.537	46.288	2.14	
South East	152.555	38.478	0.79	
South West	124.508	29.626	0.25	
Eastern	125.154	33.819	0.26	
West Midlands	94.402	31.857	−0.34	
East Midlands	88.724	29.350	−0.45	
North East	62.089	27.405	−0.96	
North West	69.372	28.625	−0.82	
Yorkshire & Humber	66.958	27.832	−0.87	

♦

Activity 4.2 Standardized house prices

Use the values of the standardized house price Z_1 in Table 4.1 to answer the following questions.

(a) Verify that $\overline{z}_1$, the sample mean standardized house price, is 0.00 (to two decimal places, since that is the accuracy of the z_{ij}).

(b) Verify that the sample variance of Z_1 is 1.00 (to two decimal places).

Activity 4.3 Standardizing household income

The mean household income (in thousands of pounds) for the nine English regions in Table 4.1 is 32.587, and the variance is 38.6. Calculate the values of the standardized household income, and hence complete the final column of Table 4.1.

4.3 The correlation matrix

Standardized variables consist simply of numbers; they have no units associated with them. Thus even if two variables are measured using completely different units, the corresponding standardized variables are comparable. So the covariance matrix based on standardized variables can be used to compare and assess relationships between the original (unstandardized) variables.

After standardization, the variance of a variable is 1, so the elements on the main diagonal of the covariance matrix are all 1.

The sample covariance between a pair of standardized variables is simply the sample (Pearson) correlation coefficient between the unstandardized variables. Thus the covariance matrix based on the standardized variables is usually known more succinctly as the **correlation matrix**.

The proof of this result is straightforward, but has been omitted. Correlation coefficients are discussed in Subsection 5.1 of the *Introduction to statistical modelling*.

Since the elements of a correlation matrix are correlation coefficients, they take values between -1 and $+1$. Element (i, j) is the correlation coefficient between the variables X_i and X_j, which is denoted $\text{Corr}(X_i, X_j)$. This correlation coefficient measures the strength of the (linear) relationship between variables X_i and X_j. The closer its value is to $+1$, the stronger is the positive linear relationship between the two variables. ($+1$ indicates a perfect linear relationship between the variables.) Similarly, an element close to -1 indicates a strong negative linear relationship between variables. When there is little relationship between two variables, the corresponding element is close to zero.

Example 4.3 Interpreting a correlation matrix

In Example 4.1, several covariance matrices for the mathematical ability of schoolboys were given, using different units for age. The variables are geometry exam score (X_1), arithmetic exam score (X_2), algebra exam score (X_3), and age of the boy (X_4). The correlation matrix for these data is

$$\begin{pmatrix} 1 & 0.540 & 0.548 & 0.099 \\ 0.540 & 1 & 0.668 & 0.002 \\ 0.548 & 0.668 & 1 & 0.169 \\ 0.099 & 0.002 & 0.169 & 1 \end{pmatrix}.$$

Perhaps the first thing that is noticeable in this correlation matrix is that all the elements on the main diagonal are exactly 1: for each j, element (j, j) corresponds to the correlation of X_j with itself, which is 1.

The largest of the elements in the lower triangle of this correlation matrix is 0.668; this corresponds to the correlation between the exam scores in algebra and arithmetic. Thus the strongest (linear) relationship is between the marks awarded for arithmetic and algebra, with higher marks in arithmetic tending to go with higher marks in algebra. Furthermore, there are moderately high correlations between the exam scores in algebra and geometry (0.548) and between arithmetic and geometry (0.540). Thus there are also moderately strong positive relationships between the exam score in geometry and the exam scores in arithmetic and algebra.

However, there is practically no linear association between age and arithmetic exam score. Indeed, there is only at best a slight association between age and exam score for either geometry or algebra.

Overall, it appears that if a schoolboy did well in one of the aspects of mathematics, he also tended to do well in the other two aspects. However, perhaps surprisingly, the age of the schoolboy is at most only weakly related to how well he performed in the exams. Note that these conclusions agree with the general impression given in the matrix scatterplot for the data, which was shown in Figure 2.4. ♦

Activity 4.4 Spotting correlation matrices

For each of the following four matrices, state why it cannot be the correlation matrix for a set of data.

(a) $\begin{pmatrix} 1 & 0.3 & -0.2 & 0.4 \\ 0.3 & 0.7 & 0.5 & 0.1 \\ -0.2 & 0.5 & 1 & -0.3 \\ 0.4 & 0.1 & -0.3 & 1 \end{pmatrix}$ (b) $\begin{pmatrix} 1 & 0.5 & 0.6 & 0.9 \\ 0.5 & 1 & 1.7 & 0.8 \\ 0.6 & 1.7 & 1 & 0.2 \\ 0.9 & 0.8 & 0.2 & 1 \end{pmatrix}$

(c) $\begin{pmatrix} 1 & 0.7 & -0.5 & -0.2 \\ 0.2 & 1 & -0.1 & 0.3 \\ -0.1 & 0.3 & 1 & 0.2 \\ 0.7 & -0.5 & -0.2 & 1 \end{pmatrix}$ (d) $\begin{pmatrix} 1 & 0.2 & -0.3 & 0.7 \\ 0.2 & 1 & 0.4 & 0.5 \\ -0.3 & 0.4 & 1 & 0.9 \end{pmatrix}$

Activity 4.5 Correlation matrix for the LEA data

In Example 1.3, data on the performance of eleven-year-old primary school students in 150 local education authorities in England were introduced. The correlation matrix for the results in English (X_1), Mathematics (X_2) and Science (X_3) is

$$\begin{pmatrix} 1 & 0.749 & 0.778 \\ 0.749 & 1 & 0.879 \\ 0.778 & 0.879 & 1 \end{pmatrix}.$$

(a) For which two subjects does there seem to be the strongest linear association?

(b) Is there a pair of subjects for which the results do not appear to be linearly related? Explain your answer.

In Subsection 2.2, you saw that when the dimension of a multivariate data set is not small, the matrix scatterplot may not be particularly helpful for exploring relationships between variables. Might it help to use the correlation matrix instead?

Unfortunately, the number of elements in a correlation matrix increases rapidly as the dimension of the data set increases. For a data set of dimension p, the lower triangle of the correlation matrix contains $p(p-1)/2$ elements. Thus p does not have to be very large before the number of elements in the correlation matrix becomes overwhelming. In Activity 4.6, the correlation matrix for a data set with nine variables is given. Since $p = 9$, the lower triangle of the correlation matrix consists of $9 \times 8/2 = 36$ elements.

Activity 4.6 Mathematical ability revisited

In Example 2.3, a data set consisting of nine mathematical ability subscores was described. You saw that a matrix scatterplot of the data is difficult to interpret because of the dimension of the data.

The lower triangle of the correlation matrix for the data is as follows.

B	0.66							
C	0.80	0.62						
D	0.63	0.34	0.79					
E	0.50	0.19	0.48	0.45				
F	0.50	0.20	0.49	0.50	0.84			
G	0.45	0.22	0.58	0.41	0.72	0.64		
H	0.57	0.25	0.58	0.42	0.57	0.58	0.55	
I	0.47	0.22	0.57	0.40	0.51	0.50	0.52	0.91
	A	B	C	D	E	F	G	H

As with the matrix scatterplot, it is difficult to pick out any detailed structure by looking at the correlation matrix. Nevertheless, some important features can be identified.

(a) What can you say in general terms about the relationships between the subscores?

(b) Identify the four pairs of subscores with the largest correlation coefficients.

(c) Identify one subscore variable which has low correlations with most of the other subscores.

(d) Compare your answers to parts (a), (b) and (c) with those you obtained in Activity 2.4.

Activity 4.6 shows that a correlation matrix can be used to identify pairs of variables with strong relationships. However, it is difficult to deduce any other structure directly from a correlation matrix — for example, whether the observations are grouped in any way. This can be done to a limited extent using a matrix scatterplot when the dimension is not too high. However, in general, other methods are required. Two methods are discussed in Parts II and III of this book.

Summary of Section 4

In this section, standardization has been described — that is, transforming variables so that they have mean 0 and variance 1. A standardized variable has no physical units. The correlation matrix has been introduced. You have seen that the covariance matrix for a standardized data set is the same as the correlation matrix for the original data.

Exercises on Section 4

Exercise 4.1 Standardizing antibody levels

In Exercise 3.1, data on antibody levels for three people who suffered both local and systemic adverse reaction to a combined diphtheria and tetanus injection were given. The data are reproduced in Table 4.2.

Table 4.2 Antibody levels in three participants

Tetanus (X_1)	Diphtheria (X_2)
2.8	1.3
3.4	1.1
3.4	2.5

(a) For the complete data set, the mean vector is $(1.986, 0.826)$ and the covariance matrix $\mathbf{S}$ is

$$\mathbf{S} = \begin{pmatrix} 0.919 & 0.213 \\ 0.213 & 0.649 \end{pmatrix}.$$

Using the mean vector and covariance matrix, calculate the values of the standardized tetanus antibody level (Z_1) and the standardized diphtheria antibody level (Z_2) for each of the participants listed in Table 4.2.

(b) The correlation between the tetanus and diphtheria antibody levels is 0.276. Write down the correlation matrix. Briefly describe the association between the tetanus and diphtheria antibody levels that is suggested by this matrix.

Exercise 4.2 Personality and course grades

In a study of US college students, the possible effect of personality on course grades was investigated. Five personality traits were measured on each student: neuroticism (X_1), extroversion (X_2), openness (X_3), agreeableness (X_4) and conscientiousness (X_5). For each personality trait, a high score indicates that the student strongly identified with the trait. The final grade that each student achieved in a psychology course was also recorded (X_6); a high grade indicates a good performance in the course.

Lounsbury, J.W., Sundstrom, E., Loveland, J.M. and Gibson, L.W. (2003) Intelligence, 'Big Five' personality traits, and work drive as predictors of course grade. *Personality and Individual Differences*, **35**, 1231–1239.

The correlation matrix, for a sample of 175 students, is

$$\begin{pmatrix} 1 & -0.38 & -0.40 & -0.57 & -0.45 & -0.11 \\ -0.38 & 1 & 0.24 & 0.40 & 0.14 & 0.01 \\ -0.40 & 0.24 & 1 & 0.29 & 0.17 & 0.16 \\ -0.57 & 0.40 & 0.29 & 1 & 0.50 & -0.01 \\ -0.45 & 0.14 & 0.17 & 0.50 & 1 & 0.18 \\ -0.11 & 0.01 & 0.16 & -0.01 & 0.18 & 1 \end{pmatrix}.$$

(a) Between which two personality traits is there the strongest association?

(b) How is neuroticism related to the other personality traits?

(c) Does there appear to be an association between any of the personality traits and the grade achieved? If so, is this association positive or negative? (In answering this question you may assume that a correlation less than 0.20 in absolute value indicates that there is little or no association.)

Exercise 4.3 Hiking experiences

In a study of visitor satisfaction, a group of hikers were asked about their experiences as they walked along a hill trail in Western Australia. As the hikers stood at various locations along the trail, they were asked to record the extent to which the location was stimulating each of fifteen emotions. These emotions ranged from negative ones, such as boring and depressing, to positive ones, such as stimulating, relaxing and pleasing. In each case, a high score indicates a strong emotional response.

Chhetri, P., Arrowsmith, C. and Jackson, M. (2004) Determining hiking experiences in nature-based tourist destinations. *Tourism Management*, **25**, 31–43.

The diagonal and the lower triangle of the correlation matrix based on the values recorded for each of the eight positive emotions are as follows.

Attracting	1							
Challenging	0.17	1						
Enjoying	0.27	0.20	1					
Exciting	0.36	0.15	0.48	1				
Motivating	0.20	0.12	0.46	0.46	1			
Pleasing	0.37	0.28	0.65	0.80	0.47	1		
Relaxing	0.38	0.11	0.42	0.51	0.33	0.40	1	
Stimulating	0.23	0.19	0.42	0.39	0.56	0.40	0.26	1

(a) Comment in general terms on the direction of the relationships between the variables.

(b) Identify the two pairs of variables with highest correlations.

(c) Identify one variable for which correlations with the other variables tend to be rather low.

(d) Briefly summarize your results.

5 Obtaining graphical and numerical summaries of multivariate data

For multivariate data sets, the calculation of numerical summaries by hand is usually tedious; and although most plots can be constructed by hand, it is often a laborious task to do so. In practice, both numerical summaries and graphical representations of multivariate data are usually obtained using a computer.

In this section, you will learn how to construct scatterplots, matrix scatterplots and profile plots using SPSS. You will also learn how to obtain mean vectors, covariance matrices and correlation matrices using SPSS.

Refer to Chapters 1 and 2 of Computer Book 3 for the work in this section.

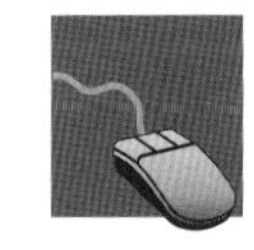

Summary of Section 5

In this section, you have learned how to use SPSS to produce graphical representations and numerical summaries of multivariate data. In particular, you have learned how to obtain 2-d scatterplots and matrix scatterplots, and how to label individual points on these plots. You have seen that transposing data in SPSS allows profile plots to be drawn. You have also learned how to calculate mean vectors, covariance matrices and correlation matrices using SPSS.

Part II Reducing dimension

Introduction to Part II

In Part I, numerical summaries and graphical techniques for displaying multivariate data were discussed. You saw that graphs such as the matrix scatterplot enable relationships between variables to be visualized and outliers to be identified, and that the strengths of relationships between variables can be quantified using the correlation matrix. However, these techniques work well only when the number of variables is not too large: their usefulness decreases as the dimension of the data set increases.

Many multivariate data sets that arise have tens, hundreds or even thousands of variables — for example, in shape and pattern recognition, bioinformatics, and meteorology. For such data sets, the techniques introduced in Part I become unwieldy. In Part II, a method for reducing the number of variables to be displayed or analysed is described. The idea is to approximate the multivariate data set by a data set that has fewer variables. This smaller data set is constructed in such a way that it can be thought of as being as good an approximation as possible to the original data set. Techniques in multivariate analysis for achieving this are known as **dimension reduction** techniques. The method discussed in Part II is called **principal component analysis**, or PCA for short. The key is to reduce the dimension without unduly distorting the main features of the original data. If the distortion is not too severe, the features of the original data can be investigated by applying the techniques discussed in Part I to the approximate data set which has lower dimension.

In Section 6, the simplest dimension reduction task is considered; this involves approximating a bivariate data set by a single variable. In Section 7, the approach used in Section 6 is extended to the task of approximating a data set of any dimension by a single variable; this variable is called the **first principal component**. A method for measuring the quality of the approximation is also presented. Often, a single-variable approximation is found to be inadequate. In Section 8, approximating a data set by two or more variables is discussed; the approximating variables are called **principal components**. You will learn how to carry out a principal component analysis using SPSS in Section 9.

6 Dimension reduction for bivariate data

The simplest dimension reduction task, the approximation of a bivariate data set by a single variable, is considered in this section. The relationship between two variables can be displayed on a two-dimensional scatterplot. Thus, in most circumstances, it is not necessary to reduce the dimension of bivariate data. However, there are situations in which it might be helpful to work with one variable instead of two. For example, it might be important to rank the data.

Reducing the dimension from two to one means that each observation is represented by one number, instead of two. This number might be the value of one of the variables, or it might be calculated using the values of both the variables — for example, by taking the average of the two variables, or the sum, or the difference.

In Subsection 6.1, single-variable approximations for a bivariate data set are discussed; linear combinations of two variables are defined in Subsection 6.2. A criterion for choosing the best linear combination to use as an approximation for a bivariate data set is introduced in Subsection 6.3.

6.1 Seeking a single-variable approximation

A bivariate data set on interest rates is described in Example 6.1. This data set is used throughout this section to illustrate the ideas involved in finding a single variable to approximate a bivariate data set.

Example 6.1 Comparing national interest rates

As part of its publication *Main Economic Indicators*, the Organization of Economic Co-operation and Development (OECD) publishes data on the interest rates in various countries. Two types of interest rate are given: short-term and long-term. For annual data, the short-term interest rates correspond to three-month rates, whereas the long-term rates generally correspond to ten-year government bonds. Table 6.1 gives the interest rates for ten countries in 2004.

OECD, *Main Economic Indicators*, January 2005.

Table 6.1 Short-term and long-term interest rates in ten countries

Country	Short-term interest rate (%)	Long-term interest rate (%)	Average rate (%)
Canada	2.31	4.58	3.445
United States	1.56	4.27	2.915
Australia	5.48	5.61	5.545
Japan	0.03	1.49	0.760
New Zealand	6.13	6.07	6.100
Czech Republic	2.36	4.75	3.555
Denmark	2.14	4.30	3.220
Norway	2.01	4.37	3.190
Sweden	2.11	4.43	3.270
United Kingdom	4.57	4.87	4.720

In New Zealand, Australia and the United Kingdom, short-term and long-term interest rates were similar in 2004, whereas in the other countries there was a difference of roughly 2% between the two types of rate. Clearly, Japan had the lowest interest rates and New Zealand the highest. However, it is not possible to order the interest rates unambiguously: for example, were interest rates higher or lower in Denmark than in Norway?

To rank the interest rates in these countries, a single measure of interest rates is required. One such measure can be calculated by simply averaging the quoted short-term and long-term interest rates. This combined interest rate is given in the final column of Table 6.1. Not surprisingly, Japan had the lowest average interest rate in 2004 and New Zealand the highest. ♦

In Example 6.1, the mean was used to obtain a single-variable approximation to the data. But is there a different, better, combination of the two variables that could have been used? How do we judge what is best? The answers to these questions depend on the qualities that are required of a good approximation.

Example 6.2 Comparing national interest rates, continued

A scatterplot of the national interest rates is shown in Figure 6.1.

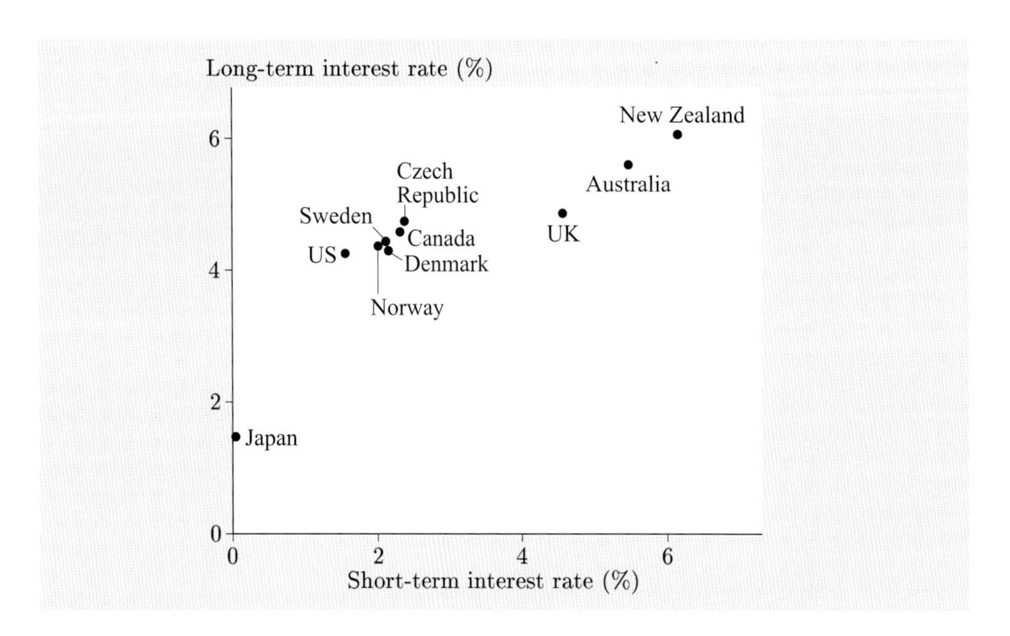

Figure 6.1 Short-term and long-term interest rates in 2004 in ten countries

From this scatterplot, it is clear that the short-term and long-term interest rates for each country are related. For example, the point representing Japan is isolated in the bottom left-hand corner of the plot, reflecting the low short-term and long-term interest rates in that country. Similarly, the high short-term and long-term interest rates in New Zealand place the point for that country in the top right-hand corner of the plot. On the other hand, the points representing Sweden, Norway and Denmark, and to a lesser extent the Czech Republic, United States and Canada, cluster together, reflecting the fact that the short-term and long-term interest rates are similar in these countries.

In any good one-dimensional approximation to these bivariate data, the same patterns should, as far as possible, be reflected. In particular, the values representing Sweden, Norway and Denmark should be close together whereas the values representing Japan and New Zealand should be quite distinct. The values of the new approximate variable should reflect *relative* differences between the countries, but it does not matter whether the value assigned to each country is numerically close to either the observed short-term or the observed long-term interest rate. ♦

Three approximations to the interest rate data are discussed in Example 6.3.

Example 6.3 Three approximations

In Example 6.1, the average interest rate was used as an approximation to the short-term and long-term interest rates. The average interest rates range from 0.760% in Japan to 6.100% in New Zealand, and the mean of the average interest rates is 3.672%. Two other possible one-dimensional approximations are as follows.

◇ The sum of the interest rates: $X_1 + X_2$.

◇ The centred average interest rate, that is, the average of the interest rates transformed to have mean zero: $0.5(X_1 + X_2) - 3.672$.

The values of the approximations are given in Table 6.2.

Table 6.2 Three approximations to short-term and long-term interest rates

Country	Average (%)	Sum (%)	Centred average (%)
Canada	3.445	6.89	−0.227
United States	2.915	5.83	−0.757
Australia	5.545	11.09	1.873
Japan	0.760	1.52	−2.912
New Zealand	6.100	12.20	2.428
Czech Republic	3.555	7.11	−0.117
Denmark	3.220	6.44	−0.452
Norway	3.190	6.38	−0.482
Sweden	3.270	6.54	−0.402
United Kingdom	4.720	9.44	1.048

Superficially, these approximations look quite different: the sums of the interest rates are more spread out than either of the two averages, and the centred average interest rates are lower than the average interest rates. Plots of these three variables are shown in Figure 6.2.

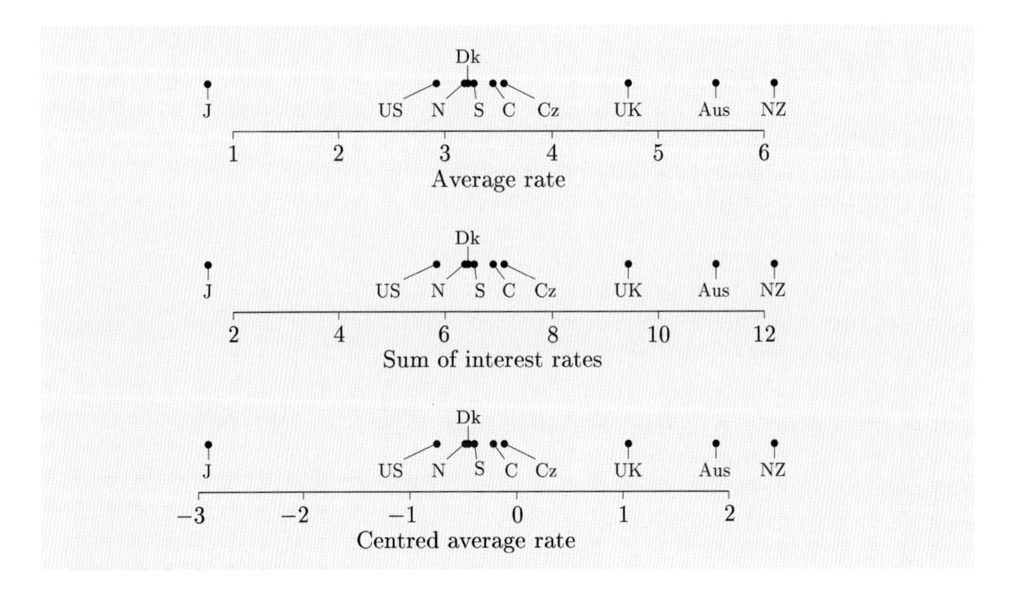

Figure 6.2 Plots of three one-dimensional approximations to the national interest rate data

Note that the relative positions of the points are identical in the three plots. All that has changed is the labelling of the axes. Thus these three approximations are essentially the same. ♦

In Example 6.3, the mean of the approximate variable was changed without effectively changing the approximation, and the scale was changed without effectively changing the quality of the approximation. The three approximations are said to be **equivalent**. The definition of equivalent approximations is given in the following box.

Equivalent approximations

Two approximations, Y_1 and Y_2, are **equivalent** if constants $c_1 \neq 0$ and c_2 can be found such that

$$Y_2 = c_1 Y_1 + c_2.$$

Thus two approximations Y_1 and Y_2 are equivalent if Y_2 can be obtained from Y_1 by multiplication by a non-zero constant, c_1, and addition of another constant, c_2.

Activity 6.1 Spotting equivalent approximations

Explain whether or not each of the following one-dimensional approximations to the pair of variables X_1 and X_2 is equivalent to taking the average, $(X_1 + X_2)/2$.

(a) $X_1 X_2/2$

(b) $0.8X_1 + 0.2X_2$

(c) $0.5X_1 - 0.5X_2$

(d) $0.5X_1 + 0.5X_2 - 1$

(e) $X_1 - X_2$

(f) $(1/\sqrt{2})X_1 + (1/\sqrt{2})X_2 - 8/\sqrt{3}$

6.2 Linear combinations of two variables

There are many ways in which two variables, X_1 and X_2, can be combined mathematically to create a new variable Y. One way is by means of a *linear combination.* A variable Y is said to be a **linear combination** of X_1 and X_2 if, for some constants α_1 and α_2,

$$Y = \alpha_1 X_1 + \alpha_2 X_2. \qquad (6.1)$$

The value of Y for observation i is given by

$$y_i = \alpha_1 x_{i1} + \alpha_2 x_{i2}.$$

The constant α_1 is called the **loading for variable X_1**. Similarly, α_2 is called the **loading for variable X_2**. Calculating the values of a linear combination is illustrated in Example 6.4.

Example 6.4 A linear combination

Suppose that X_1 represents the short-term interest rate in 2004 and X_2 represents the long-term interest rate, and that $Y = \alpha_1 X_1 + \alpha_2 X_2$ is a linear combination of X_1 and X_2. When $\alpha_1 = \alpha_2 = 1/\sqrt{2}$, the value of Y for Canada is

$$\begin{aligned} y_1 &= \alpha_1 x_{11} + \alpha_2 x_{12} \\ &= (1/\sqrt{2}) \times 2.31 + (1/\sqrt{2}) \times 4.58 \simeq 4.872. \end{aligned}$$

Similar calculations for the other nine countries give the values of the variable Y shown in the final column of Table 6.3.

Table 6.3 A one-dimensional approximation

i	Country	X_1	X_2	Y
1	Canada (C)	2.31	4.58	4.872
2	United States (US)	1.56	4.27	4.122
3	Australia (Aus)	5.48	5.61	7.842
4	Japan (J)	0.03	1.49	1.075
5	New Zealand (NZ)	6.13	6.07	8.627
6	Czech Republic (Cz)	2.36	4.75	5.028
7	Denmark (Dk)	2.14	4.30	4.554
8	Norway (N)	2.01	4.37	4.511
9	Sweden (S)	2.11	4.43	4.624
10	United Kingdom (UK)	4.57	4.87	6.675

Notice that the countries that had a high average interest rate in 2004 (notably New Zealand, Australia and the United Kingdom) have a large value of Y. The value of Y for Japan, which had a notably low average interest rate, is relatively small. ♦

Activity 6.2 Calculating Y

Using the interest rate data in Table 6.1, calculate the value of Y for Canada for each of the following pairs of values of α_1 and α_2; that is, calculate the value of $y_1 = \alpha_1 x_{11} + \alpha_2 x_{12}$.

(a) $\alpha_1 = 1$ and $\alpha_2 = 0$

(b) $\alpha_1 = 0$ and $\alpha_2 = 1$

(c) $\alpha_1 = 0.8$ and $\alpha_2 = 0.6$

(d) $\alpha_1 = 1/\sqrt{2}$ and $\alpha_2 = -1/\sqrt{2}$

(e) $\alpha_1 = 0.6$ and $\alpha_2 = -0.8$

If the linear combination Y is defined as in (6.1), then the mean of Y depends on the values of the constants α_1 and α_2 and on the means of X_1 and X_2. In practice, the linear combination Y is usually defined as follows:

$$Y = \alpha_1(X_1 - \overline{X}_1) + \alpha_2(X_2 - \overline{X}_2). \tag{6.2}$$

This ensures that the mean of Y is zero, whatever the values of α_1, α_2, $\overline{X}_1$ and $\overline{X}_2$. The formula for Y in (6.2) can be rewritten as follows:

$$Y = \alpha_1 X_1 + \alpha_2 X_2 - (\alpha_1 \overline{X}_1 + \alpha_2 \overline{X}_2).$$

For any particular data set, $\overline{X}_1$ and $\overline{X}_2$ are just the means of the values of X_1 and X_2, respectively, so they are constants. Therefore, for any given choice of α_1 and α_2, the quantity $\alpha_1 \overline{X}_1 + \alpha_2 \overline{X}_2$ is just a constant. Thus the approximations given by (6.1) and (6.2) are equivalent.

When α_1 and α_2 are both multiplied by a constant c_1, this produces an equivalent approximation. The following constraint is usually placed on the possible values of α_1 and α_2:

$$\alpha_1^2 + \alpha_2^2 = 1.$$

Note that any approximation by a linear combination for which $\alpha_1^2 + \alpha_2^2 \neq 1$ can be replaced by an equivalent approximation for which $\alpha_1^2 + \alpha_2^2 = 1$. Thus the problem of choosing between equivalent approximations can be eliminated, and the task of finding the 'best' linear combination reduced to choosing from among linear combinations (6.2), which have mean 0, for which $\alpha_1^2 + \alpha_2^2 = 1$.

The equivalent approximation is obtained by multiplying the linear combination by the constant $(\alpha_1^2 + \alpha_2^2)^{-1/2}$.

6.3 Choosing between linear combinations

Restricting the approximation Y to be a linear combination of X_1 and X_2 with $\alpha_1^2 + \alpha_2^2 = 1$ still leaves many possible different values of α_1 and α_2. What makes a good choice for α_1 and α_2? To answer this question, the quality of the resulting approximations must be compared in some way.

Example 6.5 Six linear combinations

In Activity 6.2, you calculated the value of Y for Canada for several choices of α_1 and α_2. In each case, $\alpha_1^2 + \alpha_2^2 = 1$. (You might like to check this.) The values for the other countries were calculated in a similar way, then all the values were adjusted so that the mean of Y is zero. The resulting values of Y are given in Table 6.4, together with results for the linear combination discussed in Example 6.4 ($\alpha_1 = \alpha_2 = 1/\sqrt{2}$).

Table 6.4 Values of the linear combination Y for different choices of α_1 and α_2

i	Country	(a) $\alpha_1 = 1/\sqrt{2}$, $\alpha_2 = 1/\sqrt{2}$	(b) $\alpha_1 = 1$, $\alpha_2 = 0$	(c) $\alpha_1 = 0$, $\alpha_2 = 1$	(d) $\alpha_1 = 0.8$, $\alpha_2 = 0.6$	(e) $\alpha_1 = 1/\sqrt{2}$, $\alpha_2 = -1/\sqrt{2}$	(f) $\alpha_1 = 0.6$, $\alpha_2 = -0.8$
1	Canada (C)	0.321	−0.560	0.106	−0.384	−0.471	−0.421
2	United States (US)	−1.071	−1.310	−0.204	−1.170	−0.782	−0.623
3	Australia (Aus)	2.649	2.610	1.136	2.770	1.042	0.657
4	Japan (J)	−4.118	−2.840	−2.984	−4.062	0.102	0.683
5	New Zealand (NZ)	3.434	3.260	1.596	3.566	1.177	0.679
6	Czech Republic (Cz)	−0.165	−0.510	0.276	−0.242	−0.556	−0.527
7	Denmark (Dk)	−0.639	−0.730	−0.174	−0.688	−0.393	−0.299
8	Norway (N)	−0.682	−0.860	−0.104	−0.750	−0.535	−0.433
9	Sweden (S)	−0.569	−0.760	−0.044	−0.634	−0.506	−0.421
10	United Kingdom (UK)	1.482	1.700	0.396	1.598	0.922	0.703

These values are plotted in Figure 6.3; each plot corresponds to a different choice of α_1 and α_2.

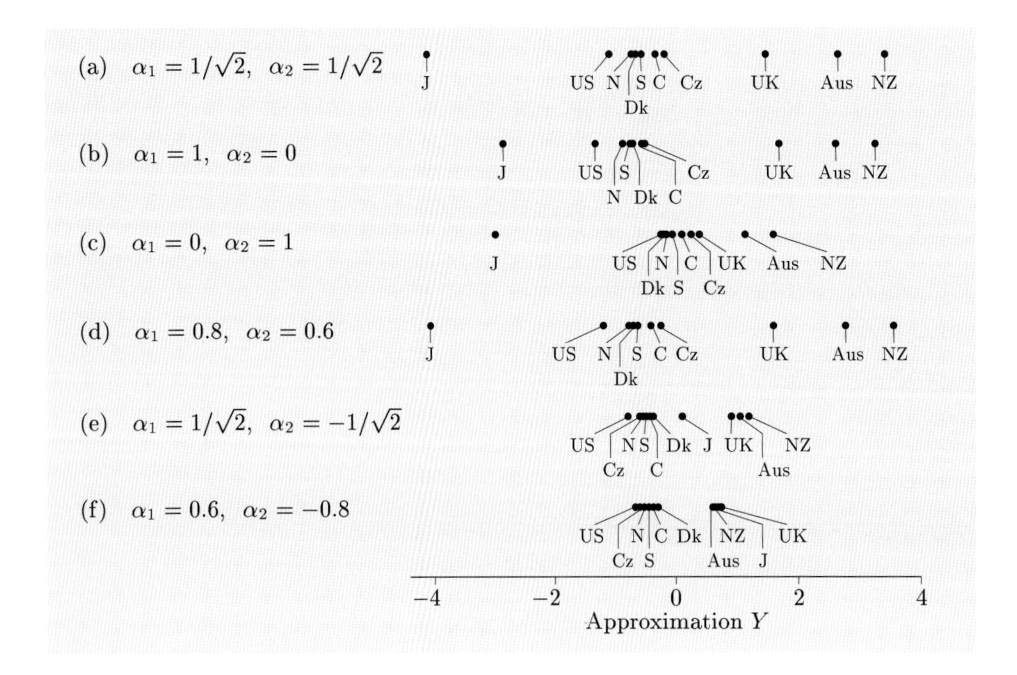

Figure 6.3 Six approximations to the interest rate data

Look at Figure 6.3(a): it is clear that the choice of $\alpha_1 = \alpha_2 = 1/\sqrt{2}$ does a reasonable job of capturing the general patterns in the data that can be seen in the scatterplot in Figure 6.1. The value for Japan (labelled J) is much lower than the values for the other countries. Similarly, the high values for the United Kingdom, Australia and New Zealand reflect the combination of high short-term and long-term interest rates in these countries. The plot also highlights the similarity in interest rates for Norway, Sweden and Denmark (and to a lesser extent Canada and the Czech Republic), as the points for these countries are clustered together.

Figures 6.3(b) and 6.3(d) are broadly similar to Figure 6.3(a). This indicates that in these cases the choices of α_1 and α_2 used to calculate Y do a good job of capturing the general patterns in the bivariate data. Figure 6.3(c) also does reasonably well, although the points for the US and the UK are not separated from the central cluster of points as in Figures 6.3(a), 6.3(b) and 6.3(d).

In contrast, Figures 6.3(e) and 6.3(f) give a radically different impression of the relationship between interest rates in the countries from that given by the 2-d scatterplot. In these plots, the point representing Japan is close to the points representing the United Kingdom, Australia and New Zealand. This indicates that $\alpha_1 = 1/\sqrt{2}$, $\alpha_2 = -1/\sqrt{2}$ and $\alpha_1 = 0.6$, $\alpha_2 = -0.8$ are poor choices. With either choice, the resulting linear combination does not provide a good approximation to the bivariate data. ♦

A choice of values for α_1 and α_2 is a good one if the dominant patterns in the bivariate data are reflected in the values of Y. However, in practice the dominant one-dimensional pattern in the data is not known in advance; if it were known then there would be no need to calculate Y using a linear combination. The choice of linear combination is therefore based on the spread of the Y values. The more bunched these values are, the more difficult it will be to identify any patterns. Thus a good choice of linear combination is one for which the spread of the Y values is large. For mathematical convenience, the measure of spread used is the sample variance.

Throughout Parts II and III, the terms variance and covariance refer to *sample* quantities.

Unfortunately, one way of increasing the variance of the points is to multiply both α_1 and α_2 by a constant c_1, where $c_1 > 1$. In this way, an equivalent approximation with large variance could be produced from a poor approximation, but it would still be a poor approximation. This problem is avoided by imposing the constraint $\alpha_1^2 + \alpha_2^2 = 1$.

Thus the best choices of α_1 and α_2 are those for which the sample variance of the resulting Y is maximized among all pairs of values α_1 and α_2 such that $\alpha_1^2 + \alpha_2^2 = 1$.

Example 6.6 Comparing linear combinations

For one of the linear combinations considered in Example 6.5, $\alpha_1 = \alpha_2 = 1/\sqrt{2}$. The resulting values of Y, adjusted so that the mean value of Y is zero, are in Table 6.4. Using these values, the variance of Y can be calculated as follows:

$$\begin{aligned} V(Y) = \frac{1}{10-1}\sum_{i=1}^{10}(y_i - \overline{y})^2 &= \frac{1}{9}\sum_{i=1}^{10} y_i^2 \\ &= \tfrac{1}{9}\left(0.321^2 + (-1.071)^2 + \cdots + 1.482^2\right) \\ &\simeq 4.493. \end{aligned}$$

The sample variance of Y for each choice of α_1 and α_2 in Table 6.4 is given in Table 6.5.

For each of the choices of α_1 and α_2 in Table 6.5, $\alpha_1^2 + \alpha_2^2 = 1$ (see Example 6.5). Hence, out of these six choices, the best choice is $\alpha_1 = 0.8$ and $\alpha_2 = 0.6$, since the variance is largest for this choice. Looking at Figure 6.3(d), this choice seems sensible. When $\alpha_1 = 0.8$ and $\alpha_2 = 0.6$, the large difference between Japan and countries such as the United Kingdom, Australia and New Zealand is emphasized. The similarity between the interest rates in the Scandinavian countries Norway, Sweden and Denmark is clear from the proximity of the points representing these countries. Moreover, in Figure 6.3(d) slight differences between the interest rates in the Scandinavian countries and the rates in the United States, Canada and the Czech Republic are also noticeable. This fine detail is not apparent in Figure 6.3(c), and arguably not quite as clear in Figures 6.3(a) and 6.3(b) as it is in Figure 6.3(d). ♦

Table 6.5 Variance of Y for six choices of α_1 and α_2

α_1	α_2	$V(Y)$
$1/\sqrt{2}$	$1/\sqrt{2}$	4.493
1	0	3.615
0	1	1.452
0.8	0.6	4.717
$1/\sqrt{2}$	$-1/\sqrt{2}$	0.574
0.6	−0.8	0.350

In Example 6.6, the value of $V(Y)$ for each choice of α_1 and α_2 was found by first calculating the value of Y for every observation. However, calculating $V(Y)$ in this way quickly becomes tedious as the number of different choices of α_1 and α_2 considered increases. Fortunately, there is an alternative way of calculating $V(Y)$. It can be shown that if Y is given by (6.1) or (6.2), then

$$V(Y) = \alpha_1^2 V(X_1) + \alpha_2^2 V(X_2) + 2\alpha_1\alpha_2 \operatorname{Cov}(X_1, X_2). \tag{6.3}$$

This formula includes the covariance between X_1 and X_2 to allow for the fact that X_1 and X_2 are generally not independent.

This means that, regardless of the number of choices of α_1 and α_2 for which $V(Y)$ needs to be evaluated, it is necessary to calculate only two variances and one covariance. The use of (6.3) is illustrated in Example 6.7.

Example 6.7 Calculating the variance of Y directly

The variance of the short-term interest rates in Table 6.1 is 3.615, and the variance of the long-term interest rates is 1.452; that is, $V(X_1) = 3.615$ and $V(X_2) = 1.452$. The covariance between X_1 and X_2 is 1.959.

The variances and the covariance have been rounded to three decimal places.

When $\alpha_1 = 1/\sqrt{2}$ and $\alpha_2 = 1/\sqrt{2}$, using Formula (6.3) gives

$$\begin{aligned} V(Y) &= \alpha_1^2 V(X_1) + \alpha_2^2 V(X_2) + 2\alpha_1\alpha_2 \operatorname{Cov}(X_1, X_2) \\ &= (1/\sqrt{2})^2 \times 3.615 + (1/\sqrt{2})^2 \times 1.452 + 2 \times (1/\sqrt{2}) \times (1/\sqrt{2}) \times 1.959 \\ &= 4.4925. \end{aligned}$$

This value is the same as that obtained in Example 6.6 (after allowing for rounding error). ♦

Activity 6.3 Calculating the variance of Y

Use Formula (6.3) to calculate the variance of Y for the national interest rate data of Example 6.1 for each of the following pairs of values of α_1 and α_2. The values of $V(X_1)$, $V(X_2)$ and $\operatorname{Cov}(X_1, X_2)$ are given in Example 6.7.

(a) $\alpha_1 = 0.8$ and $\alpha_2 = 0.6$

(b) $\alpha_1 = 1/\sqrt{2}$ and $\alpha_2 = -1/\sqrt{2}$

(c) $\alpha_1 = 0.6$ and $\alpha_2 = -0.8$

Check that the values you obtain match those given in Table 6.5.

The method for finding a 'best' linear combination Y to approximate bivariate data that has just been described is called **principal component analysis** (or PCA for short). This best linear combination Y is known as the **(first) principal component** of the bivariate data. In the context of PCA, the constant α_1 is called the **loading for variable X_1**, and the constant α_2 is the **loading for variable X_2**. The definition of the first principal component is given in the following box.

The (first) principal component of a bivariate data set

Given a bivariate data set with variables X_1 and X_2, let Y denote the following linear combination of X_1 and X_2:

$$Y = \alpha_1(X_1 - \overline{X}_1) + \alpha_2(X_2 - \overline{X}_2).$$

The constants α_1 and α_2 are called the **loadings** for variables X_1 and X_2, respectively.

The sample variance of Y is given by

$$V(Y) = \alpha_1^2 V(X_1) + \alpha_2^2 V(X_2) + 2\alpha_1\alpha_2 \operatorname{Cov}(X_1, X_2).$$

The **(first) principal component** of the data is the linear combination Y for which $V(Y)$ is maximized, subject to the constraint

$$\alpha_1^2 + \alpha_2^2 = 1.$$

It can be shown that there is just one way to choose the loadings for the principal component Y, up to a change of sign (for both loadings).

Example 6.8 The first principal component of the interest rate data

For the interest rate data, it can be shown that the maximum possible variance of Y is 4.771, and this is achieved when $\alpha_1 = 0.861$ and $\alpha_2 = 0.508$ (to three decimal places). Using these values of α_1 and α_2, the values of Y, the first principal component of these data, can be calculated. These values are given in Table 6.6.

Table 6.6 The first principal component of the national interest rate data

Country	First principal component
Canada (C)	−0.428
United States (US)	−1.232
Australia (Aus)	2.825
Japan (J)	−3.963
New Zealand (NZ)	3.619
Czech Republic (Cz)	−0.299
Denmark (Dk)	−0.717
Norway (N)	−0.793
Sweden (S)	−0.677
United Kingdom (UK)	1.665

The values of the principal component for the ten countries are plotted in Figure 6.4.

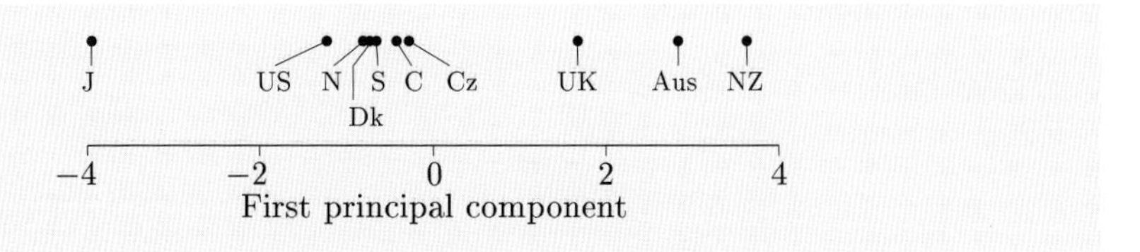

Figure 6.4 Plot of the first principal component of the interest rate data

The particularly low interest rates in Japan are indicated by the low value of the principal component for Japan; and the high values of the principal component for New Zealand, Australia and the UK correctly reflect the high interest rates in those countries. The principal component also picks up the similarity in interest rates in Norway, Denmark and Sweden, and between the interest rates in Canada and the Czech Republic. Thus the principal component is a good one-dimensional approximation to the interest rate data. Notice that Figure 6.4 looks very similar to Figures 6.3(a) and 6.3(d), which also represent good one-dimensional approximations to the interest rate data. ♦

See Example 6.5.

Activity 6.4 Land cover

In England, the percentage of land that is arable and horticultural land varies from region to region. The percentage of land that is grassland also varies from region to region. The percentages for eight regions of England in 1998 are given in Table 6.7.

Office for National Statistics (2004) *Regional Trends*, 38, HMSO, London.

Table 6.7 Percentages of land of two types in eight English regions

Region	Arable and horticultural land (X_1)	Grassland (X_2)
North	16.6	47.9
North West	15.9	45.2
Yorkshire & Humber	27.6	38.8
East Midlands	48.8	25.5
West Midlands	29.2	37.5
East Anglia	57.1	21.1
South East	41.8	27.5
South West	23.0	43.2
Average	32.5	35.8

A scatterplot of the data is shown in Figure 6.5.

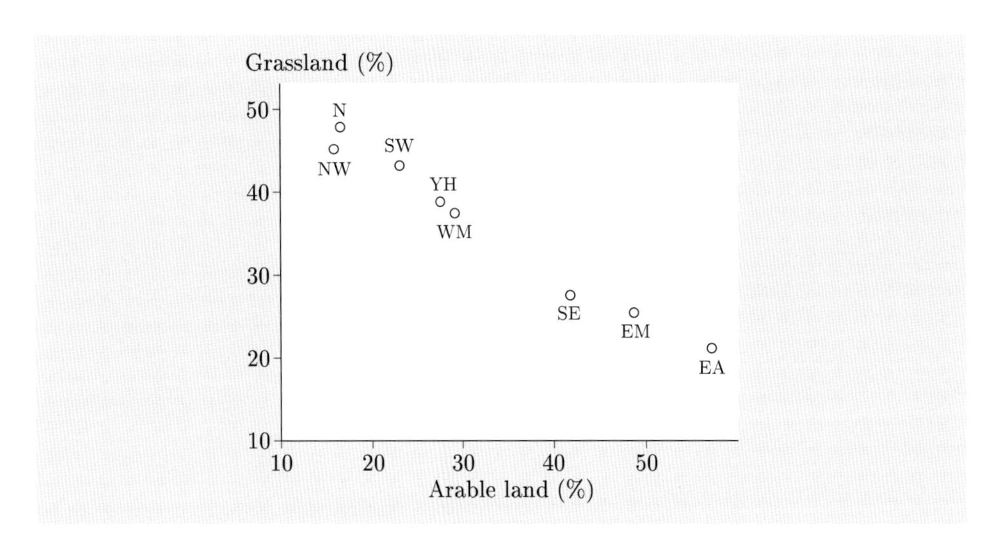

Figure 6.5 Land cover in eight English regions in 1998

(a) Describe the main features you would expect to see in a good one-dimensional approximation to the data represented in Figure 6.5.

(b) The percentage of land classified as arable and horticultural land (X_1) has variance 230.12. The percentage of land classified as grassland (X_2) has variance 98.93. The covariance of X_1 and X_2 is -149.39. Suppose that Y is a linear combination of these two variables of the form:

$$Y = \alpha_1(X_1 - \overline{X}_1) + \alpha_2(X_2 - \overline{X}_2)\,.$$

Calculate the variance of Y for each of the following pairs of values of α_1 and α_2.

(i) $\alpha_1 = 0.6$ and $\alpha_2 = 0.8$

(ii) $\alpha_1 = 0.8$ and $\alpha_2 = 0.6$

(iii) $\alpha_1 = 0.6$ and $\alpha_2 = -0.8$

(iv) $\alpha_1 = 0.8$ and $\alpha_2 = -0.6$

(c) When the variance of Y is maximized subject to the constraint $\alpha_1^2 + \alpha_2^2 = 1$, the maximum possible value of $V(Y)$ is 327.68, and this is achieved when $\alpha_1 = 0.84$ and $\alpha_2 = -0.54$ (to two decimal places). In the light of your answers to part (b), does this seem plausible?

(d) Using the values $\alpha_1 = 0.84$ and $\alpha_2 = -0.54$, calculate the value of the first principal component for the North West region. (The average values for X_1 and X_2 are given in Table 6.7.)

(e) A plot of the first principal component is shown in Figure 6.6.

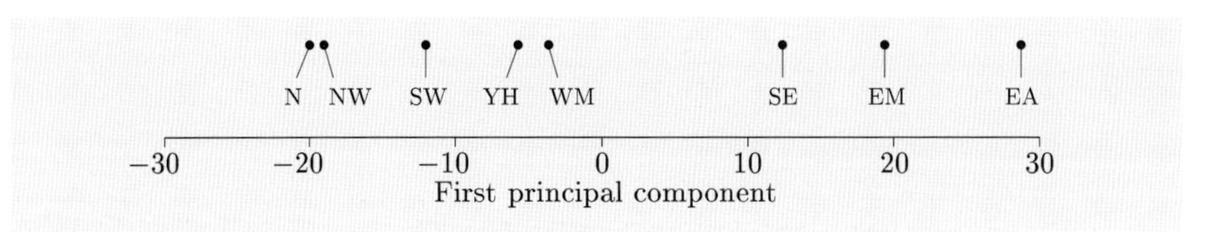

Figure 6.6 First principal component of the data in Figure 6.5

By comparing Figures 6.5 and 6.6, explain whether or not the first principal component seems to be a good one-dimensional approximation to the data.

Summary of Section 6

In this section, linear combinations of two variables X_1 and X_2 have been used to approximate bivariate data by a single variable Y. You have seen that principal component analysis provides a means of choosing the linear combination that is the 'best' approximation of bivariate data. The first principal component of X_1 and X_2 has been defined as the linear combination $Y = \alpha_1(X_1 - \overline{X}_1) + \alpha_2(X_2 - \overline{X}_2)$ that has maximum variance, subject to the constraint $\alpha_1^2 + \alpha_2^2 = 1$.

Exercises on Section 6

Exercise 6.1 Combining antibody measurements

A study investigating reactions to immunizations was described in Activity 1.1. For each young adult who took part in the study, antibodies to two different diseases were measured — tetanus (X_1) and diphtheria (X_2). Suppose that Y is a linear combination of X_1 and X_2 with mean zero, so that

$$Y = \alpha_1(X_1 - \overline{X}_1) + \alpha_2(X_2 - \overline{X}_2).$$

(a) The covariance matrix for the tetanus and diphtheria antibody measurements is

$$\mathbf{S} = \begin{pmatrix} 0.919 & 0.213 \\ 0.213 & 0.649 \end{pmatrix}.$$

Calculate the variance of Y when $\alpha_1 = 1/\sqrt{2}$ and $\alpha_2 = 1/\sqrt{2}$.

(b) Table 6.8 gives the variance of Y for a range of choices for α_1 and α_2 with $\alpha_1^2 + \alpha_2^2 = 1$. Which of the linear combinations whose variances are given in Table 6.8 will result in the best approximation to the two-dimensional data? Explain your answer.

Table 6.8 Variance of Y for several choices of α_1 and α_2

α_1	α_2	$V(Y)$
1	0	0.919
0	1	0.649
$2/\sqrt{5}$	$1/\sqrt{5}$	1.035
$1/\sqrt{5}$	$2/\sqrt{5}$	0.873
$1/\sqrt{2}$	$-1/\sqrt{2}$	0.571
$2/\sqrt{5}$	$-1/\sqrt{5}$	0.695
$1/\sqrt{2}$	$-2/\sqrt{5}$	0.533

Exercise 6.2 *Combining antibody measurements, continued*

In Exercise 6.1, data on two antibody measurements were discussed. A scatterplot of these data is shown in Figure 6.7.

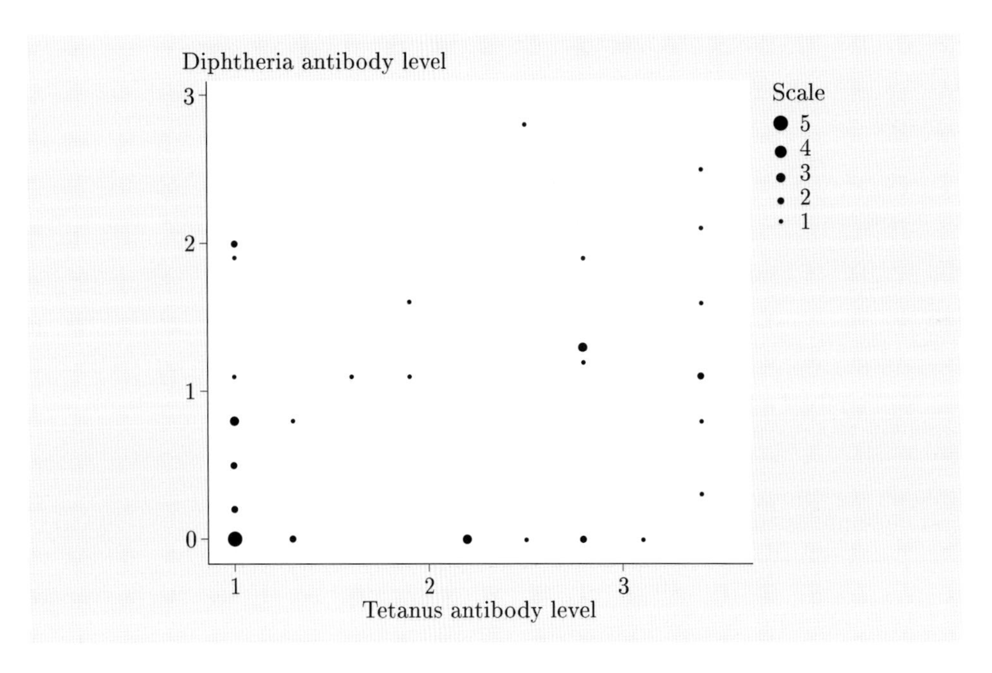

Figure 6.7 Scatterplot of tetanus and diphtheria antibody levels

The antibody responses of some individuals were the same for both diphtheria and tetanus, and hence the points representing these individuals are plotted at the same position and cannot be distinguished. The number of individuals at each point is therefore represented by the size of the dot.

(a) Briefly describe the relationship between the two antibody levels.

(b) From this scatterplot, would you expect that it would be possible to choose a good one-dimensional approximation to the data? Give a reason for your answer.

7 Dimension reduction for p variables

In Section 6, linear combinations were used to approximate bivariate data by a single variable, and a method for finding the 'best' single-variable approximation to the data, the first principal component, was described. In Subsection 7.1, the ideas introduced in Section 6 are extended to data sets of three or more variables: the first principal component of data of dimension p is defined. A method for measuring the quality of an approximation is described in Subsection 7.2. In Subsections 7.3 and 7.4, you will see why it is sometimes helpful, and may be essential, to standardize variables prior to obtaining the first principal component.

7.1 Seeking a single-variable approximation

In this subsection, the LEA performance data that were introduced in Example 1.3 are used to illustrate how the ideas involved in finding the 'best' single-variable approximation to bivariate data can be extended to data of dimension greater than two.

Example 7.1 Ranking local education authority performance

The multivariate data set relating to the performance of local education authorities that was introduced in Example 1.3 consists of three variables, relating to English (X_1), Mathematics (X_2) and Science (X_3). Each variable represents the percentage of eleven-year-old primary school students in a local education authority area who reached at least level 4 in a standardized test.

A natural aim is to rank the performance of the local authorities, and for this, a single value for each local education authority is required. When *The Times* published the data on 4 December 2003, the LEAs were ranked on the basis of the sum of the percentages for English, Mathematics and Science (that is, $X_1 + X_2 + X_3$). Does the total provide a good one-dimensional approximation to the data? Can it be improved upon? ♦

In Example 7.1, the total $X_1 + X_2 + X_3$ is a linear combination of three variables. More generally, the variable Y is a linear combination of the p variables $X_1, X_2, \ldots, X_p$ if, for constants $\alpha_1, \alpha_2, \ldots, \alpha_p$,

$$Y = \sum_{j=1}^{p} \alpha_j X_j. \qquad (7.1)$$

The value α_j is called the **loading for variable X_j**. The values $\alpha_1, \alpha_2, \ldots, \alpha_p$ are usually written in the form of a vector, $\boldsymbol{\alpha} = (\alpha_1, \alpha_2, \ldots, \alpha_p)$, which is known as a **loadings vector**.

For the total score used by *The Times* to rank LEAs, the loadings vector is $\boldsymbol{\alpha} = (1, 1, 1)$.

Example 7.2 Another linear combination of the LEA data

Suppose that the LEAs are to be ranked using the linear combination $Y = \alpha_1 X_1 + \alpha_2 X_2 + \alpha_3 X_3$, where $\alpha_1 = \frac{2}{3}$, $\alpha_2 = \frac{2}{3}$, $\alpha_3 = \frac{1}{3}$.

For the first LEA, City of London, the percentages for English, Mathematics and Science were 96.6%, 79.3% and 93.1%, respectively, so $x_{11} = 96.6$, $x_{12} = 79.3$ and $x_{13} = 93.1$. Therefore the value y_1 of Y for the City of London LEA is given by

$$\begin{aligned} y_1 &= \alpha_1 x_{11} + \alpha_2 x_{12} + \alpha_3 x_{13} \\ &= \tfrac{2}{3} \times 96.6 + \tfrac{2}{3} \times 79.3 + \tfrac{1}{3} \times 93.1 \\ &= 148.3. \end{aligned}$$ ♦

For bivariate data, the linear combination Y is usually defined so that its sample mean is zero. The same is true when the data comprise p variables $X_1, X_2, \ldots, X_p$. In practice, Y is usually defined to be

$$Y = \sum_{j=1}^{p} \alpha_j (X_j - \overline{X}_j), \qquad (7.2)$$

where $\overline{X}_j$ is the mean of X_j. The linear combinations defined by Formulas (7.1) and (7.2) represent equivalent approximations to the p-dimensional data.

An equivalent approximation is also obtained if the loadings α_j are all multiplied by the same constant.

Hence, as for bivariate data, a constraint is usually imposed on the loadings. For p-dimensional data, the constraint is as follows:

$$\sum_{j=1}^{p} \alpha_j^2 = \alpha_1^2 + \alpha_2^2 + \cdots + \alpha_p^2 = 1.$$

Note that when $p = 2$, this constraint reduces to $\alpha_1^2 + \alpha_2^2 = 1$, which is the constraint that was used in Section 6.

The 'best' single-variable approximation is the linear combination Y with loadings vector $(\alpha_1, \alpha_2, \ldots, \alpha_p)$ for which the variance of Y is maximized, subject to this constraint. The variable Y calculated using this loadings vector is known as the **(first) principal component** of $X_1, X_2, \ldots, X_p$.

The (first) principal component of a data set of dimension p

Given a data set of dimension p with variables $X_1, X_2, \ldots, X_p$, the **(first) principal component** of the data is the linear combination Y given by

$$Y = \sum_{j=1}^{p} \alpha_j (X_j - \overline{X}_j),$$

where the loadings vector $\boldsymbol{\alpha} = (\alpha_1, \alpha_2, \ldots, \alpha_p)$ is chosen so that the variance of Y is maximized, subject to the constraint

$$\sum_{j=1}^{p} \alpha_j^2 = 1.$$

Example 7.3 Ranking LEA performance, continued

For the data on local education authority performance, the first principal component is the linear combination

$$Y = \alpha_1(X_1 - \overline{X}_1) + \alpha_2(X_2 - \overline{X}_2) + \alpha_3(X_3 - \overline{X}_3),$$

where $\alpha_1^2 + \alpha_2^2 + \alpha_3^2 = 1$, for which $V(Y)$ is maximized.

It can be shown that the maximum variance is achieved when $\alpha_1 = 0.678$, $\alpha_2 = 0.583$ and $\alpha_3 = 0.449$ (to three decimal places). Using these values, the values of Y, the first principal component, vary between -20.42 and 22.20.

These values were obtained using a computer.

The ranking published in *The Times* was based on the total score. This is the same as the ranking based on the equivalent linear combination with loadings $\alpha_1 = \alpha_2 = \alpha_3 = 1/\sqrt{3}$. In general, the ranking of the LEAs based on the first principal component Y is similar to this ranking. The City of London LEA is placed first for both rankings, and the ranks of most of the LEAs differ by one or two places at most. There is one exception: the Isles of Scilly LEA was placed 60th in the ranking produced by *The Times* but is only 81st in the ranking based on the first principal component. This difference reflects the unusually poor results for English in the Isles of Scilly; although the performances in Mathematics and in Science were amongst the best in the country, the performance in English was one of the worst. In the calculation of the first principal component, the English score is given the most weight because α_1 is larger than both α_2 and α_3. However, the ranking used by *The Times* gives equal weight to the three subjects. So, for the Isles of Scilly LEA, the poor score in English has more impact on its relative standing based on the principal component than it does on its relative standing based on the total score. ♦

In Section 6, you saw that when the original data set is two-dimensional, it is not necessary to calculate each individual value of a linear combination Y in order to obtain the variance of Y: the variance of Y can be calculated directly from the variances of X_1 and X_2 and their covariance using Formula (6.3).

In general, for a data set with p variables, the variance of a linear combination Y can be calculated from the variances and covariances of the original variables $X_1, X_2, \ldots, X_p$ using the following formula:

$$V(Y) = \sum_{j=1}^{p} \alpha_j^2 V(X_j) + 2 \sum_{j,k:k>j} \alpha_j \alpha_k \operatorname{Cov}(X_j, X_k).$$

The limit on the second summation term means that the sum includes all possible pairs j and k where $k > j$.

In other words, $V(Y)$ depends on the variances of the original variables and the covariances between them. For example, for a three-dimensional data set with variables X_1, X_2 and X_3,

$$\begin{aligned} V(Y) &= \alpha_1^2 V(X_1) + \alpha_2^2 V(X_2) + \alpha_3^2 V(X_3) + 2\alpha_1\alpha_2 \operatorname{Cov}(X_1, X_2) \\ &\quad + 2\alpha_1\alpha_3 \operatorname{Cov}(X_1, X_3) + 2\alpha_2\alpha_3 \operatorname{Cov}(X_2, X_3). \end{aligned} \tag{7.3}$$

You will not be expected to calculate $V(Y)$ by hand for data sets which have dimension greater than 3.

Thus, if the covariance matrix is known, for any set of loadings $\alpha_1, \ldots, \alpha_p$, the variance $V(Y)$ can be calculated. The loadings that maximize $V(Y)$ can then be found. (This is usually done using a computer.)

Example 7.4 Calculating V(Y) for the principal component

The covariance matrix for the local education authority performance data is

$$\begin{pmatrix} 26.22 & 17.06 & 13.69 \\ 17.06 & 19.78 & 13.44 \\ 13.69 & 13.44 & 11.81 \end{pmatrix}.$$

When Y is a linear combination of the English, Mathematics and Science scores, the variance of Y is calculated using Formula (7.3), as follows:

$$\begin{aligned} V(Y) &= \alpha_1^2 V(X_1) + \alpha_2^2 V(X_2) + \alpha_3^2 V(X_3) \\ &\quad + 2\alpha_1\alpha_2 \operatorname{Cov}(X_1, X_2) + 2\alpha_1\alpha_3 \operatorname{Cov}(X_1, X_3) + 2\alpha_2\alpha_3 \operatorname{Cov}(X_2, X_3) \\ &= 26.22\alpha_1^2 + 19.78\alpha_2^2 + 11.81\alpha_3^2 \\ &\quad + 2 \times 17.06 \times \alpha_1\alpha_2 + 2 \times 13.69 \times \alpha_1\alpha_3 + 2 \times 13.44 \times \alpha_2\alpha_3. \end{aligned}$$

For the first principal component, $\alpha_1 = 0.678$, $\alpha_2 = 0.583$ and $\alpha_3 = 0.449$, so the variance is

These loadings were given in Example 7.3.

$$\begin{aligned} V(Y) &= 26.22 \times 0.678^2 + 19.78 \times 0.583^2 + 11.81 \times 0.449^2 \\ &\quad + 2 \times 17.06 \times 0.678 \times 0.583 + 2 \times 13.69 \times 0.678 \times 0.449 \\ &\quad + 2 \times 13.44 \times 0.583 \times 0.449 \\ &\simeq 50.0. \end{aligned}$$ ♦

Activity 7.1 Another linear combination for the LEA data

In ranking the LEAs, *The Times* summed the performances of each authority with respect to English, Mathematics and Science. This ranking is equivalent to using a linear combination Y of the English, Mathematics and Sciences scores with $\alpha_1 = \alpha_2 = \alpha_3 = 1/\sqrt{3}$.

(a) Calculate the variance of Y.

(b) Compare the variance of this linear combination with the variance of the first principal component, which was calculated in Example 7.4. Comment on the relative merits of the two choices of loadings vector.

7.2 How good is the approximation?

The criterion that has been used for choosing the 'best' one-dimensional approximation for a multivariate data set is based on the variance: Y_1 is regarded as providing a better approximation than Y_2 if $V(Y_1) > V(Y_2)$; and the first principal component is the linear combination Y that has the maximum variance, subject to the constraint $\sum_{j=1}^{p} \alpha_j^2 = 1$. However, the fact that Y is the linear combination with maximum variance does not mean that Y approximates the data well. A measure is needed of how good the approximation is.

The variance $V(Y)$ of a one-dimensional approximation Y measures the variability in the data that is captured by Y. This needs to be compared with the overall variability in the multivariate data. A quantity that is commonly used to measure this overall variability is the *total variance*.

For a multivariate data set with p variables, $X_1, X_2, \ldots, X_p$, the **total variance**, **TV**, is defined as follows:

$$\mathrm{TV} = \sum_{j=1}^{p} V(X_j) = V(X_1) + V(X_2) + \cdots + V(X_p).$$

The total variance is simply the sum of the variances of the individual variables. Note that the covariances between the variables do not appear in the formula for the total variance. (It may seem strange not to take the covariances into account, but there are good mathematical reasons why it does not help to include them.)

The degree to which a linear combination Y captures the total variance is given by the **percentage variance explained**, **PVE**, which is defined as follows:

$$\mathrm{PVE} = \frac{V(Y)}{\mathrm{TV}} \times 100\%.$$

When Y represents a good one-dimensional approximation to the data, the percentage variance explained is high.

It can be shown that when $\sum_{j=1}^{p} \alpha_j^2 = 1$, the percentage variance explained lies between 0% and 100%. When 0% of the variance is explained, the variance of Y is zero. In this extreme case, $y_i = \overline{Y}$ for each observation i, and hence Y cannot distinguish between the observations. When the percentage variance explained is 100%, the relative differences between the observations are represented exactly by the differences between the y_i. In this case, the original multivariate data set does not contain any more information about the differences between observations than is available from Y. This occurs only when all of the variables $X_1, \ldots, X_p$ are perfectly correlated, that is, when the correlation between X_j and X_k is either $+1$ or -1 for every pair of variables X_j and X_k.

Example 7.5 The PVE for the LEA performance data

The loadings for the first principal component Y of the LEA performance data were given in Example 7.3. The variance of the principal component is 50.0, and the variances of the English (X_1), Mathematics (X_2) and Science (X_3) scores are 26.22, 19.78 and 11.81, respectively. So, for the original multivariate data, the total variance is

See Example 7.4.

$$\mathrm{TV} = V(X_1) + V(X_2) + V(X_3) = 26.22 + 19.78 + 11.81 = 57.81.$$

Hence the percentage variance explained by the first principal component is

$$\mathrm{PVE} = \frac{V(Y)}{\mathrm{TV}} \times 100\% = \frac{50.0}{57.81} \times 100\% \simeq 86.5\%.$$

Thus most of the variability in the multivariate data is captured by the first principal component. This suggests that the approximation represented by the first principal component is a good one. ♦

Activity 7.2 Calculating the percentage variance explained

Calculate the percentage variance explained by the first principal component for each of the following bivariate data sets. In each case, comment on the quality of the approximation.

(a) The interest rate data described in Example 6.1: the variance of the first principal component is $V(Y) = 4.771$, and the variances of the two variables, X_1 and X_2, are $V(X_1) = 3.615$ and $V(X_2) = 1.452$.

(b) The land cover data described in Activity 6.4: the variance of the principal component is $V(Y) = 327.68$, and the variances of the two variables are $V(X_1) = 230.12$ and $V(X_2) = 98.93$.

7.3 Standardization

In Subsection 7.2, the percentage variance explained was introduced as a means of measuring how well a linear combination Y approximates a multivariate data set. Generally, when the percentage variance explained is close to 100%, Y represents a good approximation to the multivariate data set. However, the percentage variance explained sometimes provides a misleading impression about the quality of the approximation: it can be close to 100% whilst the approximation reflects few (or perhaps only one) of the variables in the multivariate data set.

In this subsection, several examples of multivariate data for which this problem arises are discussed. You will see how such situations can be avoided by standardizing the variables.

Example 7.6 House price and household income

In Example 1.2, a data set consisting of the average house price, X_1, and the average household income, X_2, in nine English regions was discussed. The covariance matrix for these data, with entries rounded to the nearest integer, is

$$\begin{pmatrix} 2645 & 306 \\ 306 & 39 \end{pmatrix}.$$

See Examples 3.3 and 3.4.

Hence the total variance for these data is given by

$$\text{TV} = V(X_1) + V(X_2) = 2645 + 39 = 2684.$$

The loadings for the first principal component, obtained using a computer, are $\alpha_1 = 0.993$ and $\alpha_2 = 0.115$, and the variance of the first principal component is 2680. Therefore the percentage variance explained by this principal component is

$$\text{PVE} = \frac{V(Y)}{\text{TV}} \times 100\% = \frac{2680}{2684} \times 100\% \simeq 99.9\%.$$

The percentage variance explained is very close to 100%, which suggests that the first principal component represents an extremely good one-dimensional approximation to the data. ♦

In Example 7.6, the variance explained by the first principal component Y is almost as large as the total variance of the multivariate data set. It is tempting to think that the first principal component must be an excellent substitute for the multivariate data set. However, as you will see in Example 7.7, this is not the case.

Example 7.7 House price and household income, continued

The first principal component Y of the house price and household income data is of the form

$$Y = \alpha_1(X_1 - \overline{X}_1) + \alpha_2(X_2 - \overline{X}_2),$$

where X_1 is house price and X_2 is household income. This is equivalent to

$$Y = \alpha_1 X_1 + \alpha_2 X_2 = 0.993X_1 + 0.115X_2.$$

Some of the intermediate steps in the calculation of values of Y are shown in Table 7.1.

Table 7.1 Intermediate steps in the calculation of a principal component

Region	X_1	X_2	$\alpha_1 X_1$	$\alpha_2 X_2$
London	221.5	46.3	219.9	5.3
South East	152.6	38.5	151.5	4.4
South West	124.5	29.6	123.6	3.4
Eastern	125.2	33.8	124.3	3.9
West Midlands	94.4	31.9	93.7	3.7
East Midlands	88.7	29.4	88.1	3.4
North East	62.1	27.4	61.7	3.2
North West	69.4	28.6	68.9	3.3
Yorkshire & Humber	67.0	27.8	66.5	3.2

Notice that the spread of values for $\alpha_1 X_1$ is much larger than that for $\alpha_2 X_2$. In consequence, the variation in the linear combination Y reflects almost exclusively the variation in average house price X_1. By comparison, the contribution of the variation in average household income X_2 is very minor. This can also be seen from the scatterplot in Figure 7.1.

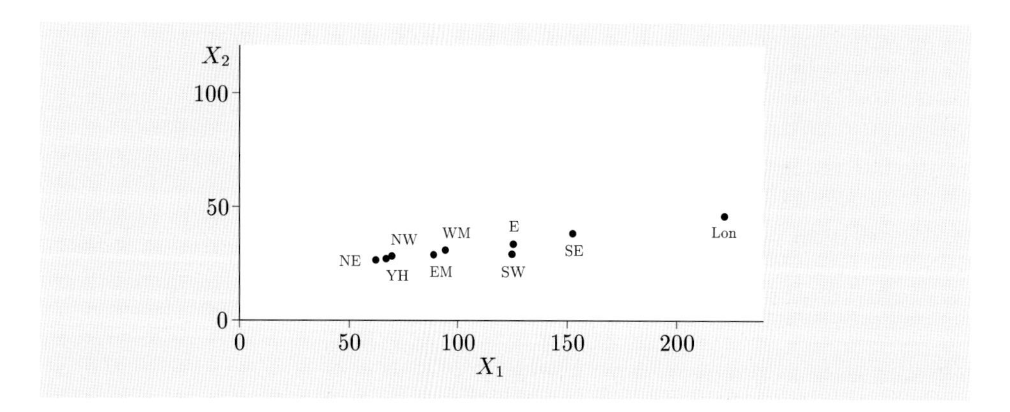

Figure 7.1 Scatterplot of the house price and household income data

Note that the scales used to plot house price (X_1) and household income (X_2) are the same. The points are spread out much more horizontally than they are vertically, reflecting the much larger variance observed for X_1 (2645) than for X_2 (39).

The principal component Y is defined so that it captures as much as possible of the variation in the bivariate data. Looking at Figure 7.1, the main variation in the bivariate data is horizontally, as a result of differences in average house prices. Any differences between regions resulting from differences in household income are small by comparison. Thus setting Y to be very similar to the average house price (X_1) is sufficient to capture this dominant variation. ♦

In general, if the variances of X_1 and X_2 are very different, then the principal component tends to reflect the variable with the greater variance, and to ignore the other variable. So, for example, if $V(X_1)$ is much greater than $V(X_2)$, as in Example 7.7, then α_1 will be much greater than α_2 in absolute value. Another example where this occurs is given in Activity 7.3.

Activity 7.3 National athletics ability

In athletics, the national records for a particular event give the best performance ever achieved by competitors from each nation. This activity concerns one such set of national records, giving men's national records for 55 countries in eight events in 1984. The events are races over distances ranging from 100 metres to a marathon (26.2 miles). Summary statistics for the eight variables, the records for the eight events in seconds, are given in Table 7.2.

Belcham, P. and Hymans, R. (eds) (1984) *IAAF/ATFS Track and Field Statistics Handbook for the 1984 Los Angeles Olympic Games*. International Amateur Athletic Federation, London.

Table 7.2 Summary statistics for the national records data (in seconds)

Event	Minimum	Maximum	Mean	Variance
100 m	9.93	12.18	10.47	0.12
200 m	19.72	23.20	20.94	0.42
400 m	43.86	52.94	46.44	2.12
800 m	102.0	121.2	107.6	14.6
1500 m	210.6	254.4	221.9	87.5
5000 m	780.6	1002.0	830.7	2 310.7
10 000 m	1642.8	2122.8	1739.3	11 764.4
Marathon	7693.2	9882.0	8197.4	306 497.3

(a) In a principal component analysis of these data, which variable will be given the largest loading? Explain your answer.

(b) The first principal component Y has loadings $\alpha_1 = 0.000\,33$ for the 100 m and $\alpha_8 = 0.98$ for the marathon. Compare the effects of an improvement in a country's best performance of one second in the 100 m and of one second in the marathon on the value of Y for that country. Hence comment on the relevance of the ranking of countries provided by the first principal component.

(c) The percentage variance explained by the first principal component is 99.5%. Comment on the quality of the approximation to the data provided by the first principal component. Does this contradict your answer to part (b)? Explain your answer.

For the data described in Activity 7.3, the principal component Y reflects primarily the variables which have the greatest variance. This is not appropriate if all variables are to be considered on equal terms. In practice, this problem is avoided by transforming the variables so that the variances of the variables are equal. This is usually done by standardizing the variables, as described in Section 4.

When a variable is standardized, it is transformed so that the sample mean is 0 and the sample variance is 1. So if the variables are standardized then they will all have sample variance equal to 1. Furthermore, the covariance matrix of the standardized variables will be the same as the correlation matrix of the unstandardized variables.

Example 7.8 Standardized house price and household income

A scatterplot of the standardized house price (Z_1) and standardized household income (Z_2) is shown in Figure 7.2.

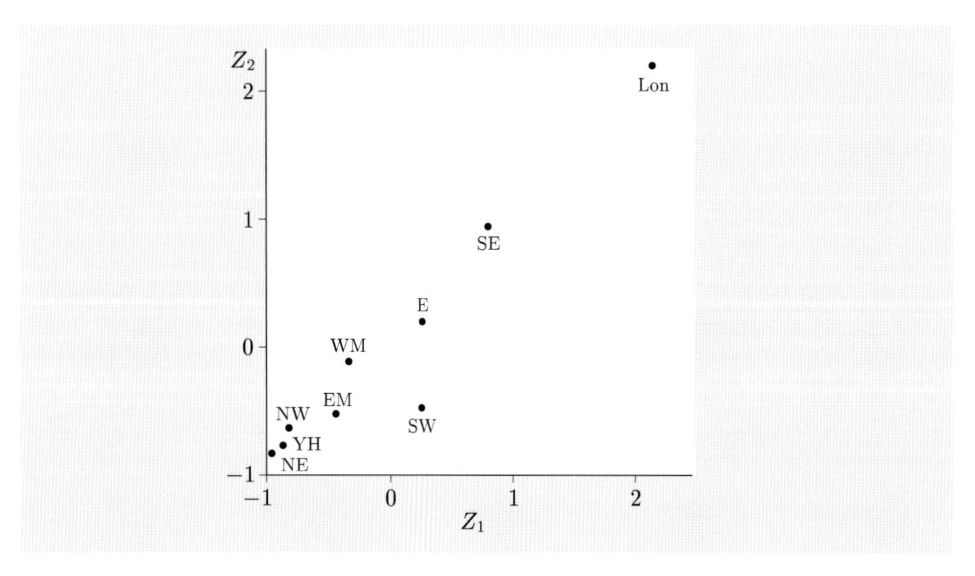

Figure 7.2 Scatterplot of standardized house price and standardized household income

Notice that the scales used for the two variables are the same, so the variation horizontally looks similar to the variation vertically: a difference of one unit in the standardized house price is the same as a difference of one unit in the standardized household income. (Though, of course, one unit of standardized house price corresponds to more money than one unit of standardized household income.) ♦

After standardizing the variables $X_1, X_2, \ldots, X_p$ in a multivariate data set, the first principal component of the standardized variables $Z_1, Z_2, \ldots, Z_p$ can be found. This is the linear combination Y of the form

$$Y = \sum_{j=1}^{p} \alpha_j Z_j = \alpha_1 Z_1 + \alpha_2 Z_2 + \cdots + \alpha_p Z_p,$$

with maximum variance, subject to the constraint $\sum_{j=1}^{p} \alpha_j^2 = 1$. Note that this formula involves Z_j, rather than $Z_j - \overline{Z}_j$, because $\overline{Z}_j$ is necessarily zero.

Example 7.9 The first principal component of the standardized data

The loadings for the first principal component Y of the standardized house price and household income data are $\alpha_1 = \alpha_2 = 1/\sqrt{2}$.

It can be shown that for bivariate standardized data, the best choices for α_1 and α_2 are always $\pm 1/\sqrt{2}$.

The variance of Y can be found using Formula (6.3):

$$V(Y) = \alpha_1^2 V(Z_1) + \alpha_2^2 V(Z_2) + 2\alpha_1\alpha_2 \operatorname{Cov}(Z_1, Z_2).$$

Since the covariance matrix for the standardized data is the same as the correlation matrix for the original data, the variance of Y can be calculated directly from the correlation matrix for the unstandardized variables. The correlation matrix is

$$\begin{pmatrix} 1 & 0.958 \\ 0.958 & 1 \end{pmatrix}.$$

Therefore

$$\begin{aligned} V(Y) &= \alpha_1^2 \times 1 + \alpha_2^2 \times 1 + 2\alpha_1\alpha_2 \times 0.958 \\ &= (1/\sqrt{2})^2 \times 1 + (1/\sqrt{2})^2 \times 1 + 2 \times (1/\sqrt{2}) \times (1/\sqrt{2}) \times 0.958 \\ &= 0.5 + 0.5 + 0.958 = 1.958. \end{aligned}$$

For standardized data, the variance of each variable is 1. The total variance is equal to the number of variables, which is 2 in this case. Thus, when using the standardized data, the percentage variance explained by the first principal component is

$$\text{PVE} = \frac{V(Y)}{\text{TV}} \times 100\% = \frac{1.958}{2} \times 100\% = 97.9\%.$$

This is less than the 99.9% obtained when working with the original data. In this case, a considerable amount of the variation in the data is captured by the first principal component when working with the standardized data. However, note that the loadings α_1 and α_2 for the principal component Y are equal: house price and household income contribute equally to the first principal component Y. Figure 7.3 displays the values of the first principal component Y for each of the nine regions.

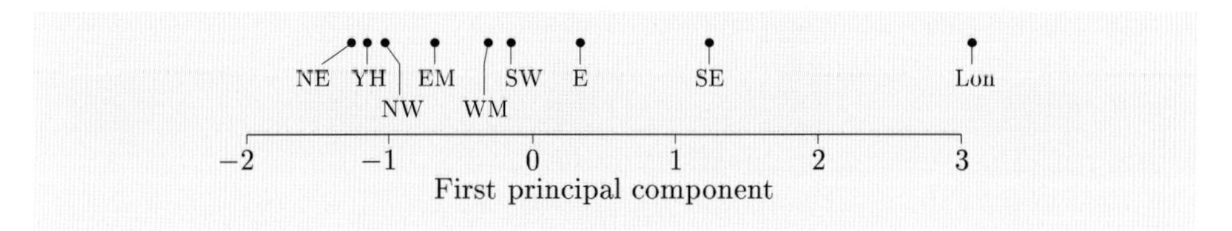

Figure 7.3 Values of the first principal component Y for the standardized house price and standardized household income data

It is clear that the first principal component has captured the dominant one-dimensional pattern in Figure 7.2. The regions where standardized house prices and standardized household incomes are low tend to lie in the lower left-hand corner of the plot, whereas London and the South East, where standardized house prices and standardized annual household incomes are high, lie in the top right-hand corner of the plot. The first principal component in Figure 7.3 has captured the separation between the points representing the Eastern and South West regions that is apparent in Figure 7.2 but not in the scatterplot of the unstandardized data in Figure 7.1. ♦

Activity 7.4 Air quality

This activity brings together several of the ideas discussed so far in this section.

As part of routine monitoring of air quality, concentrations of various chemicals in the air are recorded at various locations across the UK. Five of the chemicals that are included in this monitoring are benzene (C_6H_6), carbon monoxide (CO), nitrogen dioxide (NO_2), ozone (O_3) and sulphur dioxide (SO_2). The average concentrations of these chemicals (in $\mu g/m^3$) during 2004 are available for 22 locations.

These data were obtained from the UK National Air Quality Information Archive, http://www.airquality.co.uk, in March 2005.

(a) Summary statistics of the average concentrations in 2004 for the five chemicals across the 22 locations are given in Table 7.3.

Table 7.3 Summary statistics for chemical concentrations in the air

Chemical	Minimum	Maximum	Mean	Variance
C_6H_6	0.81	2.48	1.32	0.118
CO	200	1000	355	38 788
NO_2	17	110	32.3	384
O_3	15	53	39.8	80.7
SO_2	1	17	7.05	24.3

Comment on the relative variability of the measurements for the chemicals.

(b) Calculate the total variance of the (unstandardized) data set. If the carbon monoxide concentration is used as a one-dimensional approximation Y for the data, calculate the percentage variance explained by Y.

(c) The correlation matrix of the data is as follows.

	C_6H_6	CO	NO_2	O_3	SO_2
C_6H_6	1	0.732	0.860	−0.804	0.283
CO	0.732	1	0.800	−0.785	0.247
NO_2	0.860	0.800	1	−0.881	0.136
O_3	−0.804	−0.785	−0.881	1	−0.272
SO_2	0.283	0.247	0.136	−0.272	1

Calculate the total variance of the standardized data and the percentage variance explained by the standardized carbon monoxide concentrations.

(d) The first principal component of the standardized data is

$$Y = 0.489Z_{C_6H_6} + 0.475Z_{CO} + 0.502Z_{NO_2} - 0.499Z_{O_3} + 0.183Z_{SO_2},$$

where $Z_{C_6H_6}$, Z_{CO}, Z_{NO_2}, Z_{O_3} and Z_{SO_2} are the standardized concentrations of benzene, carbon monoxide, nitrogen dioxide, ozone and sulphur dioxide, respectively. The variance of Y is 3.52. Calculate the percentage variance explained by this linear combination.

(e) In your opinion, which of the two one-dimensional approximations to the data is the more useful — that used in part (b) or that in part (d)? Justify your answer.

7.4 Combining variables measured in different units

In each of the multivariate data sets considered so far in Sections 6 and 7, all the variables in the data set can be measured in the same units. For example, for the national interest rate data in Example 6.1 and the land cover data in Activity 6.4, all the variables are percentages; in Example 7.6, both house price and household income are measured in £000s; and in Activity 7.4, the chemical concentrations are all measured in $\mu g/m^3$. However, for many multivariate data sets, the variables cannot all be measured in the same units. For such data sets, it makes little sense to search for a one-dimensional approximation to the data among linear combinations of the unstandardized variables. The variables must be standardized before seeking an approximation. This is illustrated in Example 7.10.

Example 7.10 Mathematical ability revisited

A multivariate data set relating to the ability in mathematics of a group of English schoolboys was described in Activity 2.3 and Example 4.1. Exam scores in three different aspects of mathematics were recorded — geometry (X_1), arithmetic (X_2) and algebra (X_3). The age of each boy at the time they were tested (X_4) was also recorded.

Numerically, for any choice of loadings α_1, α_2, α_3 and α_4, the following linear combination can be calculated for each boy:

$$Y = \alpha_1(X_1 - \overline{X}_1) + \alpha_2(X_2 - \overline{X}_2) + \alpha_3(X_3 - \overline{X}_3) + \alpha_4(X_4 - \overline{X}_4).$$

But what units would the quantity Y have? Each of the variables X_1, X_2 and X_3 represents the number of marks on an exam paper. So it is not unreasonable to combine these variables using a linear combination. However, the variable X_4 represents the age of a boy. This could be measured in years or months or some other unit of time, but not in marks scored. So it is not possible to assign sensible units to the quantity Y, and hence, it could be argued, the values of Y are meaningless.

However, whatever units a variable X is measured in, the corresponding standardized variable Z has no units associated with it: it is *scale-free*. So linear combinations of standardized variables make sense whether or not the unstandardized variables are measured in the same units.

Let Z_1 represent the standardized geometry score, Z_2 the standardized arithmetic score, Z_3 the standardized algebra score, and Z_4 the standardized age for the mathematical ability data set.

A one-dimensional approximation to the standardized data is given by a linear combination Y of the form

$$Y = \alpha_1 Z_1 + \alpha_2 Z_2 + \alpha_3 Z_3 + \alpha_4 Z_4,$$

where $\alpha_1^2 + \alpha_2^2 + \alpha_3^2 + \alpha_4^2 = 1$.

It can be shown that the maximum value of $V(Y)$ is 2.193, and this is achieved with the following loadings: $\alpha_1 = 0.545$, $\alpha_2 = 0.579$, $\alpha_3 = 0.593$ and $\alpha_4 = 0.130$. Thus the first principal component depends almost equally on the three standardized exam scores, and the standardized age has little impact on it. Since there are four variables, the total variance of the standardized data is 4. The variance of Y, the first principal component, is 2.193, so

$$\text{PVE} = \frac{V(Y)}{\text{TV}} \times 100\% = \frac{2.193}{4} \times 100\% \simeq 54.8\%.$$

Although the principal component captures over half of the variation in the standardized data, there is still a large amount that is not accounted for by this one-dimensional approximation. ♦

Activity 7.5 Is standardization necessary?

Four situations in which the first principal component of a multivariate data set is sought are described below. For each situation, state whether it only makes sense to consider linear combinations of the standardized data or whether linear combinations of the original unstandardized data could be considered.

(a) In a study of vegetable oils, the percentages of seven fatty acids were measured.

(b) A study was conducted on the impact of price-cap regulation on local telephone companies in the USA. For each telephone company, ten 'input' variables were recorded, five for residential users and five for business users. For both categories of user the variables were as follows.

- ◇ Average interval in days for installation.
- ◇ Number of initial trouble reports.
- ◇ Number of initial out-of-service trouble reports.
- ◇ Number of all other trouble reports.
- ◇ Number of repeat trouble reports.

(c) In a study of eco-efficiency in the New Zealand economy, fourteen variables were measured for 46 industry sectors. These fourteen variables included land (in ha/\$), energy (in EmJ/\$, a measure of total energy adjusted for energy quality), minerals (in tonne/\$) and carbon dioxide emissions (in tonne/\$).

(d) In a study of religious quest, the responses to twelve questions were obtained from 415 churchgoers in the UK. An individual's response to each question was restricted to a three-point scale, with 'no' coded as 1, 'don't know' coded as 2, and 'yes' coded as 3.

Summary of Section 7

In this section, linear combinations of p variables have been introduced. The (first) principal component of a data set of dimension p has been defined as the linear combination Y of the p variables that maximizes the variance $V(Y)$, subject to a constraint on the loadings. You have learned how to calculate the variance of a linear combination from the covariance matrix of the data and the loadings. The percentage variance explained (PVE) has been introduced to measure the quality of an approximation to a multivariate data set. You have seen that when variables are measured in the same units, but have very different variances, it is sensible to standardize the variables prior to obtaining the first principal component, and that if the variables are measured in different units, it is essential to standardize the variables.

Exercises on Section 7

Exercise 7.1 Dominating variables

Scatterplots of observations from four bivariate distributions are shown in Figure 7.4.

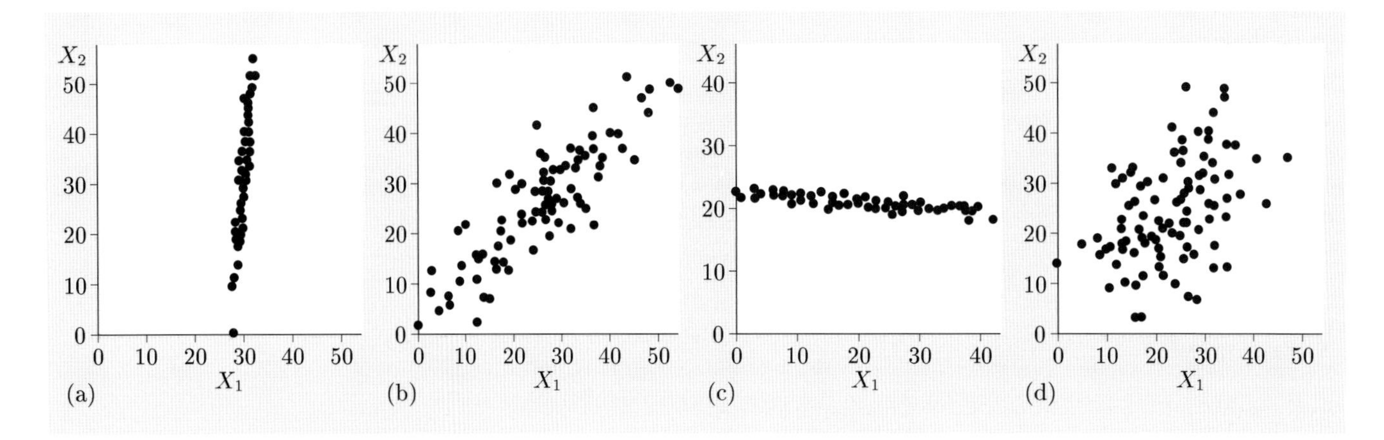

Figure 7.4 Four scatterplots of bivariate data

For each scatterplot, state whether or not the first principal component is likely to be dominated by one of the variables. If so, say which of X_1 and X_2 is likely to dominate, and explain your choice.

Exercise 7.2 A single measure of national athletics ability

This exercise is based on the national athletics data introduced in Activity 7.3. The eight variables were standardized, and the first principal component of the standardized data was obtained. The loadings for the standardized variables are given in Table 7.4.

(a) Comment on the relative sizes of the loadings, and hence suggest an interpretation of the first principal component.

(b) The variance of the first principal component is 6.622. Calculate the percentage variance explained by this component. Does the first principal component provide a good approximation to the full eight-dimensional data set? Explain your answer.

Table 7.4 Loadings for the first principal component of the (standardized) national records data

Event	Loading
100 m	0.318
200 m	0.337
400 m	0.356
800 m	0.369
1500 m	0.373
5000 m	0.364
10 000 m	0.367
Marathon	0.342

8 Higher-dimensional approximations

So far, attention has focused on finding a reasonable one-dimensional approximation to a multivariate data set. However, there are many situations in which the first principal component does not provide a particularly good approximation. In Subsection 8.1, you will see how a better approximation can be obtained by using an additional linear combination of the variables called the *second principal component*. In Subsection 8.2, the idea of using additional linear combinations is extended: additional linear combinations are chosen so that each captures as much as possible of the remaining variation in the multivariate data set. Methods for deciding how many principal components to use are described in Subsection 8.3.

8.1 The second principal component

In most of the examples discussed so far in Part II, the first principal component has provided a good approximation to the multivariate data set. The percentage variance explained has usually been above 80%, indicating that most of the variation in the data has been captured. However, this has not always been the case. In Example 7.10, you saw that the first principal component of the mathematical ability data set captures only 54.8% of the total variance. What is to be done?

The answer is to approximate the data set using two linear combinations of the variables instead of one. The second linear combination is chosen so that it captures as much as possible of the remaining 45.2% of the variation in the data set, and is called the *second principal component* of the data set. An approximation consisting of two linear combinations has advantages over the original data set; for example, the approximate data could be displayed on a scatterplot.

Example 8.1 Capturing more variance

In Example 7.10, you saw that the first principal component Y for the standardized mathematical ability data set captures only 54.8% of the total variance in the data set. So what accounts for the rest of the variability?

Scatterplots of Y against the four standardized variables in the data set (geometry score, arithmetic score, algebra score and age) are shown in Figure 8.1.

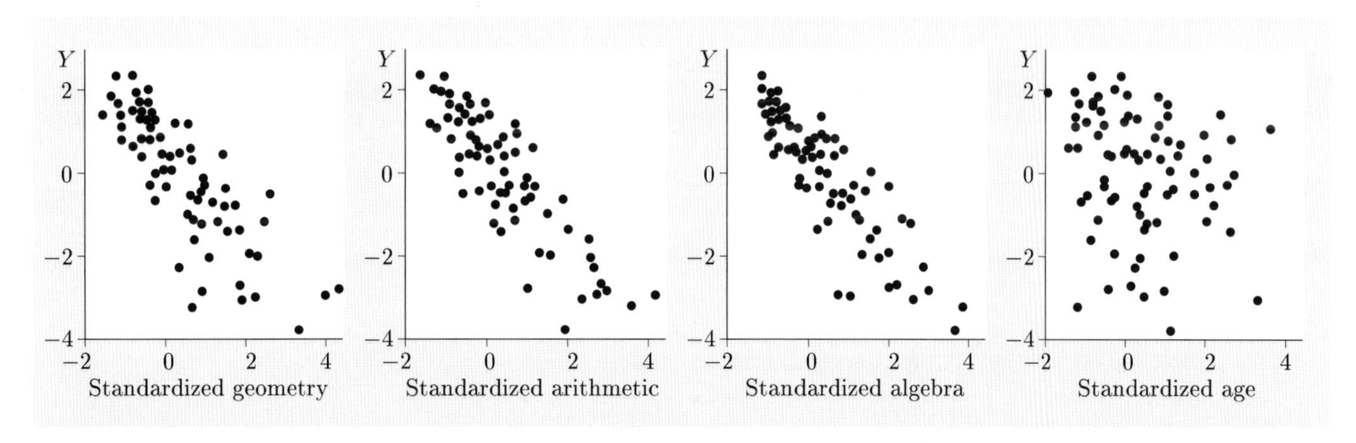

Figure 8.1 The first principal component Y plotted against the four standardized variables in the mathematical ability data set

These plots show that there is a fairly strong correlation between the Y values and the scores awarded for geometry, arithmetic and algebra. This indicates that the value y_i calculated for individual i reflects the individual's score on each of the three exams quite well. However, there is little correlation between Y and age. This indicates that little of the variability in the ages of the boys is captured by the first principal component Y. ♦

In Sections 6 and 7, the first principal component has been denoted by Y, and the loadings vector by $\boldsymbol{\alpha} = (\alpha_1, \ldots, \alpha_p)$. From now on, all quantities relating to the first principal component will be given the subscript 1. Thus the first principal component will be denoted by Y_1 and its loadings vector by $\boldsymbol{\alpha}_1 = (\alpha_{11}, \ldots, \alpha_{1p})$.

The second principal component, which is denoted by Y_2, is defined in a similar manner to Y_1: for unstandardized data $X_1, \ldots, X_p$,

$$Y_2 = \sum_{j=1}^{p} \alpha_{2j}(X_j - \overline{X}_j);$$

and for standardized data $Z_1, \ldots, Z_p$,

$$Y_2 = \sum_{j=1}^{p} \alpha_{2j} Z_j.$$

In either case, the loadings $\alpha_{21}, \ldots, \alpha_{2p}$ are constants such that $\sum_{j=1}^{p} \alpha_{2j}^2 = 1$. But how should the values of $\alpha_{21}, \ldots, \alpha_{2p}$ be chosen?

First, the variable Y_2 should capture variability that is not already captured by Y_1. One way of achieving this is to insist that the linear combinations Y_1 and Y_2 are *uncorrelated*. In other words, $\text{Corr}(Y_1, Y_2)$, the (sample) correlation between Y_1 and Y_2, must be zero.

In addition, Y_2 should capture as much as possible of the remaining variability — that is, of the variability not accounted for by Y_1.

These two requirements are met if the loadings $\alpha_{21}, \ldots, \alpha_{2p}$ are chosen to maximize the variance $V(Y_2)$ subject to two conditions: first, that $\sum_{j=1}^{p} \alpha_{2j}^2 = 1$, and secondly, that Y_2 and Y_1 are uncorrelated. The linear combination Y_2 associated with this choice of loadings $\alpha_{21}, \ldots, \alpha_{2p}$ is known as the **second principal component**.

Needless to say, the calculations are best done by a computer!

Example 8.2 A second linear combination for the mathematical ability data set

For the standardized mathematical ability data set of Example 7.10, the second principal component is a linear combination of the form

$$Y_2 = \alpha_{21} Z_1 + \alpha_{22} Z_2 + \alpha_{23} Z_3 + \alpha_{24} Z_4,$$

satisfying $\alpha_{21}^2 + \alpha_{22}^2 + \alpha_{23}^2 + \alpha_{24}^2 = 1$ and $\text{Corr}(Y_1, Y_2) = 0$.

It can be shown that $V(Y_2)$ is maximized when $\alpha_{21} = -0.042$, $\alpha_{22} = -0.212$, $\alpha_{23} = 0.031$ and $\alpha_{24} = 0.976$, and the variance of the second principal component is $V(Y_2) = 1.001$.

A scatterplot of the first and second principal components is shown in Figure 8.2.

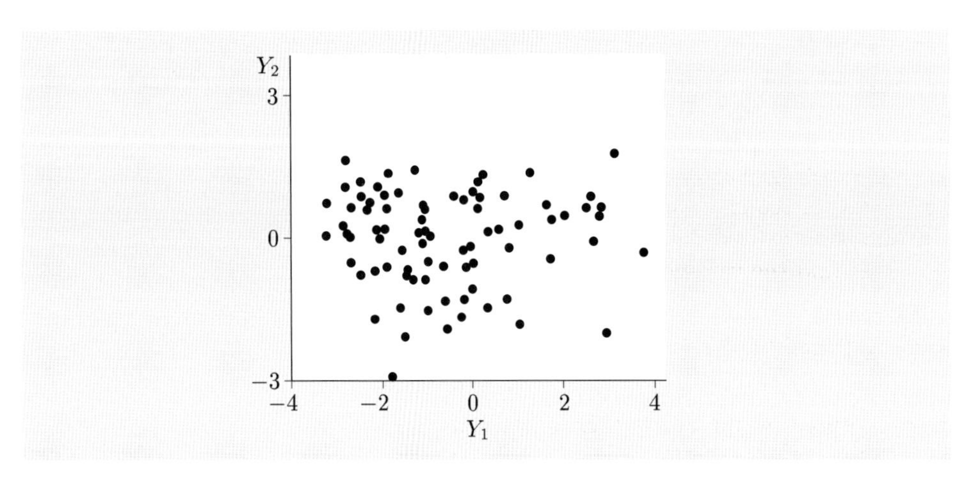

Figure 8.2 The first and second principal components of the mathematical ability data

The lack of correlation between the two components is apparent in this plot: there seems to be little relationship, if any, between them.

In Example 7.10, you saw that the values of the first three loadings, α_{11}, α_{12} and α_{13}, are similar and reasonably large, but the value of α_{14} is much smaller. This indicates that Y_1 generally represents ability in mathematics and does not reflect the age of the schoolboy taking the test. In contrast, for Y_2, only α_{24} is large (in absolute value). Thus Y_2 almost exclusively reflects the age of the schoolboy. ♦

In Example 7.10, the loadings were denoted α_1, α_2, α_3 and α_4.

In Figure 8.2, the points are more spread out horizontally (that is, in the Y_1 direction) than vertically (the Y_2 direction). By definition, Y_1 is the linear combination satisfying the constraint that the sum of the squares of the loadings is 1 that has maximum variance. So $V(Y_2)$ must be less than or equal to $V(Y_1)$.

Having decided to include a second principal component in order to improve the approximation for a multivariate data set, it is useful to have some measure of how worthwhile this has been. In Subsection 7.2, you saw that the percentage variance explained is used to measure the quality of the approximation provided by the first principal component, Y_1. The percentage variance explained can also be calculated for Y_2:

$$\text{PVE} = \frac{V(Y_2)}{\text{TV}} \times 100\%.$$

Thus the percentage variance explained by Y_2 measures the proportion of the total variance captured by Y_2.

A measure of how well Y_1 and Y_2 together capture the total variance is also useful. The **cumulative variance** captured by the first and second principal components, Y_1 and Y_2, is simply $V(Y_1) + V(Y_2)$. The **cumulative percentage variance explained** (**CPVE**) is defined as follows:

$$\text{CPVE by } Y_1 \text{ and } Y_2 = \frac{V(Y_1) + V(Y_2)}{\text{TV}} \times 100\%.$$

Example 8.3 Calculating the CPVE

The variance of the first principal component Y_1 of the mathematical ability data set is 2.193, and the variance of the second principal component Y_2 is 1.001. So the cumulative variance captured by Y_1 and Y_2 is

See Examples 7.10 and 8.2.

$$V(Y_1) + V(Y_2) = 2.193 + 1.001 = 3.194.$$

Thus the cumulative percentage variance explained by Y_1 and Y_2 is

$$\text{CPVE by } Y_1 \text{ and } Y_2 = \frac{V(Y_1) + V(Y_2)}{\text{TV}} \times 100\% = \frac{3.194}{4} \times 100\% \simeq 79.9\%.$$

In other words, nearly 80% of the variance in this multivariate data set of dimension 4 can be captured by the bivariate data set consisting of Y_1 and Y_2. ♦

Activity 8.1 Calculating the percentage variance explained

In Activity 7.5(c), a multivariate data set of dimension 14 was described; the variables correspond to different measures of eco-efficiency. One-dimensional and two-dimensional approximations to the standardized data are found. The variance of the first principal component is 4.672, and the variance of the second principal component is 3.394.

(a) Obtain the percentage variance explained by the first and second principal components separately.

(b) Obtain the cumulative variance captured by the two principal components, and hence obtain the CPVE.

(c) Briefly interpret these results. Is it necessary to use a second principal component? Has a good approximation to the data been achieved?

8.2 Approximations using more than two linear combinations

In Activity 8.1, you saw that using two principal components may leave uncaptured a considerable amount of the variation in a multivariate data set. In such cases, further principal components are used. These are defined in a similar way to the second principal component: each principal component is a linear combination that captures as much as possible of the variance that has not been captured by the preceding principal components; and each is uncorrelated with the preceding principal components.

For multivariate data $X_1, \ldots, X_p$, the **kth principal component**, denoted Y_k, has the following form:

$$Y_k = \sum_{j=1}^{p} \alpha_{kj}(X_j - \overline{X}_j).$$

For standardized data $Z_1, \ldots, Z_p$, it takes the simpler form

$$Y_k = \sum_{j=1}^{p} \alpha_{kj} Z_j.$$

In both cases, the loadings α_{kj} satisfy the constraint $\sum_{j=1}^{p} \alpha_{kj}^2 = 1$.

As for the second principal component, restrictions are placed on the values of the loadings vector $\boldsymbol{\alpha}_k = (\alpha_{k1}, \ldots, \alpha_{kp})$ to ensure that the kth principal component captures variation in the data that is not accounted for by any of the preceding $k-1$ principal components. This is done by requiring that the kth principal component Y_k has zero correlation with each of the previous principal components $Y_1, \ldots, Y_{k-1}$.

Thus the loadings $\alpha_{k1}, \ldots, \alpha_{kp}$ of the kth principal component are chosen to maximize the variance $V(Y_k)$ subject to the following conditions: $\sum_{j=1}^{p} \alpha_{kj}^2 = 1$ and Y_k is uncorrelated with $Y_1, \ldots, Y_{k-1}$.

The requirement for zero correlations means that more restrictions are placed on the values of the loadings vector $\boldsymbol{\alpha}_k$ than on each of $\boldsymbol{\alpha}_1, \ldots, \boldsymbol{\alpha}_{k-1}$, so

$$V(Y_1) \geq V(Y_2) \geq \cdots \geq V(Y_k).$$

Thus the principal components individually successively capture less and less of the variability in the original multivariate data.

So far in Part II, the emphasis has been on approximating multivariate data using a data set of lower dimension. This aim is compromised as the number of principal components increases. However, another reason for obtaining several components is to gain insight into the structure of the data. It is hoped that such structure may be revealed by the first few principal components, particularly if these can be interpreted in a plausibly 'intuitive' way.

Example 8.4 Interpreting principal components

The researchers who analysed the eco-efficiency data set discussed in Activities 7.5(c) and 8.1 decided to approximate the 14-dimensional data set by using the first five principal components of the standardized data. The loadings associated with each of the principal components are given in Table 8.1.

Jollands, N., Lermit, J. and Patterson, M. (2004) Aggregate eco-efficiency indices for New Zealand — a principal components analysis. *Journal of Environmental Management*, **73**, 293–305.

Table 8.1 Principal component loadings for the eco-efficiency data set

	Principal component loadings				
Variable	1	2	3	4	5
Water input	0.0487	0.0206	0.1584	0.1148	0.9477
Land	0.0511	0.0206	−0.1815	0.6386	0.1166
Energy	−0.1147	0.5187	−0.0337	−0.0230	0.0329
Minerals	0.0159	0.0659	0.6939	0.1892	−0.1654
Water discharge	0.1950	0.1216	0.6286	0.1191	−0.0875
Ammonia	0.4005	0.0779	−0.1262	0.1912	−0.0706
BOD_5	0.4501	0.0826	−0.0485	−0.1272	0.0054
DRP	0.4424	0.0763	−0.0301	−0.1733	0.0093
Nitrate	0.0887	0.0242	−0.1605	0.6483	−0.1870
TKN	0.4429	0.0769	−0.0335	−0.1501	0.0020
TPD	0.3889	0.0914	−0.0921	−0.0166	0.0200
CO_2 emissions	−0.1138	0.5082	−0.0498	−0.0372	−0.0115
CH_4 emissions	0.0728	0.4117	−0.0785	0.0209	−0.0877
NO_2 emissions	−0.1069	0.4996	−0.0310	−0.0280	0.0628
Variance	4.6720	3.3943	1.8670	1.3314	0.9872

The loadings for the first principal component for Ammonia, BOD_5, DRP, TKN and TPD are similar and large compared to the other loadings, which are all much closer to zero. Thus the first principal component may be interpreted in broad terms as representing an average or a sum of the (standardized) variables Ammonia, BOD_5, DRP, TKN and TPD. These five variables relate to measures of water pollution in the industry sectors. So the loadings of the first principal component suggest that the dominant pattern in the data relates to the water pollution produced by each sector.

The second principal component has large non-zero loadings for Energy and for CO_2, CH_4 and NO_2 emissions (all emissions associated with energy use). The other variables all have loadings close to zero for the second principal component. So the second principal component may be interpreted in broad terms as representing energy use in the different sectors.

The third principal component has large non-zero loadings for Minerals and Water discharge. The authors interpret this component as relating to 'material intensity' associated with the combination of high mineral inputs and water discharge, as arise in the mining industry. Intuitive interpretations can also be given to the other two principal components.

The data have been standardized, so the total variance is equal to the number of variables, which is 14. The cumulative variance captured by the five principal components is

$$4.6720 + 3.3943 + 1.8670 + 1.3314 + 0.9872 = 12.2519.$$

Thus the cumulative percentage variance explained by the first five principal components is

$$\text{CPVE} = \frac{12.2519}{14} \times 100\% \simeq 87.5\%.$$

Thus the five principal components provide a good approximation to this 14-dimensional data set. ♦

As you have just seen in Example 8.4, to interpret a principal component, it is often convenient to focus on the signs of the loadings, and to ignore variables with loadings that are close to zero (which contribute little to the value of the principal component). Activity 8.2 will give you some practice at interpreting principal components.

Activity 8.2 Interpreting principal components for the national athletics records data

National athletics records data for 55 countries in eight running events were described in Activity 7.3. The data were standardized and the first three principal components were obtained, with a CPVE of 95.7%. The loadings for the three components are given in Table 8.2.

Table 8.2 Principal component loadings for national running events

	Principal component		
Event	1	2	3
100 m	0.318	0.567	0.334
200 m	0.337	0.461	0.361
400 m	0.356	0.249	−0.562
800 m	0.369	0.013	−0.534
1500 m	0.373	−0.140	−0.153
5000 m	0.364	−0.312	0.191
10 000 m	0.367	−0.306	0.183
Marathon	0.342	−0.439	0.263

The loadings for the first component are all positive and take similar values. This suggests that this component represents overall performance in running events across the eight events.

(a) Identify the two variables with the smallest loadings in absolute value for the second principal component. Hence suggest an interpretation for the second principal component based on the other six variables.

(b) Identify the variables with the four largest loadings (in absolute value) for the third principal component. Hence suggest an interpretation for the third principal component based on these four loadings.

(c) A scatterplot of the first two principal components is shown in Figure 8.3.

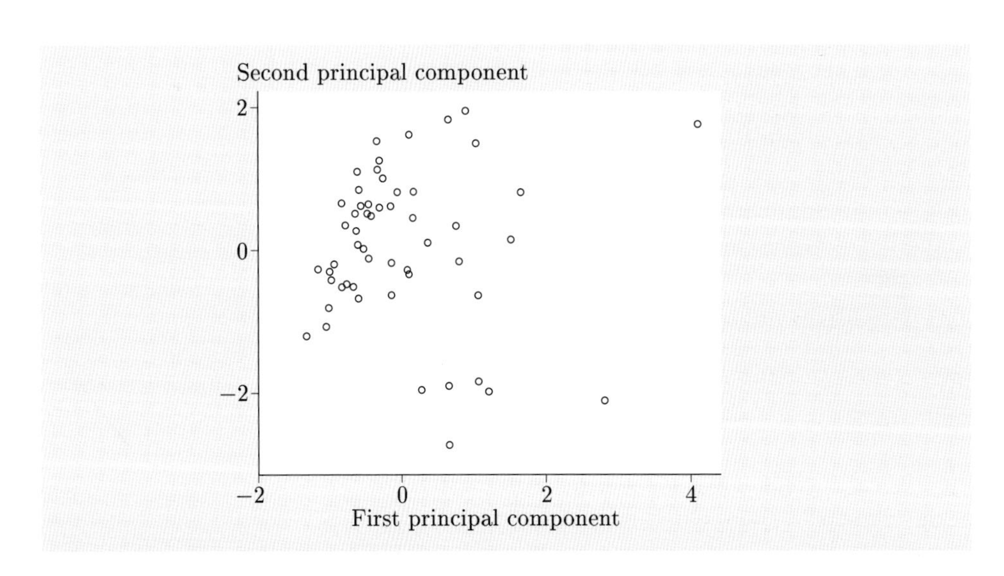

Figure 8.3 The first two principal components of the national athletics data

Identify any groups of countries and outliers that are apparent from this scatterplot. In what way are any outliers and smaller groups of countries different from the main groups in their performance in the athletics events?

8.3 How many components?

The maximum number of principal components that can be used to approximate a data set is equal to the dimension of the original data set. For example, a bivariate data set can be represented by at most two principal components, and a data set with p variables by a maximum of p principal components. When the number of principal components is equal to the dimension, the principal components then represent the data exactly, and the CPVE is 100%. This is illustrated in Example 8.5.

Example 8.5 Mathematical ability revisited

The mathematical ability data set discussed in Examples 7.10, 8.1 and 8.2 consists of four variables: geometry, arithmetic and algebra scores and age. Therefore a total of four principal components can be used to represent these data.

The variances associated with the four principal components are given in Table 8.3.

Table 8.3 Variances for the mathematical ability data set

Principal component	Variance
1	2.193
2	1.001
3	0.495
4	0.311

Notice that each variance is smaller than the preceding one. Also, the cumulative variance of the four principal components is

$$V(Y_1) + V(Y_2) + V(Y_3) + V(Y_4) = 2.193 + 1.001 + 0.495 + 0.311 = 4.000.$$

This is equal to the total variance for the standardized data set. Hence the cumulative percentage variance explained by the four principal components is 100%. Using four components certainly accounts for all the variability in the data. However, the point of obtaining principal components is to approximate the original data set with a data set of smaller dimension: the aim is to obtain a good approximation with fewer than four components. But how many components should be used? ♦

Activity 8.3 Maximum number of principal components

(a) For each of the data sets described in Activity 7.5, state the maximum number of principal components that can be used to approximate it.

(b) You are told that, for a particular data set of dimension 10, it is better to use five principal components than four, because the CPVE is higher with five than with four. Identify the flaw in this argument. What additional information do you need in order to decide whether using five components provides a more useful approximation than using four?

One of the key decisions to make in a principal component analysis is the number of components to use to approximate the data. If too many components are used, then the opportunity to simplify and reduce dimension will have been missed. However, if too few components are used, too much information will have been lost.

Various strategies have been proposed for deciding how many components to use. Four are described in this subsection: a pragmatic approach, two numerical approaches and a graphical approach. Note that if it is decided to use k components, it is always the first k that are used, namely $Y_1, \ldots, Y_k$.

The pragmatic approach

Sometimes the maximum number of components to keep is known in advance. For example, you may want to depict the data graphically on a two-dimensional scatterplot. In this case, you would obtain the first two principal components.

With this method it is important to take note of how well these two components capture the variation in the data. If the cumulative percentage variance explained is high, you can be fairly sure that the 2-d scatterplot reasonably reflects the data as a whole. In other cases, the cumulative percentage variance explained may be low, indicating that although you have obtained the best possible two-dimensional approximation, it still is not very good.

Numerical cut-offs

Instead of fixing the number of components in advance, another common approach is to fix the cumulative percentage variance explained that is required. For example, you could insist that at least 90% of the variance is explained. This could lead to many components being taken if the percentage variance explained by each component is not very high.

Alternatively, each component could be assessed based on its variance. Under this scheme, it might be argued that if the variance of a component is lower than that of one of the original variables, then the component is not worth including. When the original variables all have different variances, the issue arises as to whether you should use as cut-off the variable with the highest variance, that with lowest variance, or an intermediate value. In practice, the cut-off is usually taken to be the mean of the variances of the original variables. When principal component analysis is applied to standardized data, this variance-based criterion is easier to apply. In this case, each variable has variance 1, so only components with variance greater than 1 are used. This criterion is sometimes referred to as **Kaiser's criterion**, after the man who is credited with first suggesting it.

Example 8.6 *Choosing the number of components*

The New Zealand eco-efficiency data set introduced in Activity 7.5(c) comprises fourteen variables. Thus for these data a total of fourteen principal components can be found. Table 8.4 gives the variance for each of the components and the corresponding cumulative percentage variance explained, based on the standardized data.

Notice first that for the last two components the variance is zero (to four decimal places). So these two components are effectively constants. If a cut-off based on a CPVE of 90% is used, then the appropriate number of components is six. Alternatively, according to Kaiser's criterion, only components with variance greater than 1 should be included, so four components should be used. Though as the fifth principal component has a variance that is only just below 1, it would not be unreasonable to include this component as well. ♦

Table 8.4 Variance and CPVE

Principal component	Variance	CPVE
1	4.6720	33.4
2	3.3943	57.5
3	1.8670	71.0
4	1.3314	80.4
5	0.9872	87.5
6	0.7623	93.0
7	0.4777	96.4
8	0.2772	98.4
9	0.1481	99.4
10	0.0554	99.8
11	0.0169	99.9
12	0.0106	100.0
13	0.0000	100.0
14	0.0000	100.0

Activity 8.4 Number of components for the mathematical ability data

In Example 8.5, the variances of all four principal components for the standardized mathematical ability data set were given (see Table 8.3).

(a) How many principal components should be retained if the cumulative percentage variance explained is to be at least 90%?

(b) Use Kaiser's criterion to decide how many principal components should be retained.

Graphical approach

One approach to the analysis of multivariate data holds that major structure lies in only a few dimensions. For example, in the mathematical ability data set, the major structure is essentially an ability to do mathematics. The test results in geometry, algebra and arithmetic are simply reflections of that ability. The extra dimensions just represent 'noise', perhaps as a result of the particular questions that were set. According to this approach, the contrast between 'structural' components and the noise is reflected in the variances of the components. Thus it is assumed that structural components will account for a relatively large amount of variance. In contrast, the 'noise' components will have much smaller variances. Thus the point at which the variances become small indicates which components capture only noise and hence should be ignored.

It is possible to judge this point by looking at the variances in a table. However, looking at the numbers in this way is not a good way of assessing their relative sizes. Instead, the variance of the component is plotted against the component number to produce a diagram called a **scree plot**. An example of a scree plot is depicted in Figure 8.4.

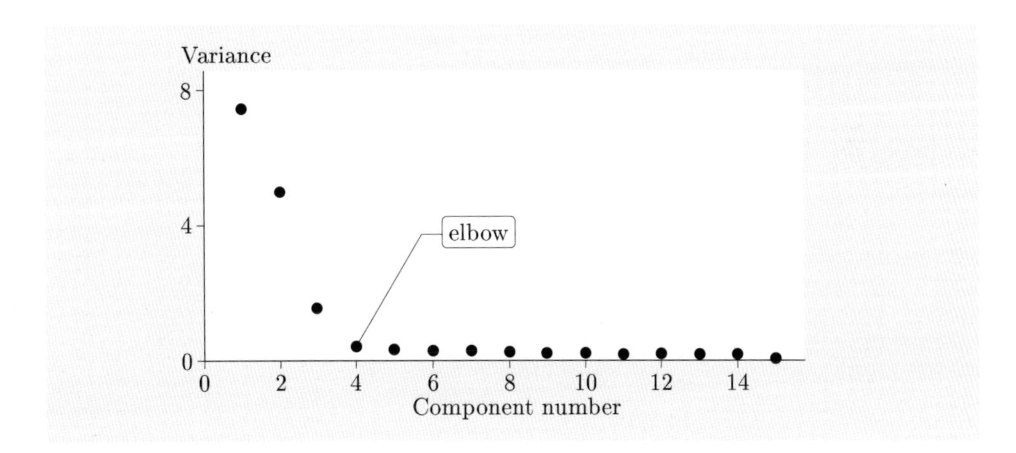

Figure 8.4 Scree plot

In any scree plot, the variance for component k decreases with k. In this scree plot, the drop is initially quite steep, then it flattens out. The point at which the scree plot first flattens out is the **elbow** in the graph. In this course, the component immediately before the elbow is taken to be the last useful component. In Figure 8.4 the elbow occurs at component 4, so the third component is the last useful component. The elbow is quite clear in Figure 8.4, but for other data sets it may not be so obvious.

Activity 8.5 Choosing the number of components from a scree plot

Figure 8.5 shows four scree plots, each obtained from a data set of dimension 20.

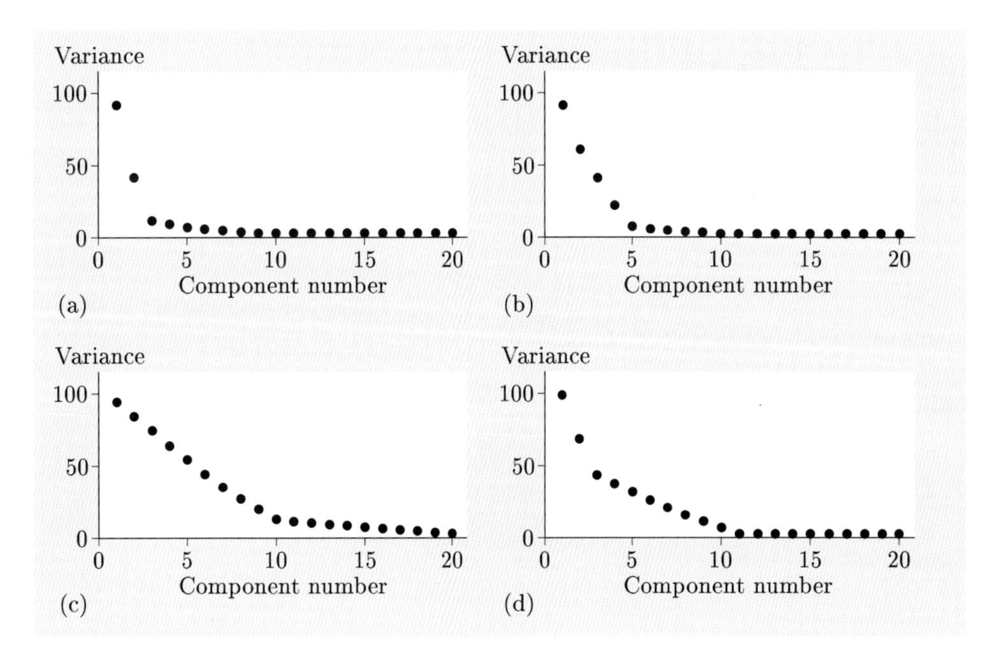

Figure 8.5 Four scree plots

In each case, identify the appropriate number of components to retain.

Summary of Section 8

In this section, the second and subsequent principal components for a data set have been defined. The kth principal component is the linear combination Y_k with maximum variance subject to two constraints — first, that the sum of the squares of its loadings is 1, and secondly, that it is uncorrelated with components 1 to $k-1$. The interpretation of principal components in terms of the underlying structure of the data has been illustrated. The cumulative percentage variance explained has been introduced as a measure of the quality of approximations consisting of two or more components.

At most p principal components can be obtained for a data set of dimension p. Several methods for choosing the appropriate number of principal components to use have been discussed. These include a pragmatic approach, numerical cut-offs including Kaiser's criterion, and a graphical method based on locating the elbow of a scree plot.

Exercise on Section 8

Exercise 8.1 Hiking data: how many components?

Data on hiking experiences were introduced in Exercise 4.3. Hikers recorded the strength of various emotional responses at locations along a trail. Eight of the emotional responses corresponded to positive emotions such as enjoyment and pleasure. Principal components were found for the standardized data based on these positive emotions.

(a) What is the maximum number of principal components that can be found?

(b) The variances of the first eight principal components are given in Table 8.5. The cumulative percentage variance explained is also given for seven of the components.

(i) Complete the entry for the second principal component.

(ii) How many components should be retained if at least 85% of the variance is to be explained?

(iii) How many components should be retained using Kaiser's criterion?

Table 8.5 Variance and CPVE

Principal component	Variance	CPVE
1	3.664	45.5
2	0.979	
3	0.951	69.9
4	0.737	79.1
5	0.594	86.6
6	0.516	93.0
7	0.419	98.3
8	0.140	100.0

(c) A scree plot for these data is shown in Figure 8.6.

Figure 8.6 Scree plot for the principal components of the hiking data

Use this scree plot to decide how many principal components should be retained.

9 Dimension reduction in practice

In Sections 6 to 8, you have learned how multivariate data can be approximated by a series of principal components. In practice, the task of obtaining the loadings for these principal components is almost always done with the help of a computer. In this section, you will learn how to use SPSS to find principal components based on either standardized or unstandardized data. You will also learn how to obtain a scree plot in SPSS.

Refer to Chapters 3 and 4 of Computer Book 3 for the work in this section.

Summary of Section 9

In this section, you have learned how to use SPSS to find the principal components of a multivariate data set. The use of SPSS to obtain principal components based on both standardized and unstandardized data has been described. You have also learned how to obtain and use output from SPSS to help decide how many principal components to use to approximate a multivariate data set.

Part III Discrimination

Introduction to Part III

In Parts I and II, several multivariate techniques for exploring the relationships between variables and between observations have been discussed. In particular, scatterplots have been used to plot multivariate data, and principal component analysis has been applied to produce approximations of lower dimension than the original data set. Scatterplots can be very helpful when the data consist of two or more groups: if different plotting symbols are used for observations in different groups, then differences between groups can be explored visually using scatterplots.

In Part III, a multivariate analysis technique aimed specifically at characterizing known subgroups of observations is described. This technique, which is called **canonical discrimination**, produces low-dimensional approximations to the data in which differences between the subgroups are emphasized as much as possible. These approximations can be used to design rules for predicting which group a newly obtained observation is likely to belong to. Such rules, which are called **allocation rules**, are used in fields as diverse as medicine (for example, to diagnose a medical condition using test results), credit scoring (to determine a client's likely creditworthiness), and archaeology (to identify provenance of artefacts).

In Section 10, a means of quantifying how well a linear combination of variables distinguishes between, or **separates**, groups of multivariate observations is introduced. Distinct linear combinations of the variables result in different amounts of separation between the groups. In canonical discrimination, which is described in Section 11, the linear combination that maximizes the separation between the groups is found. Sometimes, using two or more linear combinations achieves a better separation of the groups; obtaining further linear combinations to separate groups and assessing their usefulness for this purpose is the subject of Section 12. Allocation rules are defined in Section 13, and are used to decide to which group a newly obtained observation belongs. The implementation of canonical discrimination using SPSS is described in Section 14.

10 The separation of groups

Many multivariate data sets consist of two or more groups of observations. Several such data sets are described in this section, and are used to introduce some of the ideas upon which the techniques discussed in Part III depend. In Subsection 10.1, scatterplots are used to display groups, some useful terminology is introduced, and the purpose of discrimination is outlined. In Subsection 10.2, measures of spread within groups and between groups are defined for the situation where there are two groups, and a numerical measure of separation between two groups is introduced. These measures are generalized to an arbitrary number of groups in Subsection 10.3. Measures of the relationships between variables both between groups and within groups are described briefly in Subsection 10.4.

10.1 Representing groups in multivariate data

A data set that will be used to illustrate many of the ideas introduced in Part III is described in Example 10.1.

Example 10.1 Characteristics of counterfeit banknotes

Sophisticated counterfeit banknotes can be hard to spot, as there may be only slight differences between a counterfeit note and a genuine note. Forensic scientists are interested in discovering the characteristics that distinguish counterfeit notes from genuine notes. One way of doing this is by comparing measurements made on known counterfeit notes with similar measurements made on known genuine notes.

One set of data was collected for a Swiss 1000-franc note belonging to the second series of banknotes issued by the Swiss National Bank between about 1911 and 1956. Six measurements were made on each of 100 genuine notes and 100 counterfeit notes. The six measurements, all relating to one side of the banknote, are shown in Figure 10.1.

Flury, B. and Riedwyl, H. (1988) *Multivariate Statistics: a practical approach.* Chapman and Hall, London.

Figure 10.1 Measurements taken on Swiss 1000-franc banknotes. (Reproduced from Flury and Riedwyl)

The measurements were as follows.

Length X_1:	the length of the note
Left width X_2:	the width at the left edge of the note
Right width X_3:	the width at the right edge of the note
Bottom X_4:	the width of the bottom border
Top X_5:	the width of the top border
Diagonal X_6:	the length of the diagonal of the central motif

As it was anticipated that the variability of these measurements from note to note would be small, each note was projected onto a screen in order to enlarge it prior to measurement. Thus each measurement is given in millimetres (mm) for the enlarged image of the note.

A matrix scatterplot of these data using different plotting symbols for counterfeit notes and genuine notes is shown in Figure 10.2.

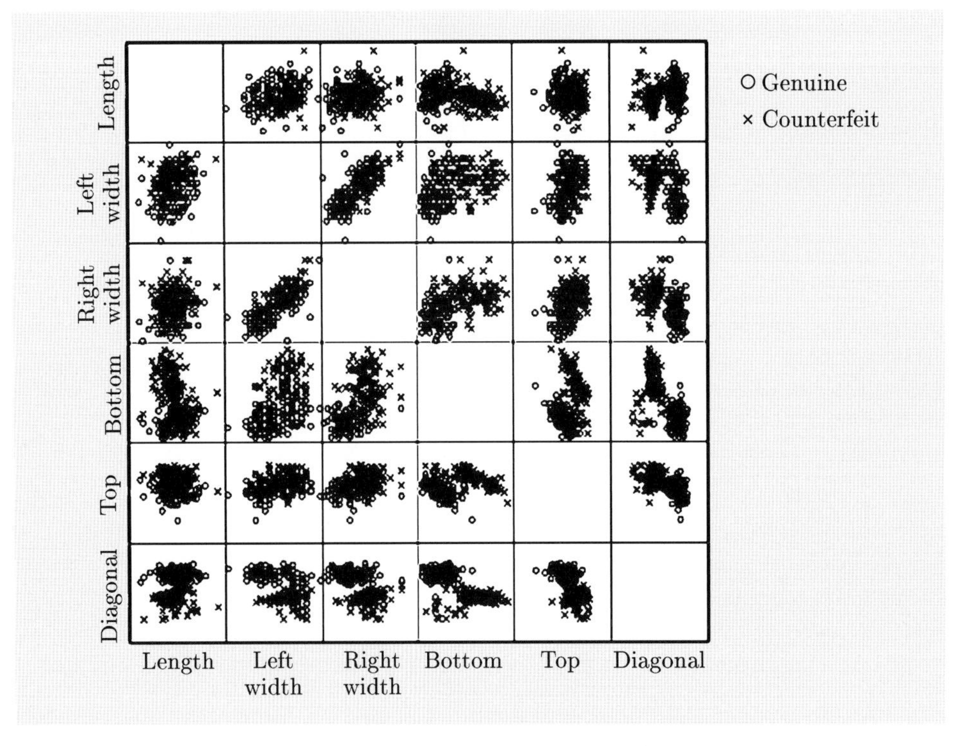

Figure 10.2 Measurements on genuine and counterfeit Swiss banknotes

The scatterplot reveals that some measurements tend to differ systematically between the two groups of notes. For example, look along the bottom row of the scatterplot. Notice that the observations fall into two clumps, corresponding to the genuine notes and the counterfeit notes: the genuine notes tend to have longer diagonals (X_6) than the counterfeit notes. Similarly, in the fourth row of the scatterplot, you can see that the genuine notes tend to have shorter bottom borders (X_4) than the counterfeit notes, though the two clumps are less easily distinguishable in this row than in the bottom row as they overlap more. On the other hand, looking at the top row, it is clear that the two groups cannot be distinguished on the basis of their lengths (X_1). ♦

At this point it is useful to introduce some terminology. A set of points lying close together on a scatterplot is often referred to as a **cloud of points**. The points corresponding to observations in a particular subgroup of the data are referred to as the cloud of points for that group. On a scatterplot, two groups are said to be **well separated** if the areas of the scatterplot occupied by the two clouds of points corresponding to these groups do not overlap (or do not overlap much). A variable that takes different values for different groups is said to **separate the groups**. Thus, in Example 10.1, the diagonal (X_6) separates the two groups of banknotes.

In Example 10.1, a matrix scatterplot was used to investigate how the measurements on two groups of banknotes differ. Scatterplots can also be used when there are three or more groups. This is illustrated in Example 10.2.

Example 10.2 Tracing sources of opium

In a study of opium, the concentrations of various amino acids from samples of (legally) cultivated opium were measured. The opium was cultivated in various regions of India. Fifty of the samples came from three divisions: Chittorgarh (15 samples), Kota (17 samples) and Mandsaur (18 samples). A scatterplot of the concentrations (in g% of total amino acids) of two of the amino acids, glycine and phenylalanine, is shown in Figure 10.3.

Krishna Reddy, M.M., Ghosh, P., Rasool, S.N., Sarin, R.K. and Sashidhar, R.B. (2005) Source identification of Indian opium based on chromatographic fingerprinting of amino acids. *Journal of Chromatography A*, **1088**, 158–168.

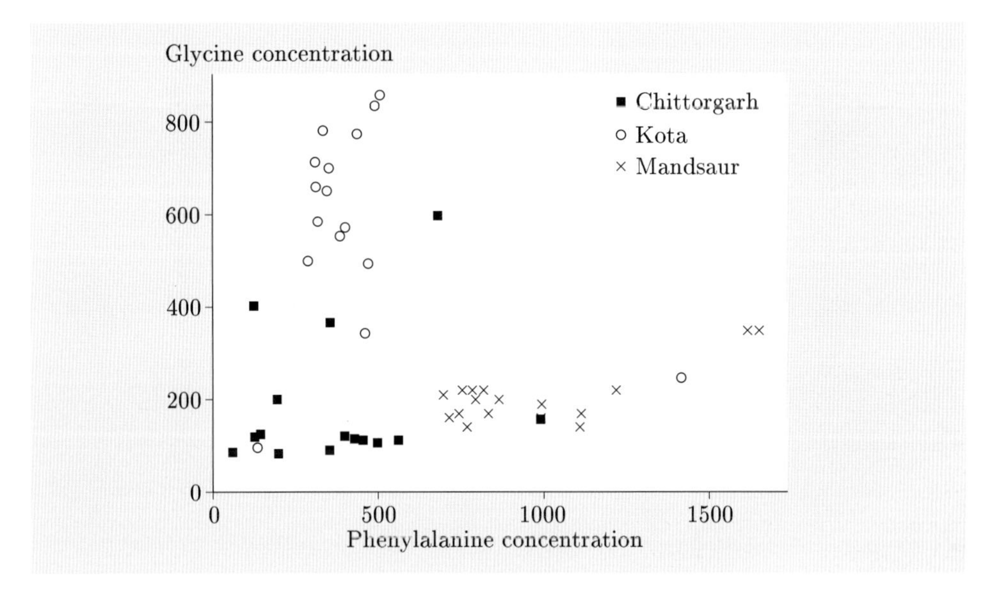

Figure 10.3 Concentrations of two amino acids in 50 samples of opium

In the scatterplot, the cloud of points for Kota is located above the clouds for Chittorgarh and Mandsaur, though there is some overlap: samples from Kota tend to have higher glycine concentrations than samples from Chittorgarh and Mandsaur. Thus glycine concentration separates Kota quite well from the other two regions.

However, glycine concentration does not separate the samples from Chittorgarh and Mandsaur. The clouds of points corresponding to Chittorgarh and Mandsaur lie at similar heights, since samples from these two locations tend to have similar glycine concentrations. ♦

Activity 10.1 Separating groups

In Example 10.2, you saw that glycine concentration separates samples from Kota and samples from the other two locations, but does not separate samples from Chittorgarh and samples from Mandsaur. Comment on the extent to which phenylalanine concentration separates samples from the three locations.

Matrix scatterplots can be used to examine the ways in which groups of observations differ. However, they are useful only when the number of variables is fairly small: as the number of variables increases, the number of subplots increases and the size of each subplot decreases. An approach is required that will work regardless of the number of variables.

One possibility is to use principal component analysis (PCA) to find a lower-dimensional approximation to the data set which captures as much as possible of the variation in the data. When the differences between groups are large, the groups are likely to be distinct on a scatterplot of the first two principal components.

Example 10.3 PCA applied to the banknote data

The Swiss banknote data set described in Example 10.1 comprises six variables. A lower-dimensional approximation to the data was obtained using principal component analysis. Since the variances of the variables differ substantially — from 0.130 for X_2, the width of the note at the left edge, to 2.087 for X_4, the width of the bottom border — the analysis was based on the standardized variables $Z_1, \ldots, Z_6$.

The first principal component captures nearly 50% of the variation, and the second principal component captures a further 21%, so together the first two principal components represent a reasonable approximation to the data as a whole. The first and second principal components Y_1 and Y_2 correspond to the following linear combinations:

$$Y_1 = -0.01Z_1 + 0.47Z_2 + 0.49Z_3 + 0.41Z_4 + 0.37Z_5 - 0.49Z_6,$$
$$Y_2 = 0.82Z_1 + 0.34Z_2 + 0.25Z_3 - 0.27Z_4 - 0.09Z_5 + 0.27Z_6.$$

The first principal component balances the four width measurements, Z_2, Z_3, Z_4 and Z_5, against the length of the diagonal of the central motif, Z_6. The length of the note, Z_1, barely contributes to the first principal component, but it plays a strong role in the second principal component. A scatterplot of the first two principal components is shown in Figure 10.4.

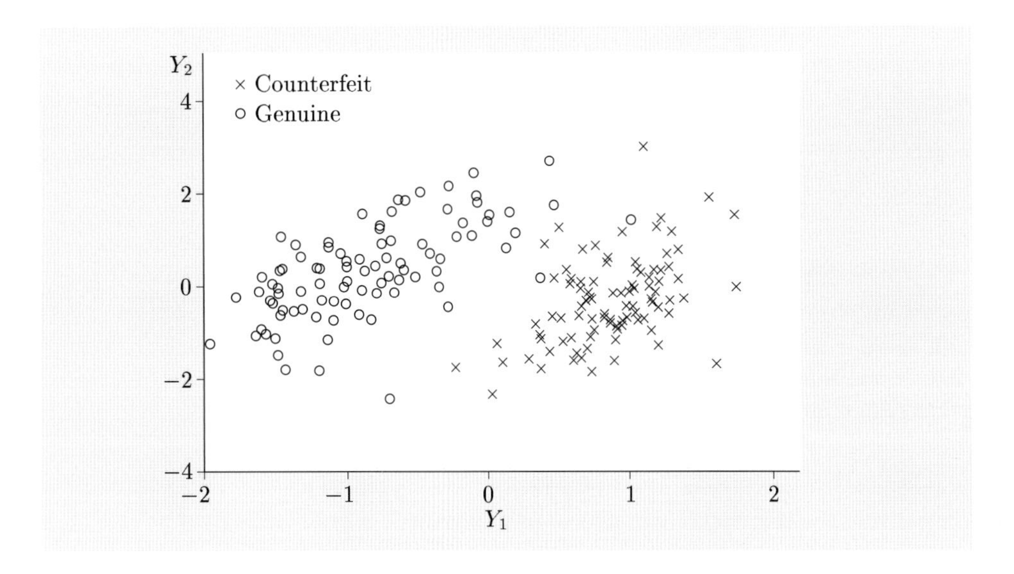

Figure 10.4 The first two principal components for the banknote data

The cloud of points representing the counterfeit notes is well separated from the cloud of points representing the genuine notes. However, the range of values of Y_2 is very similar for genuine notes and counterfeit notes, so Y_2 does not separate the groups very well. Y_1 separates them a little better, but there are many points corresponding to genuine notes that lie to the right (along the x-axis) of points corresponding to counterfeit notes. In fact, the groups are well separated only when Y_1 and Y_2 are considered together: the boundary between the two clouds lies roughly on a diagonal line through the scatterplot. ♦

In Example 10.3, principal component analysis was used to approximate the original data by a data set of lower dimension, whilst retaining enough information to identify differences between the groups. However, if the primary focus is to highlight differences between groups, is it possible to find linear combinations of the variables which do a better job of emphasizing differences between groups than the principal components? In Example 10.4, you will see that the answer to this question is yes.

Example 10.4 Separating counterfeit and genuine banknotes

Imagine drawing a diagonal from the top left-hand corner of the scatterplot in Figure 10.4 to the bottom right-hand corner. Starting at the top left-hand corner of the plot, imagine yourself moving down the diagonal towards the bottom right-hand corner, looking to the right and left of the diagonal as you move. The first points you will see are those corresponding to the genuine notes. Then, about halfway, you will begin to see points corresponding to counterfeit notes. In fact, the two groups will be nearly perfectly separated: with only a few exceptions, the genuine notes will come into view before the counterfeit notes.

You may find it helpful to draw a diagonal on Figure 10.4.

In geometrical terms, the points are being *projected* onto the diagonal.

This imaginary diagonal corresponds to a linear combination of the variables $Z_1, \ldots, Z_6$, and illustrates that it is possible to obtain a single linear combination that separates the two groups very well indeed. In fact, the following linear combination D does even better than this diagonal:

$$D = -0.002Z_1 - 0.262Z_2 + 0.278Z_3 + 1.028Z_4 + 0.757Z_5 - 0.787Z_6.$$

Histograms of the values of D for the two groups of banknotes are shown in Figure 10.5.

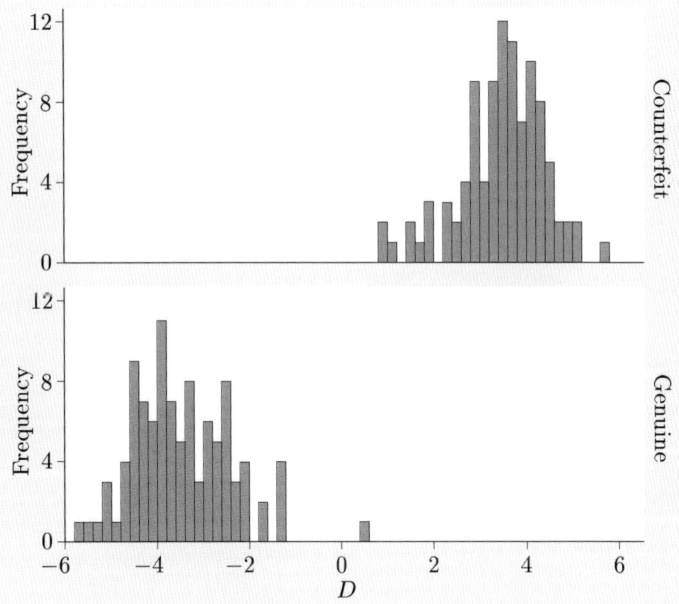

Figure 10.5 Histograms of the values of D for counterfeit and genuine banknotes

The value of D is above zero for all the counterfeit notes, and below zero for all the genuine notes except one; and for this note, the value of D is lower than the lowest value obtained for the counterfeit notes. Thus approximating the data by the linear combination D makes it possible to separate completely the two types of banknote.

This separation of the two types of notes is useful as it provides a way of predicting to which group a newly obtained note belongs. If, as Figure 10.5 suggests, counterfeit notes have positive values of D and genuine notes have negative values, a good prediction of whether a new note is counterfeit or genuine simply depends on the value of D for the note. ♦

In general terms, the reason why the single linear combination D described in Example 10.4 does better at separating the groups than the first two principal components is as follows. Principal components are defined so as to maximize the variance, without regard to group membership. However, the linear combination D was obtained specifically with the aim of maximizing the difference between the two groups.

The technique for finding linear combinations D that separate the groups as much as possible is called **canonical discrimination**, or **discrimination** for short. Discrimination has two main aims: first, to summarize the features that best distinguish known subgroups of observations; and secondly, to provide a way of deciding to which group a newly obtained observation belongs. These aims are addressed in the remaining sections of this book.

10.2 A measure of separation

As noted in Subsection 10.1, the goal of discrimination is to find a linear combination of the variables that emphasizes the differences between the groups. The extent to which this goal is achieved can be assessed subjectively by looking at a plot of the values of the linear combination, such as the histograms in Figure 10.5. Ideally, the clouds of points representing the groups should be clearly separated from each other. However, when there is some overlap, it is harder to evaluate visually how well the groups are separated. A mathematical measure of separation is therefore required. In this subsection, a measure of separation is defined for two groups.

Any reasonable measure of separation should depend on how far apart observations in one group are from observations in the other group. The further apart, on average, observations in different groups are, the larger the measured separation should be. However, the separation should also reflect the variability within groups, because for a given average difference between the groups, the groups will be better separated if the variation within each group is small than if the variation within each group is large. For example, if the two clouds of points in Figure 10.4 were to expand in size around their means, the two clouds would overlap more and hence they would become less well separated, even though the distance between their means would not have changed.

Example 10.5 Separation between counterfeit and genuine banknotes

Figure 10.6 gives the frequency distributions for the counterfeit notes (broken blue line) and the genuine notes (solid black line) with respect to each of the six variables described in Example 10.1.

A frequency distribution is obtained by joining the midpoints of the tops of the bars of a histogram, to give an impression of the shape of the distribution.

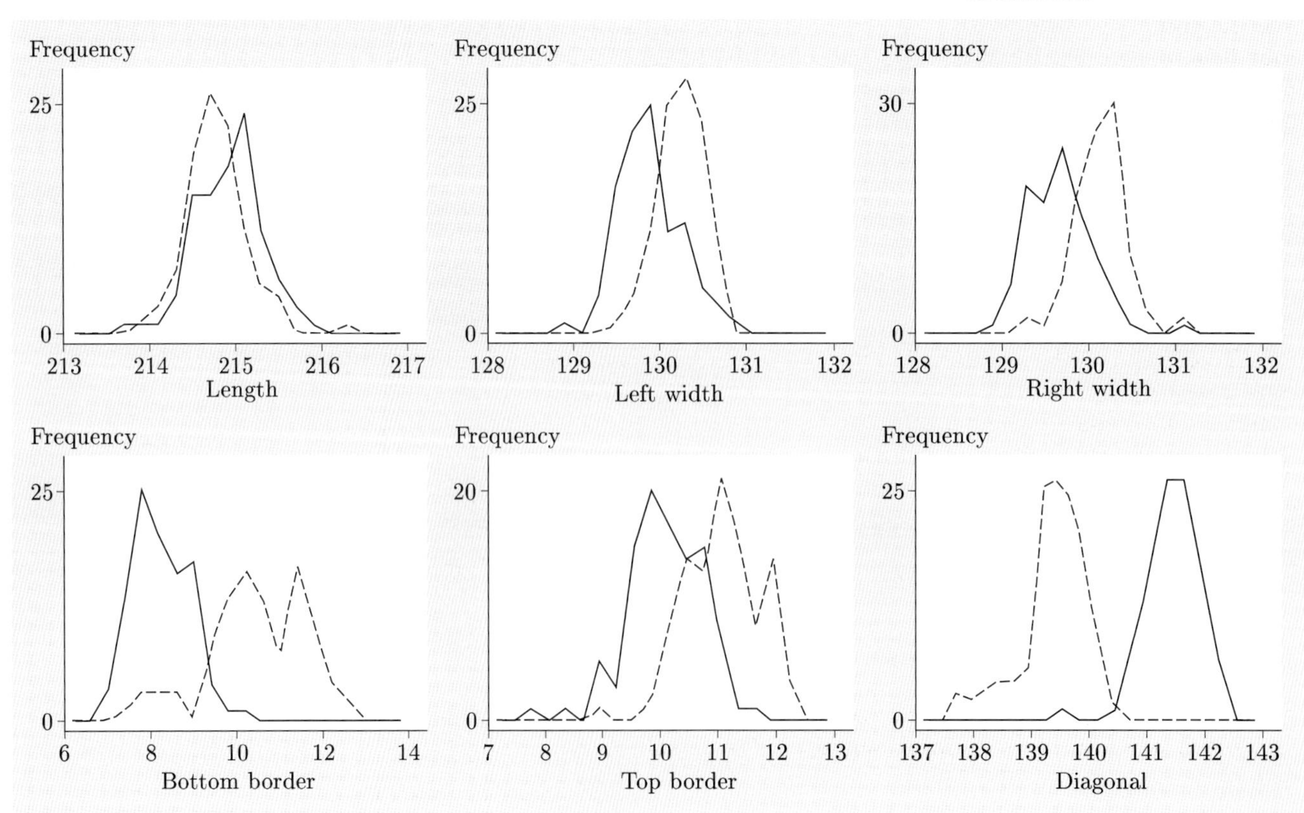

Figure 10.6 Frequency distributions for the six attributes measured on Swiss 1000-franc banknotes

Notice that there appears to be a clear separation between diagonals of counterfeit notes and genuine notes. There is also a reasonable separation between counterfeit notes and genuine notes with respect to the bottom border. However, the distributions of the length of the notes for the counterfeit notes and the genuine notes overlap to a large extent. The distributions for the other three variables also overlap, but to a lesser degree.

The relative separation between the counterfeit notes and the genuine notes with respect to each of the six variables is reflected in the means and standard deviations for each of the groups; these are given in Table 10.1.

Table 10.1 Means and standard deviations of six measurements on counterfeit and genuine notes

	Counterfeit		Genuine		
Variable	Mean	SD	Mean	SD	Grand mean
Length	214.82	0.35	214.97	0.39	214.895
Left width	130.30	0.26	129.94	0.36	130.120
Right width	130.19	0.30	129.72	0.36	129.955
Bottom border	10.53	1.13	8.30	0.64	9.415
Top border	11.13	0.64	10.17	0.65	10.650
Diagonal	139.45	0.56	141.52	0.45	140.485

The last column of Table 10.1 contains, for each variable, the mean for the two groups combined. This mean is called the **grand mean**. It is called the *grand* mean in order to distinguish it from the group means.

The mean lengths of the counterfeit notes and the genuine notes are very similar, and hence both are close to the grand mean. In fact, the differences between the group means and the grand mean are much less than the standard deviations within each group. For example, for the counterfeit notes the difference between the group mean and the grand mean is $214.82 - 214.895 = -0.075$; this is much smaller in absolute value than 0.35, the standard deviation for the counterfeit group. Therefore the length does not separate the two groups very well. In contrast, for the diagonal measurement, the differences between the group means and the grand mean are larger than the standard deviations within the groups. For example, for the counterfeit group, the difference between the group mean and the grand mean is $139.45 - 140.485 = -1.035$; this is greater in absolute value than 0.56, the standard deviation for the counterfeit group. The diagonal measurement thus separates the groups well. For the other variables, the differences between the group means and the grand mean, relative to the corresponding standard deviations, are somewhere in between. ♦

In Example 10.5, the amount of separation was described in relation to the difference between the group mean and the grand mean, relative to the standard deviation for the group. A variable achieves good separation if, for each group, the difference between the group mean and the grand mean is large (in absolute value) compared to the standard deviation for the group. However, there are two such measures, one for each group. These two measures must therefore be combined to produce a single measure of separation.

To obtain a single scale on which to assess differences between means, a weighted average of the two sample variances is used. This is denoted V_w and is called the **within-groups variance**. If group 1 is of size n_1 and has standard deviation s_1, and group 2 is of size n_2 and has standard deviation s_2, then the within-groups variance is defined as follows:

$$V_w = \frac{(n_1 - 1)s_1^2 + (n_2 - 1)s_2^2}{N - 2}, \qquad (10.1)$$

where $N = n_1 + n_2$ is the combined size of the two groups. The within-groups variance is thus a measure of the average spread within the groups.

The differences (in absolute value) between the group means and the grand mean are also combined into a single quantity, called the **between-groups variance**, denoted V_b. If the mean of group 1 is $\overline{x}_1$ and the mean of group 2 is $\overline{x}_2$, then the between-groups variance is defined as follows:

$$V_b = \frac{n_1(\overline{x}_1 - \overline{\overline{x}})^2 + n_2(\overline{x}_2 - \overline{\overline{x}})^2}{N - 2}, \tag{10.2}$$

where $\overline{\overline{x}}$ is the grand mean. The between-groups variance increases as the difference between the group means $\overline{x}_1$ and $\overline{x}_2$ increases. It is zero if the group means are equal, in which case the group means are also equal to the grand mean. Thus the between-groups variance is a measure of how far the group means are from the grand mean, and hence from each other.

In Part III, the double-bar notation is used to distinguish the grand mean from the group means.

A measure of separation between two groups is given by the ratio of the between-groups variance to the within-groups variance:

$$\text{separation} = \frac{V_b}{V_w}. \tag{10.3}$$

This measure of separation can never be negative. Furthermore, it takes the value zero only if the means for the two groups are equal. A large value of the separation is obtained when V_b is large and V_w is small.

Example 10.6 Calculating separations

The data in Table 10.1 can be used to calculate the separation between genuine notes and counterfeit notes with respect to each of the six measurements. Suppose the counterfeit notes are labelled as group 1 and the genuine notes as group 2. There were 100 notes in each of the groups, so $n_1 = n_2 = 100$ and $N = 200$. The between-groups variance for the length variable X_1 is calculated using Formula (10.2):

$$\begin{aligned} V_b &= \frac{n_1(\overline{x}_1 - \overline{\overline{x}})^2 + n_2(\overline{x}_2 - \overline{\overline{x}})^2}{N - 2} \\ &= \frac{100 \times (214.82 - 214.895)^2 + 100 \times (214.97 - 214.895)^2}{200 - 2} \\ &\simeq 0.005\,682. \end{aligned}$$

The within-groups variance is obtained using Formula (10.1):

$$\begin{aligned} V_w &= \frac{(n_1 - 1)s_1^2 + (n_2 - 1)s_2^2}{N - 2} \\ &= \frac{(100 - 1) \times 0.35^2 + (100 - 1) \times 0.39^2}{200 - 2} \\ &= 0.1373. \end{aligned}$$

Then the separation for length is found using Formula (10.3):

$$\text{separation} = \frac{V_b}{V_w} \simeq \frac{0.005\,682}{0.1373} \simeq 0.04.$$

The separations between the counterfeit notes and the genuine notes with respect to the other five variables are given in Table 10.2.

Table 10.2 Separations of counterfeit and genuine Swiss 1000-franc banknotes by different variables

Variable	Separation
Length	0.04
Left width	0.33
Right width	0.51
Bottom border	1.49
Top border	0.56
Diagonal	4.19

The length of the diagonal of the central motif gives the best separation between genuine notes and counterfeit notes. The bottom border gives the next best separation. In contrast, the length of the notes gives a separation close to zero. ♦

Activity 10.2 will give you some practice at calculating separations. Note that the grand mean $\overline{\overline{x}}$ may be obtained from the group means and the group sizes as follows:

$$\overline{\overline{x}} = \frac{n_1\overline{x}_1 + n_2\overline{x}_2}{N}. \tag{10.4}$$

Activity 10.2 Diagnosing heart disease

In a study of heart disease, measurements were taken on 120 patients with heart disease and 150 patients without heart disease. Four of the variables recorded for each patient were age, resting blood pressure, serum cholesterol and maximum heart rate. Differences between the distributions of each of these variables for patients who had heart disease and for patients who did not have heart disease are of interest.

These data were obtained in May 2005 from the Statlog database. Newman, D.J., Hettich, S., Blake, C.L. and Merz, C.J. (1998) UCI repository of machine learning databases, http://www.ics.uci.edu/~mlearn.

The mean and standard deviation for each of these variables for each group of patients are given in Table 10.3.

Table 10.3 Means and standard deviations of four variables for patients with heart disease and patients without heart disease

	Heart disease present		Heart disease absent	
Variable	Mean	SD	Mean	SD
Age	56.6	8.12	52.7	9.51
Blood pressure	134.4	19.1	128.9	16.5
Cholesterol	256.6	48.0	244.2	54.0
Maximum heart rate	138.9	23.1	158.3	19.3

(a) For each of the variables, obtain the between-groups variance and the within-groups variance, and hence calculate the separation between patients with heart disease and patients without heart disease.

(b) Which variable gives the best separation between the two groups of patients? Which gives the least separation? Explain your answer.

The separation has been defined as the ratio of the between-groups variance to the within-groups variance. This provides an intuitive explanation of why discrimination differs from principal component analysis. In principal component analysis, the aim is to choose an approximation in which the overall variation (which includes both between-groups and within-groups variation) is maximized. However, in discrimination, good separation is achieved by maximizing the ratio of the between-groups variance to the within-groups variance, and this is done by increasing the between-groups variance while reducing or restricting the within-groups variance.

10.3 Measuring separation when there are more than two groups

In Subsection 10.2, a measure of separation for two groups was introduced. However, as Example 10.7 shows, in practice, there are often more than two groups to separate.

Example 10.7 Processing satellite images

Satellites can be used to study the use of land over large regions. Digital images are captured by the satellites using radiation from a part of the spectrum — for example, the green part of the spectrum, or a non-visible part such as infrared. Each point in an image (a pixel) relates to a small area of land. For the process to be useful, the value of each pixel should depend on what type the corresponding piece of land happens to be. For pixels from one particular image, all the land was grey soil. Some of the areas of grey soil were simply classified as grey soil, while some areas were classified as damp grey soil and the rest as very damp grey soil. So for these data there are three groups: grey soil, damp grey soil and very damp grey soil. ♦

The measure of separation introduced in Subsection 10.2 can be generalized to three or more groups. The definition is given in the following box.

Measure of separation for G groups

Suppose that a multivariate data set comprises observations on G groups, and that group g has size n_g, and that $\overline{x}_g$ and s_g are the mean and standard deviation of a variable X in group g. Let N denote the total number of observations in the G groups: $N = n_1 + \cdots + n_G$.

The **grand mean** is denoted $\overline{\overline{x}}$ and is given by

$$\overline{\overline{x}} = \frac{1}{N} \sum_{g=1}^{G} n_g \overline{x}_g. \qquad (10.5)$$

The **between-groups variance** of X, denoted V_b, and the **within-groups variance** of X, denoted V_w, are defined as follows:

$$V_b = \frac{1}{N-G} \sum_{g=1}^{G} n_g (\overline{x}_g - \overline{\overline{x}})^2, \qquad (10.6)$$

$$V_w = \frac{1}{N-G} \sum_{g=1}^{G} (n_g - 1) s_g^2. \qquad (10.7)$$

The **separation** achieved by X is given by the ratio of the between-groups variance to the within-groups variance:

$$\text{separation} = \frac{V_b}{V_w}.$$

When $G = 2$, Formulas (10.6) and (10.7) for the between-groups variance and the within-groups variance coincide with Formulas (10.2) and (10.1). As for the case of two groups, the between-groups variance is a measure of the spread of the group means around the grand mean, and the within-groups variance is a measure of the spread of observations within each group, averaged over the groups. Just as for two groups, the separation is defined to be the ratio of the between-groups variance to the within-groups variance. It measures the spread of the group means, relative to the average spread of observations within the groups.

Example 10.8 Separation of satellite images

For the satellite image described in Example 10.7, 961 of the pixels correspond to grey soil, 415 of the pixels to damp grey soil, and 1038 of the pixels to very damp grey soil. For the first spectral band in which measurements were taken, Band A, the mean and variance of the measurements in each of the groups are given in Table 10.4.

These data were obtained in July 2005 from the Statlog database. Newman, D.J., Hettich, S., Blake, C.L. and Merz, C.J. (1998) UCI repository of machine learning databases, http://www.ics.uci.edu/~mlearn.

Table 10.4 Measurements for spectral band A

Soil type	Number of pixels	Mean	Variance
Grey soil	961	87.48	25.398
Damp grey soil	415	77.41	30.735
Very damp grey soil	1038	69.01	28.967

For these data, there are three groups and $N = 961 + 415 + 1038 = 2414$. The grand mean $\overline{\overline{x}}$ is obtained using Formula (10.5):

$$\begin{aligned}\overline{\overline{x}} &= \frac{n_1\overline{x}_1 + n_2\overline{x}_2 + n_3\overline{x}_3}{N}\\ &= \frac{961 \times 87.48 + 415 \times 77.41 + 1038 \times 69.01}{2414}\\ &= \frac{187\,825.81}{2414} \simeq 77.8069.\end{aligned}$$

The between-groups variance V_b is calculated using Formula (10.6):

$$V_b = \frac{n_1(\overline{x}_1 - \overline{\overline{x}})^2 + n_2(\overline{x}_2 - \overline{\overline{x}})^2 + n_3(\overline{x}_3 - \overline{\overline{x}})^2}{N-3}$$

$$= \frac{961(87.48 - 77.8069)^2 + 415(77.41 - 77.8069)^2 + 1038(69.01 - 77.8069)^2}{2411}$$

$$\simeq 70.64.$$

The within-groups variance V_w is found using Formula (10.7):

$$V_w = \frac{(n_1 - 1)s_1^2 + (n_2 - 1)s_2^2 + (n_3 - 1)s_3^2}{N-3}$$

$$= \frac{960 \times 25.398 + 414 \times 30.735 + 1037 \times 28.967}{2411}$$

$$\simeq 27.85.$$

Hence the separation achieved by the Band A measurements is

$$\text{separation} = \frac{V_b}{V_w} \simeq \frac{70.64}{27.85} \simeq 2.54. \quad \blacklozenge$$

Activity 10.3 Separations for different spectral bands

In the satellite image which was the focus of Example 10.8, measurements were also taken using three other spectral bands, labelled B, C and D. The means and variances of the Band B measurements for the three soil types are given in Table 10.5.

Table 10.5 Measurements for spectral band B

Soil type	Number of pixels	Mean	Variance
Grey soil	961	105.50	47.138
Damp grey soil	415	90.94	66.565
Very damp grey soil	1038	77.42	59.091

(a) Calculate the between-groups variance and the within-groups variance for Band B measurements, and hence estimate the separation for Band B.

(b) In Example 10.8, the separation for Band A was found to be 2.54. The separations for Bands C and D are 2.70 and 2.49, respectively. Use these results and the separation for Band B that you calculated in part (a) to compare the degree of separation achieved by the four sets of measurements, A, B, C and D. Which set of measurements best separates the three types of soil? Explain your answer.

10.4 Between-groups and within-groups covariance matrices

For a variable X, the between-groups variance V_b summarizes the spread of the group means of X, and the within-groups variance V_w summarizes the spread of the observations on X within each group. However, for multivariate data, the variance is not sufficient to describe all the variability in a data set. Another important measure of variability is the covariance. When there are p variables, $p(p-1)/2$ covariances are required, one for each possible pair of variables. Similarly, when multivariate data consist of data from different groups, it is not sufficient to calculate between-groups variances and within-groups variances for all the variables. Between-groups covariances and within-groups covariances are also required.

Within-groups covariances and between-groups covariances are defined analogously to within-groups variances and between-groups variances. Since several different variables are involved, it is necessary to be specific about which variable is being referred to. So from now on the within-groups variance for X_j will be denoted $V_w(X_j)$, and the between-groups variance for X_j will be denoted $V_b(X_j)$.

The **within-groups covariance** for a pair of variables X_i and X_j, which is denoted $\text{Cov}_w(X_i, X_j)$, is the weighted average of the covariances for X_i and X_j calculated for each of the groups separately.

The **between-groups covariance** between variables X_i and X_j, which is denoted $\text{Cov}_b(X_i, X_j)$, is the covariance between the group means for variables X_i and X_j. The between-groups covariance depends only on the mean values of X_i and X_j within the groups. A positive value of $\text{Cov}_b(X_i, X_j)$ indicates that groups with a high mean value of X_i also tend to have a high mean value of X_j. In contrast, a negative value of $\text{Cov}_b(X_i, X_j)$ indicates that groups with a high mean value of X_i tend to have a low mean value of X_j. The between-groups covariance is zero if there is no relationship between the mean values for X_i and for X_j in the groups. Furthermore, $\text{Cov}_b(X_i, X_i)$, the between-groups covariance between X_i and itself, is simply the between-groups variance for X_i as defined in Formula (10.6); that is, $\text{Cov}_b(X_i, X_i) = V_b(X_i)$.

The within-groups variances and covariances are usually displayed in the form of a matrix, the **within-groups covariance matrix W**. Like the ordinary covariance matrix, **W** has p rows and p columns. Element (i, j) of **W** corresponds to $\text{Cov}_w(X_i, X_j)$, the within-groups covariance between variables X_i and X_j. Similarly, the between-groups variances and covariances are usually displayed as a matrix, the **between-groups covariance matrix B**. This matrix also has p rows and p columns. Element (i, j) of **B** corresponds to $\text{Cov}_b(X_i, X_j)$, the between-groups covariance between variables X_i and X_j.

You will not be expected to calculate within-groups covariances and between-groups covariances in this course, so the formulas have been omitted. Although the calculations are not complicated, they are tedious and are best done by computer. However, you will be expected to be able to interpret within-groups and between-groups covariance matrices.

You are, however, expected to know how to calculate within-groups and between-groups variances, as described in Subsection 10.3.

Example 10.9 The within-groups and between-groups covariance matrices

The variables measured on genuine and counterfeit Swiss 1000-franc banknotes are as follows.

See Example 10.1.

Length X_1: the length of the note
Left width X_2: the width at the left edge of the note
Right width X_3: the width at the right edge of the note
Bottom borderX_4: the width of the bottom border
Top border X_5: the width of the top border
Diagonal X_6: the length of the diagonal of the central motif

The within-groups covariance matrix **W** and the between-groups covariance matrix **B**, calculated for these six variables, with elements rounded to three decimal places, are shown below.

$$\mathbf{W} = \begin{pmatrix} 0.137 & 0.045 & 0.041 & -0.022 & 0.017 & 0.009 \\ 0.045 & 0.099 & 0.066 & 0.016 & 0.019 & -0.024 \\ 0.041 & 0.066 & 0.108 & 0.020 & 0.015 & 0.005 \\ -0.022 & 0.016 & 0.020 & 0.847 & -0.377 & 0.119 \\ 0.017 & 0.019 & 0.015 & -0.377 & 0.413 & -0.049 \\ 0.009 & -0.024 & 0.005 & 0.119 & -0.049 & 0.256 \end{pmatrix}$$

$$\mathbf{B} = \begin{pmatrix} 0.006 & -0.014 & -0.018 & -0.084 & -0.036 & 0.078 \\ -0.014 & 0.033 & 0.043 & 0.203 & 0.087 & -0.188 \\ -0.018 & 0.043 & 0.056 & 0.265 & 0.114 & -0.246 \\ -0.084 & 0.203 & 0.265 & 1.256 & 0.541 & -1.166 \\ -0.036 & 0.087 & 0.114 & 0.541 & 0.233 & -0.502 \\ 0.078 & -0.188 & -0.246 & -1.166 & -0.502 & 1.082 \end{pmatrix}$$

First, notice that both matrices are symmetrical because the covariance for X_i and X_j, whether within-groups or between-groups, is the same as the covariance for X_j and X_i.

Secondly, note that the diagonals contain the within-groups and between-groups variances, so the separation for each variable can be obtained from the matrices **W** and **B**. For example, the separation for X_6 is $1.082/0.256 \simeq 4.23$. This agrees with the value given in Table 10.2, to one decimal place.

The difference in the second decimal place is due to rounding error.

Also observe that the pattern of positive and negative covariances is different in **W** and in **B**. For example, the within-groups covariance for X_4 and X_5 is -0.377, whereas the between-groups covariance for these two variables is 0.541. Thus they are negatively related within groups, but positively related between groups. ♦

Example 10.9 illustrates that the relationship between two variables within groups can be quite different to their relationship between groups. When this happens, a combination of the two variables will be better at separating the groups than either of the variables separately. Exploiting this property is the subject of Section 11.

Activity 10.4 will give you some practice at interpreting within-groups and between-groups covariance matrices.

Activity 10.4 W and B for the heart disease data

In Activity 10.2, data on 120 patients with heart disease and 150 patients without heart disease were described. Four variables were measured on each of the 270 patients: age (X_1), blood pressure (X_2), cholesterol (X_3), and maximum heart rate (X_4). The within-groups and between-groups covariance matrices are

$$\mathbf{W} = \begin{pmatrix} 79.53 & 39.2 & 92.15 & -66.37 \\ 39.20 & 312.50 & 143.33 & 10.75 \\ 92.15 & 143.33 & 2644.09 & 36.84 \\ -66.37 & 10.75 & 36.84 & 444.31 \end{pmatrix},$$

$$\mathbf{B} = \begin{pmatrix} 3.76 & 5.25 & 11.94 & -18.68 \\ 5.25 & 7.47 & 16.84 & -26.35 \\ 11.94 & 16.84 & 37.97 & -59.40 \\ -18.68 & -26.35 & -59.40 & 92.93 \end{pmatrix}.$$

(a) Which variable has the smallest within-groups variance? Which has the largest between-groups variance?

(b) Obtain the separations for the four variables, and compare the results with those you obtained in Activity 10.2.

(c) Identify a pair of variables for which the between-groups covariance and the within-groups covariance have different signs. Describe the relationship between these variables.

(d) Hence suggest how the separation achieved using maximum heart rate could be improved by combining it with one or more additional variables.

Summary of Section 10

In this section, the idea of separating groups has been introduced. The within-groups variance and the between-groups variance have been defined, and a measure of separation based on the ratio of the between-groups variance to the within-groups variance has been described. You have learned how to calculate separations, and how to compare the abilities of different variables to separate groups. The within-groups and between-groups covariance matrices have been discussed. The within-groups covariance matrix **W** describes the average variation between observations within each group. The between-groups covariance matrix **B** describes the variation of group means around the grand mean. You have learned how to interpret the matrices **W** and **B**, and hence identify combinations of variables that may give better separation than can be achieved using the variables separately.

Exercise on Section 10

Exercise 10.1 *Separating the sources of opium*

In Example 10.2 and Activity 10.1, data on the identification of sources of opium were described. The data relate to 50 samples of opium from three divisions: Chittorgarh (15 samples), Kota (17 samples) and Mandsaur (18 samples). Concentrations were measured of four amino acids: glycine (G), phenylalanine (F), isoleucine (I) and aspartic acid (D). The mean concentrations for each of these amino acids for each division are given in Table 10.6. The corresponding variances of the concentrations are also given.

Table 10.6 Means and variances of four amino acids measured in samples of opium grown in three Indian divisions

Amino	Mean			Variance		
acid	Chittorgarh	Kota	Mandsaur	Chittorgarh	Kota	Mandsaur
G	0.185	0.597	0.203	0.0227	0.0449	0.0036
F	0.369	0.427	0.965	0.0622	0.0724	0.0813
I	0.263	0.240	0.391	0.0572	0.0151	0.0549
D	0.575	0.647	0.727	0.1917	0.1371	0.0411

(a) Calculate the between-groups variance for glycine.

(b) Calculate the within-groups variance for phenylalanine.

(c) Use your answers to parts (a) and (b) to calculate the missing values in Table 10.7.

Table 10.7 Between-groups variances, within-groups variances and separations

Amino acid	V_b	V_w	Separation
G		0.0233	
F	0.0789		
I	0.0049	0.0420	0.12
D	0.0041	0.1186	0.03

(d) If there were sufficient resources to measure only one amino acid, which one would be most useful for indicating the division from which a sample came? Explain your answer.

11 Linear combinations for separation

In Section 10, the degree to which groups are separated by a variable was measured by the separation; this is defined as the ratio of the between-groups variance to the within-groups variance. Calculating this separation for each variable in a multivariate data set allows the single variable that best differentiates between the groups to be identified.

However, for most data sets, the separation between groups can be increased by using a linear combination of variables. In Subsection 11.1, you will learn how to calculate the between-groups and within-groups variances for a linear combination from the between-groups and within-groups covariance matrices, and hence calculate the separation achieved by the linear combination. Canonical discrimination, which involves finding the linear combination that best separates the groups, is described in Subsection 11.2. Discrimination using standardized variables is discussed in Subsection 11.3.

11.1 Linear combinations

A linear combination D of variables $X_1, \ldots, X_p$ has the general form

$$D = \sum_{j=1}^{p} \alpha_j (X_j - \overline{\overline{X}}_j),$$

Linear combinations of p variables were introduced in Subsection 7.1.

where $\overline{\overline{X}}_j$ is the grand mean of X_j and $\alpha_1, \ldots, \alpha_p$ are constants known as loadings. In Subsection 7.1, you learned how to calculate the variance of the linear combination D directly from the covariance matrix of $X_1, \ldots, X_p$ using the following formula:

$$V(D) = \sum_{j=1}^{p} \alpha_j^2 \, V(X_j) + 2 \sum_{j,k:k>j} \alpha_j \alpha_k \operatorname{Cov}(X_j, X_k). \tag{11.1}$$

The limit on the second summation term means that the sum includes all possible pairs j and k where $k > j$.

Similarly, the within-groups variance of D can be calculated directly from $\mathbf{W}$, the within-groups covariance matrix for $X_1, \ldots, X_p$, and the between-groups variance of D can be calculated directly from $\mathbf{B}$, the between-groups covariance matrix for $X_1, \ldots, X_p$, using the following formulas:

$$V_w(D) = \sum_{j=1}^{p} \alpha_j^2 \, V_w(X_j) + 2 \sum_{j,k:k>j} \alpha_j \alpha_k \operatorname{Cov}_w(X_j, X_k), \tag{11.2}$$

$$V_b(D) = \sum_{j=1}^{p} \alpha_j^2 \, V_b(X_j) + 2 \sum_{j,k:k>j} \alpha_j \alpha_k \operatorname{Cov}_b(X_j, X_k). \tag{11.3}$$

You will not be expected to calculate the variances for linear combinations of more than three variables by hand.

Notice the similarity between these formulas and Formula (11.1). The only difference is that all the (ordinary) variances and covariances have been replaced by the corresponding within-groups and between-groups variances and covariances.

For any linear combination D, the separation between the groups achieved by D is defined as the ratio of the between-groups variance of D to the within-groups variance of D:

$$\text{separation} = \frac{V_b(D)}{V_w(D)}. \tag{11.4}$$

Calculation of the separation for a linear combination of two variables is illustrated in Example 11.1 using the Swiss 1000-franc banknote data that was described in Example 10.1.

Example 11.1 Separation achieved by a linear combination of two variables

In Example 10.6, it was shown that the two measurements that are the least effective in separating the counterfeit notes and the genuine notes are X_1, the length of the banknote, and X_2, the width at the left edge: the width at the left edge achieves a separation of 0.33, and using the length results in a separation of only 0.04. Can a linear combination of these two variables do better?

Consider the following linear combination:

$$\begin{aligned} D &= 0.6(X_1 - \overline{\overline{X}}_1) - 0.8(X_2 - \overline{\overline{X}}_2) \\ &= 0.6(X_1 - 214.895) - 0.8(X_2 - 130.120). \end{aligned}$$

The means are given in Table 10.1. (See Example 10.5.)

For a linear combination of two variables, X_1 and X_2, Formulas (11.2) and (11.3) are as follows:

$$V_w(D) = \alpha_1^2 \, V_w(X_1) + \alpha_2^2 \, V_w(X_2) + 2\alpha_1\alpha_2 \operatorname{Cov}_w(X_1, X_2), \tag{11.5}$$

$$V_b(D) = \alpha_1^2 \, V_b(X_1) + \alpha_2^2 \, V_b(X_2) + 2\alpha_1\alpha_2 \operatorname{Cov}_b(X_1, X_2). \tag{11.6}$$

For the linear combination D above, $\alpha_1 = 0.6$ and $\alpha_2 = -0.8$.

The within-groups and between-groups variances and covariances required are given in the within-groups and between-groups covariance matrices, **W** and **B**; their values are as follows:

$$V_w(X_1) = 0.137, \quad V_w(X_2) = 0.099, \quad \text{Cov}_w(X_1, X_2) = 0.045,$$
$$V_b(X_1) = 0.006, \quad V_b(X_2) = 0.033, \quad \text{Cov}_b(X_1, X_2) = -0.014.$$

The covariance matrices are given in Example 10.9.

Hence, using Formulas (11.5) and (11.6),

$$\begin{aligned} V_w(D) &= (0.6)^2 \times 0.137 + (-0.8)^2 \times 0.099 + 2 \times 0.6 \times (-0.8) \times 0.045 \\ &= 0.069\,48, \end{aligned}$$

$$\begin{aligned} V_b(D) &= (0.6)^2 \times 0.006 + (-0.8)^2 \times 0.033 + 2 \times 0.6 \times (-0.8) \times (-0.014) \\ &= 0.036\,72. \end{aligned}$$

So the separation achieved by the linear combination D is

$$\frac{V_b(D)}{V_w(D)} = \frac{0.036\,72}{0.069\,48} \simeq 0.53.$$

This separation is better than that achieved by either the length or the left width alone. There are two reasons for this improvement. First, the within-groups variance of D is less than the within-groups variance for either the length or the left width. Secondly, the between-groups variance of D is greater than the between-groups variance for either the length or the left width. So the difference between the mean values for the counterfeit notes and the genuine notes has been increased, while the spread of the observations within the groups has decreased. ♦

Activity 11.1 Trying other values of α_1 and α_2

This activity will give you some practice at calculating the separation for several linear combinations of the variables X_1 and X_2 for the banknotes. The variances and covariances required were given in Example 11.1.

(a) For each of the following choices of α_1 and α_2, calculate the between-groups variance and the within-groups variance with respect to the linear combination

$$D = \alpha_1(X_1 - 214.895) + \alpha_2(X_2 - 130.120).$$

(i) $\alpha_1 = 0.8$ and $\alpha_2 = -0.6$

(ii) $\alpha_1 = 1$ and $\alpha_2 = 0$

(iii) $\alpha_1 = 0$ and $\alpha_2 = 1$

(iv) $\alpha_1 = 0.6$ and $\alpha_2 = 0.8$

(b) Use the values you found in part (a) to calculate the values of the missing entries in Table 11.1.

Table 11.1 Between-groups variances, within-groups variances and separations resulting from linear combinations of the length and left width of banknotes

α_1	α_2	$V_b(D)$	$V_w(D)$	$V_b(D)/V_w(D)$
1	0			
0.8	0.6	0.002 28	0.166 52	0.01
$1/\sqrt{2}$	$1/\sqrt{2}$	0.005 50	0.163 00	0.03
0.6	0.8			
0	1			
0.8	−0.6			
$1/\sqrt{2}$	$-1/\sqrt{2}$	0.033 50	0.073 00	0.46
0.6	−0.8	0.036 72	0.069 48	0.53

(c) Which choice of α_1 and α_2 among those listed in Table 11.1 leads to the differences between the values of D for the counterfeit notes and the genuine notes being emphasized the most? Explain your answer.

11.2 Canonical discrimination

In Subsection 11.1, you have seen that the separation between groups can be improved by considering linear combinations of the variables of the form

$$D = \sum_{j=1}^{p} \alpha_j (X_j - \overline{\overline{X}}_j).$$

The technique of **canonical discrimination**, or **discrimination** for short, consists of finding the linear combination D for which the separation is maximized, subject to the constraint $\sum_{j=1}^{p} \alpha_j^2 = 1$ on the loadings $\alpha_1, \ldots, \alpha_p$.

Canonical discrimination is sometimes referred to in the statistical literature under other names.

The linear combination D that maximizes the separation is called the **(first) discriminant function**. For convenience, the discriminant function is often written in the form

$$D = \left(\sum_{j=1}^{p} \alpha_j X_j \right) - c,$$

where

$$c = \sum_{j=1}^{p} \alpha_j \overline{\overline{X}}_j.$$

It can be shown that the loadings for the discriminant function are unique up to a change of sign for all the loadings. It does not matter which of D and $-D$ is used.

Note that the grand mean of D is zero, that is, $\overline{\overline{D}} = 0$.

Example 11.2 Discriminant function based on length and left width

In Example 11.1 and Activity 11.1, you explored the effect of different choices of α_1 and α_2 on the linear combination

$$D = \alpha_1 (X_1 - 214.895) + \alpha_2 (X_2 - 130.120).$$

It can be shown that the separation for D is maximized when $\alpha_1 = 0.481$ and $\alpha_2 = -0.877$. Thus the first discriminant function based on the two variables X_1 and X_2 is

$$\begin{aligned} D &= 0.481(X_1 - 214.895) - 0.877(X_2 - 130.120) \\ &\simeq 0.481X_1 - 0.877X_2 + 10.75. \end{aligned}$$

For this discriminant function, $V_b(D) \simeq 0.038\,58$ and $V_w(D) \simeq 0.069\,87$. So the separation achieved by this choice of α_1 and α_2 is approximately 0.55. Note that this is greater than any of the values listed in Table S.4.

You may wish to check the values of these variances and the separation for D.

It is not surprising that in this linear combination, the greater weight is given to X_2, the width at the left edge of the note. This measurement is far better at separating the groups by itself than is X_1, the length of the note (see Example 10.6). Note that D tends to be positive for relatively long, narrow notes (that is, notes with large values of X_1 and small values of X_2), and negative for short wide notes (those with small values of X_1 and large values of X_2). Thus D measures the shape of the notes, its value increasing as the notes become longer and thinner.

Since there are only two variables involved, the canonical discriminant function D can be interpreted geometrically. A scatterplot of the lengths of the notes and widths at the left edge is shown in Figure 11.1 (overleaf).

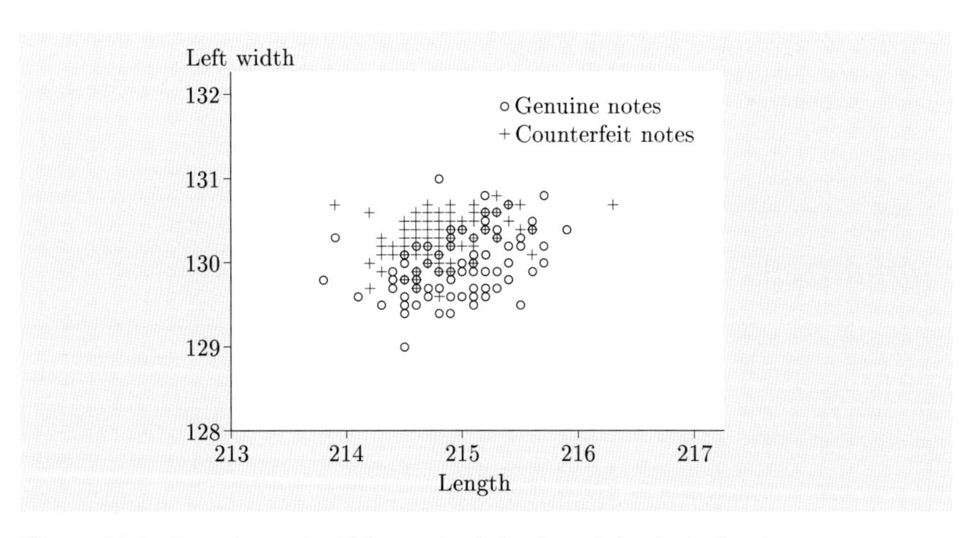

Figure 11.1 Lengths and widths at the left edge of the Swiss banknotes

Short wide notes (D negative) are located towards the top left-hand corner of the scatterplot, whereas long narrow notes (D positive) tend to lie towards the bottom right-hand corner. The value of D increases as you move diagonally from one corner to the other. The scatterplot shows that counterfeit notes are more likely to be short and wide (with D negative), and genuine notes tend to be long and narrow (with D positive). However, there is a good deal of overlap between the two clouds of points, so D does not separate the groups very well. ♦

Equivalent linear combinations were defined in Subsection 6.1: two linear combinations Y_1 and Y_2 are equivalent if constants $c_1 \neq 0$ and c_2 can be found such that $Y_2 = c_1 Y_1 + c_2$. Suppose that D_1 and D_2 are equivalent linear combinations and that $D_2 = c_1 D_1 + c_2$, where $c_1 \neq 0$. In this case, $V_w(D_2) = c_1^2 V_w(D_1)$ and $V_b(D_2) = c_1^2 V_b(D_1)$. Hence, if the separations for D_1 and D_2 are denoted $\text{Sep}(D_1)$ and $\text{Sep}(D_2)$, then

For any random variable X, and constants $a \neq 0$ and b,
$$V(aX+b) = a^2 V(X).$$

$$\text{Sep}(D_2) = \frac{V_b(D_2)}{V_w(D_2)} = \frac{c_1^2 V_b(D_1)}{c_1^2 V_w(D_2)} = \frac{V_b(D_1)}{V_w(D_1)} = \text{Sep}(D_1).$$

That is, the separations for D_1 and D_2 are the same.

The property $\overline{\overline{D}} = 0$, together with the restriction $\sum_{j=1}^{p} \alpha_j^2 = 1$ placed on the loadings $\alpha_1, \ldots, \alpha_p$ of the discriminant function D, ensure that the function is unique (up to a change in sign). However, since the separations achieved by equivalent linear combinations are equal, if D_1 is a discriminant function and $D_2 = c_1 D_1 + c_2$ ($c_1 \neq 0$), then D_2 could just as well be used as a discriminant function; and in this case, D_1 and D_2 are said to be **equivalent discriminant functions**.

Since equivalent linear combinations achieve the same separation, a more general definition of the discriminant function could be used which allows any one of a class of equivalent linear combinations to be chosen.

Restrictions other than $\sum_{j=1}^{p} \alpha_j^2 = 1$ are often placed on the values of $\alpha_1, \ldots, \alpha_p$ when defining the discriminant function. The constants $\alpha_1, \ldots, \alpha_p$ are often restricted in such a way that $V_w(D) = 1$. SPSS places this restriction on the constants, and from now on, unless stated otherwise, 'the' discriminant function always refers to the linear combination with mean zero which satisfies the condition $V_w(D) = 1$. This choice is popular because it makes it easier to compare discriminant functions from different analyses. In effect, it standardizes the values of D, after allowing for any group differences. An example of this alternative way of specifying the loadings is given in Example 11.3.

Example 11.3 Alternative loadings for the banknote data

The discriminant function for the Swiss 1000-franc banknote data based on the length and the width at the left edge can be written as

$$D = \alpha_1(X_1 - 214.895) + \alpha_2(X_2 - 130.120),$$

where $\alpha_1 = 0.481$ and $\alpha_2 = -0.877$. For this choice of α_1 and α_2, $V_w(D) \simeq 0.070$.

See Example 11.2.

Dividing both α_1 and α_2 by $\sqrt{0.070}$ has the effect of dividing both $V_w(D)$ and $V_b(D)$ by 0.070, so for these new loadings, $V_w(D) = 1$. This produces a second discriminant function, with loadings $\alpha_1 = 0.481/\sqrt{0.070} \simeq 1.818$ and $\alpha_2 = -0.877/\sqrt{0.070} \simeq -3.315$:

$$\begin{aligned} D_2 &= 1.818(X_1 - 214.895) - 3.315(X_2 - 130.120) \\ &\simeq 1.818X_1 - 3.315X_2 + 40.669. \end{aligned}$$

Dividing the loadings by the constant $\sqrt{0.070}$ does not affect the separation achieved: D and D_2 are equivalent. The only difference between D and D_2 is that the loadings of D_2 are scaled so that $V_w(D_2) = 1$. ♦

Activity 11.2 Equivalence of discriminant functions

Six measurements were made on each Swiss 1000-franc banknote, as described in Example 10.1. The discriminant function based on all six variables may be written as follows:

$$\begin{aligned} D = &-0.005(X_1 - 214.895) - 0.832(X_2 - 130.120) + 0.849(X_3 - 129.955) \\ &+ 1.117(X_4 - 9.415) + 1.179(X_5 - 10.650) - 1.557(X_6 - 140.485). \end{aligned}$$

(a) Write down the discriminant function in the form

$$D = \left(\sum_{j=1}^{6} \alpha_j X_j \right) - c.$$

(b) Another linear combination has the form

$$\begin{aligned} D_2 = &\ 0.010X_1 + 1.664X_2 + 1.698X_3 + 2.234X_4 \\ &+ 2.358X_5 + 3.114X_6 - 919.825. \end{aligned}$$

Is D_2 equivalent to D? Explain your answer.

The main results of this subsection are summarized in the following box.

Canonical discrimination

In canonical discrimination, a linear combination of the p variables in a multivariate data set that best separates the groups is sought.

This linear combination is of the form

$$D = \sum_{j=1}^{p} \alpha_j (X_j - \overline{\overline{X}}_j)$$

or, equivalently,

$$D = \left(\sum_{j=1}^{p} \alpha_j X_j \right) - c, \quad \text{where } c = \sum_{j=1}^{p} \alpha_j \overline{\overline{X}}_j.$$

The **first discriminant function** D is the linear combination for which the separation is maximized, subject to a constraint on the loadings $\alpha_1, \alpha_2, \dots, \alpha_p$.

Commonly, the constraint placed on the loadings is that $\sum_{j=1}^{p} \alpha_j^2 = 1$. Often the loadings are restricted so that $V_w(D) = 1$, as this makes it easier to compare discriminant functions from different analyses.

11.3 Group-standardization of variables

In principal component analysis, using standardized variables instead of unstandardized variables can lead to substantially different results. However, as you will see, provided that the standardized variables are defined in a suitable way, this is not the case for canonical discrimination: the results are the same whether or not the variables are standardized, but using standardized variables makes it easier to interpret the discriminant function.

The standardized version Z_j of a variable X_j is usually defined so that Z_j has mean 0 and standard deviation 1 (and hence variance 1).

In canonical discrimination, the standardized version Z_j of a variable X_j is defined so that Z_j has mean 0 and within-groups variance 1, using the formula

$$Z_j = \frac{X_j - \overline{\overline{X}}_j}{\sqrt{V_w(X_j)}}.$$

To distinguish this type of standardization from that defined in Subsection 4.2, the variable Z_j will be called the **group-standardized** variable.

The discriminant function D may thus be written as follows:

$$D = \sum_{j=1}^{p} \alpha_j (X_j - \overline{\overline{X}}_j) = \sum_{j=1}^{p} \alpha_j \sqrt{V_w(X_j)}\, Z_j = \sum_{j=1}^{p} a_j Z_j,$$

where $a_j = \alpha_j \sqrt{V_w(X_j)}$. Thus the discriminant function can be written in terms of the group-standardized variables simply by multiplying the loadings $\alpha_1, \ldots, \alpha_p$ by the corresponding within-groups standard deviations. For each observation, the value of D is unchanged by this transformation, and hence the between-groups and within-groups variances of D are unchanged. In consequence, the value of the separation is also the same.

In other words, the discriminant function D may equivalently be written in terms of the group-standardized variables Z_j as

$$D = \sum_{j=1}^{p} a_j Z_j,$$

where the loadings a_j are given by

$$a_j = \alpha_j \sqrt{V_w(X_j)}.$$

Example 11.4 Group-standardization for the Swiss banknotes

The discriminant function D (with $V_w(D) = 1$) for the Swiss 1000-franc banknote data, based on the length (X_1) and the width at the left edge (X_2), is

$$D = 1.818(X_1 - \overline{\overline{X}}_1) - 3.315(X_2 - \overline{\overline{X}}_2).$$

See Example 11.3.

Thus $\alpha_1 = 1.818$ and $\alpha_2 = -3.315$. To express D as a linear combination of the group-standardized variables Z_1 and Z_2, the within-groups variances of X_1 and X_2 are required: $V_w(X_1) = 0.137$ and $V_w(X_2) = 0.099$. Thus the values of a_1 and a_2, the loadings for the group-standardized variables Z_1 and Z_2, are given by

These variances may be obtained from the within-groups covariance matrix $\mathbf{W}$, given in Example 10.9.

$$a_1 = \alpha_1 \sqrt{V_w(X_1)} = 1.818 \times \sqrt{0.137} \simeq 0.673,$$
$$a_2 = \alpha_2 \sqrt{V_w(X_2)} = -3.315 \times \sqrt{0.099} \simeq -1.043.$$

Hence

$$D = 0.673 Z_1 - 1.043 Z_2.$$

With this choice of a_1 and a_2, the separation is 0.55, the same as when using the unstandardized variables. ♦

As you have just seen, group-standardization changes only the coefficients of the discriminant function: it does not change the values of the discriminant function. Group-standardization makes it easier to interpret the discriminant function. Since all the variables are group-standardized, it makes sense to compare the sizes of their loadings: the larger the loading is in absolute value, the more important the corresponding variable is to the discriminant function. Therefore group-standardization is usually applied before a discriminant function is interpreted.

Example 11.5 Interpreting the loadings

For the Swiss 1000-franc banknote data, the first discriminant function, based on the length and the width at the left edge, can be written as

$$D = 0.673Z_1 - 1.043Z_2.$$

Since the loadings for the two variables have opposite signs, it is the *difference* between the length and the width at the left edge that matters in distinguishing between genuine notes and counterfeit notes. Thus the shape of the note matters rather than its size. Furthermore, the width at the left edge is almost twice as important as the length of the note. ♦

Activity 11.3 Interpreting the discriminant function for the banknotes

The discriminant function for the Swiss 1000-franc banknotes, based on all six variables, can be written as follows:

$$D = -0.005(X_1 - 214.895) - 0.832(X_2 - 130.120) + 0.849(X_3 - 129.955) + 1.117(X_4 - 9.415) + 1.179(X_5 - 10.650) - 1.557(X_6 - 140.485).$$

See Activity 11.2.

(a) Write D in terms of the group-standardized variables $Z_1, \ldots, Z_6$. (You will need the within-groups covariance matrix $\mathbf{W}$; this is given in Example 10.9.)

(b) Use the expression for D that you obtained in part (a) to interpret the discriminant function. In particular, identify which measurements are important, and whether any measurements appear not to be helpful.

(c) In Example 11.5, the loading for the length was 0.673. How does this value compare with the loading you obtained in part (a)? Explain why these two values are so different.

The main results of this subsection are summarized in the following box.

Group-standardization

In canonical discrimination, Z_j, the group-standardized version of the variable X_j, is defined as follows:

$$Z_j = \frac{X_j - \overline{\overline{X}}_j}{\sqrt{V_w(X_j)}}.$$

The mean of Z_j is 0, and its within-groups variance is 1.

The first discriminant function

$$D = \alpha_1(X_1 - \overline{\overline{X}}_1) + \alpha_2(X_2 - \overline{\overline{X}}_2) + \cdots + \alpha_p(X_p - \overline{\overline{X}}_p)$$

may be written as

$$D = a_1 Z_1 + a_2 Z_2 + \cdots + a_p Z_p,$$

where the loadings a_j are given by

$$a_j = \alpha_j \sqrt{V_w(X_j)}.$$

The separation achieved by the discriminant function D is the same whether D is based on unstandardized or on group-standardized variables.

Summary of Section 11

In this section, canonical discrimination has been introduced; this involves finding a linear combination of variables that best separates the groups in a multivariate data set. In order to ensure uniqueness (up to a change in sign for all the loadings), a constraint is placed on the loadings.

The linear combination that maximizes the separation is called the (first) discriminant function. You have seen that equivalent linear combinations achieve the same separation. Therefore, given a discriminant function, any equivalent linear combination may be used instead as a discriminant function.

Canonical discrimination using standardized variables has also been discussed. You have seen that, provided that the variables are standardized appropriately, the results using standardized and unstandardized variables are the same. However, using standardized variables makes it easier to interpret the discriminant function.

Exercises on Section 11

Exercise 11.1 Comparing discriminant functions

Suppose that the following linear combination is a discriminant function D for a data set with three variables X_1, X_2 and X_3:

$$D = 0.3(X_1 - 1) + 0.4(X_2 + 2) - 0.5(X_3 - 4).$$

Which of the following linear combinations are also discriminant functions for this data set? Explain your answer in each case.

(a) $D = 3(X_1 - 1) + 4(X_2 + 2) - 0.5(X_3 - 4)$.

(b) $D = 0.9X_1 + 1.2X_2 - 1.5X_3 + 7.5$.

(c) $D = Z_1 + Z_2 - Z_3$ when $V_w(X_1) = 0.09$, $V_w(X_2) = 0.16$ and $V_w(X_3) = 0.25$.

(d) $D = Z_1 + Z_2 - Z_3$ when $V_w(X_1) = 11.1$, $V_w(X_2) = 6.25$ and $V_w(X_3) = 4$.

Exercise 11.2 Tracing the opium sources

A data set consisting of measurements on samples of opium cultivated legally in three divisions of India was described in Example 10.2 and Exercise 10.1. Concentrations of four amino acids were measured for each sample: glycine (X_1), phenylalanine (X_2), isoleucine (X_3) and aspartic acid (X_4).

When written in terms of the group-standardized variables, a discriminant function using all four variables is

$$D = 0.968Z_1 - 0.233Z_2 + 0.169Z_3 - 0.508Z_4.$$

Interpret this function.

12 Separation of groups in more than one dimension

When the first discriminant function does not adequately separate all the groups, it is sometimes possible to separate the groups better by using additional linear combinations of the variables. In Subsection 12.1, the second discriminant function is defined. The number of discriminant functions that can be found is limited by the number of groups and the number of variables in the data set. The maximum number that can be found is discussed in Subsection 12.2, and their usefulness in Subsection 12.3.

12.1 The second discriminant function

Often, a single discriminant function is enough to separate adequately all the groups in a set of data. However, as Example 12.1 shows, this is not always the case.

Example 12.1 Provenancing stone artefacts

Outcrops of the same type of rock in different locations can have slightly different chemical compositions. These differences are of interest to archaeologists, as they provide a means of identifying the sources of stone used to fashion stone artefacts. In one study, researchers studied the chemical composition of steatite rocks taken from quarries in different locations in North America.

Truncer, J., Glascock, M.D. and Neff, H. (1998) Steatite source characterization in Eastern North America: New results using instrumental neutron activation analysis. *Archaeometry*, **40**, 23–44.

Four of the quarries studied were Boyce Farm Quarry in Pennsylvania, Chula Quarry in Virginia, Lawrenceville East Quarry in Virginia and Susquehanna Quarry in Maryland. For each sample of stone, the concentrations of six chemical elements (in parts per billion) were measured. These elements were cobalt (Co), chromium (Cr), iron (Fe), manganese (Mn), scandium (Sc) and samarium (Sm). The first discriminant function based on these six variables is

$$D = 0.612X_1 - 1.710X_2 - 1.698X_3 - 0.443X_4 - 2.649X_5 - 0.019X_6 + 24.097,$$

where X_1, X_2, X_3, X_4, X_5 and X_6 are the log concentrations of cobalt, chromium, iron, manganese, scandium and samarium, respectively.

Figure 12.1 shows histograms of the values of D for each of the quarries. The values of D for the samples from Boyce Farm are noticeably lower than the values for the samples from Chula and Lawrenceville East, so D separate Boyce Farm from Chula and Lawrenceville East well. However, the values of D for samples from Chula quarry overlap with those from Lawrenceville East and Susquehanna. So this discriminant function does not separate samples from Chula, Lawrenceville East and Susquehanna quarries very well. ♦

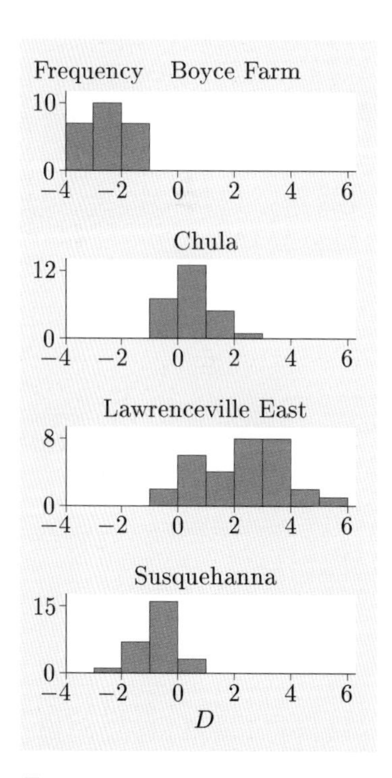

Figure 12.1 Histograms of values of the discriminant function for samples taken from four quarries

Example 12.1 shows that sometimes the discriminant function D does not clearly separate all the groups. So what is to be done in such situations?

The solution is to look for a second linear combination, D_2, which separates the groups in a way that has not already been exploited by the first discriminant function, D_1. (Choosing this second linear combination is similar in many ways to choosing a second principal component.) This is achieved by requiring that the within-groups covariance between D_1 and D_2 is zero. Then, subject to this condition being satisfied, the loadings for D_2 are chosen so that the separation achieved by D_2 is maximized. The corresponding linear combination is called the **second discriminant function**.

In order to distinguish the expressions for the first and second discriminant functions, from now on, an extra subscript will be used for their loadings. Thus

$$D_1 = \alpha_{11}(X_1 - \overline{\overline{X}}_1) + \cdots + \alpha_{1p}(X_p - \overline{\overline{X}}_p),$$
$$D_2 = \alpha_{21}(X_1 - \overline{\overline{X}}_1) + \cdots + \alpha_{2p}(X_p - \overline{\overline{X}}_p).$$

As for the first discriminant function, to ensure that D_2 is unique (up to a change of sign), the loadings of the second discriminant function are constrained either so that $\sum_{j=1}^{p} \alpha_{2j}^2 = 1$ or so that $V_w(D_2) = 1$.

Other constraints are sometimes used. These may produce non-equivalent discriminant functions. They will not be used in this book.

The second discriminant function can also be written in the form

$$D_2 = \left(\sum_{j=1}^{p} \alpha_{2j} X_j \right) - c_2,$$

where $c_2 = \sum_{j=1}^{p} \alpha_{2j} \overline{\overline{X}}_j$. Alternatively, it can be written in terms of the group-standardized variables $Z_1, \ldots, Z_p$, as follows:

$$D_2 = \sum_{j=1}^{p} a_{2j} Z_j,$$

where $a_{2j} = \alpha_{2j}\sqrt{V_w(X_j)}$.

Example 12.2 Separating quarries

The first discriminant function for the quarries data described in Example 12.1 is

$$D_1 = 0.612X_1 - 1.710X_2 - 1.698X_3 - 0.443X_4 - 2.649X_5 - 0.019X_6 + 24.097.$$

Since the four quarries are not well separated by D_1, the second discriminant function D_2 is obtained:

$$D_2 = 0.072X_1 - 3.080X_2 - 0.385X_3 - 0.598X_4 + 1.585X_5 - 0.622X_6 - 25.104.$$

For each observation, the values of D_1 and D_2 can be calculated. A scatterplot of the values is shown in Figure 12.2, with the four quarries identified using different plotting symbols.

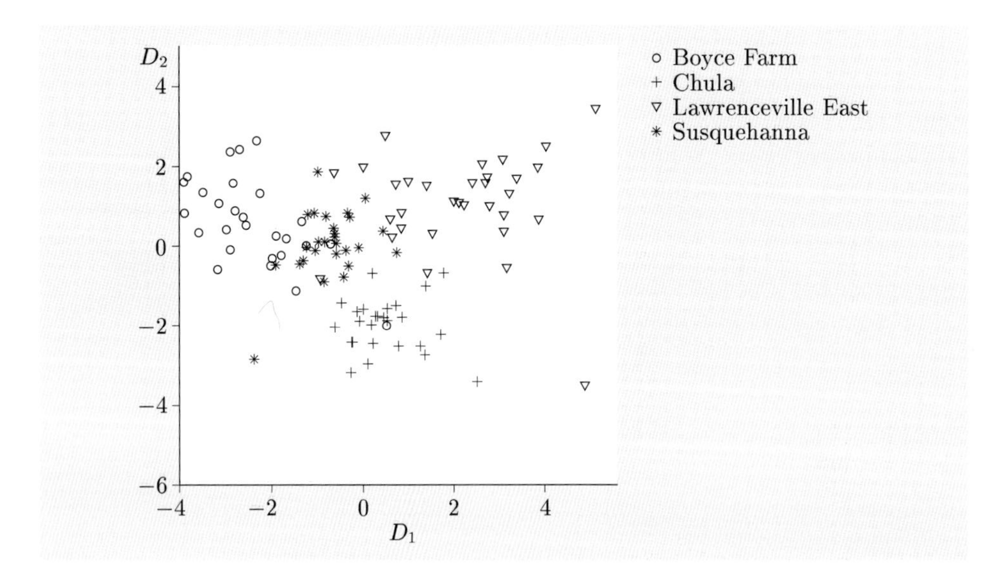

Figure 12.2 Scatterplot of D_1 and D_2 for samples taken from four quarries

Notice that the groups are more clearly separated in this scatterplot than in the histograms in Figure 12.1. Compared with the other quarries, samples from the Chula quarry generally have a lower value for D_2. As a result, the cloud of points corresponding to Chula quarry lies below those for Lawrenceville East and Susquehanna. Together, D_1 and D_2 separate the four groups much better than D_1 does on its own. ♦

Activity 12.1 Processing satellite images revisited

Data relating to a satellite image were introduced in Example 10.7. From this image, data for 2414 pixels are available. Each pixel corresponds to grey soil, damp grey soil or very damp grey soil. For each pixel, four measurements were taken, each measurement corresponding to a different spectral band.

(a) The first discriminant function, D_1, written in terms of Z_1, Z_2, Z_3 and Z_4, the group-standardized measurements using spectral bands A, B, C and D, respectively, is

$$D_1 = 0.286Z_1 + 0.440Z_2 + 0.191Z_3 + 0.156Z_4.$$

Interpret this discriminant function.

(b) The second discriminant function, D_2, for these data, based on group-standardized variables, is

$$D_2 = 1.706Z_1 - 1.056Z_2 - 0.556Z_3 + 0.005Z_4.$$

Interpret D_2.

(c) A scatterplot of values of D_1 and D_2 is shown in Figure 12.3.

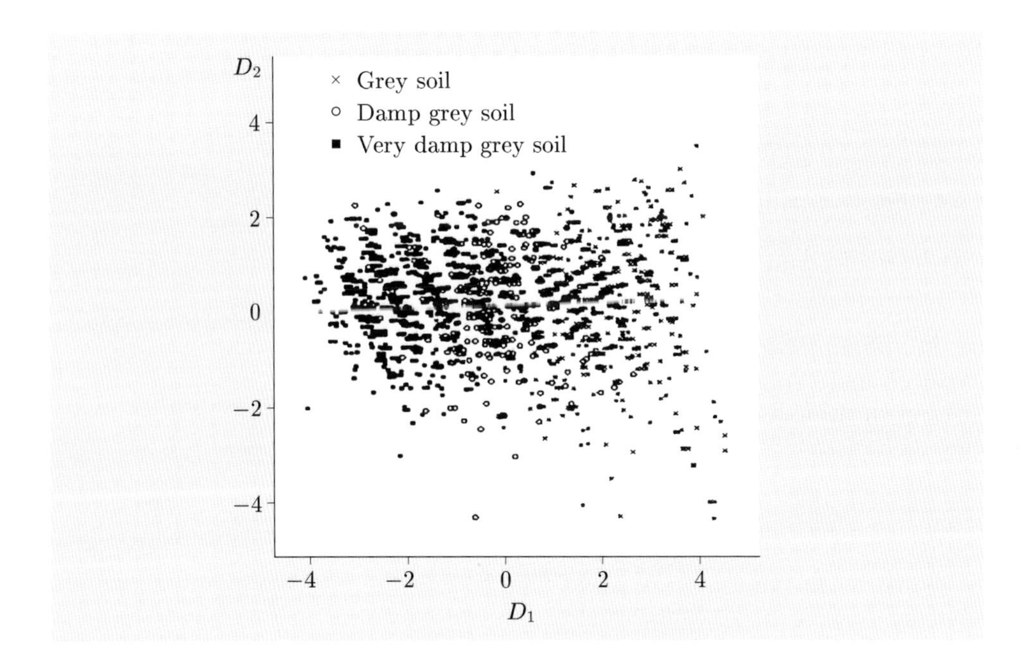

Figure 12.3 The first two discriminant functions for the satellite image data

The diagonal strips on the scatterplot are due to rounding, and may be ignored.

(i) Describe in broad terms the locations of the clouds of points corresponding to the three groups.

(ii) How well does the first discriminant function separate the three types of soil? Does the second discriminant function improve the separation? Explain your answer.

12.2 How many discriminant functions can be found?

In Subsection 12.1, you saw that using a second discriminant function can improve the separation between groups. If two discriminant functions do not separate the groups well, then a third can be sought, and so on. In general, the kth discriminant function D_k is chosen in such a way that the within-groups covariance between D_k and each of $D_1, \ldots, D_{k-1}$ is zero. But is there a limit to the number of discriminant functions that can be found?

In principal component analysis, it is not possible to find more principal components than there are variables because, in any given analysis, each principal component has to be chosen so that it is uncorrelated with all previous principal components. The restriction that each discriminant function should have zero within-groups covariance with each preceding discriminant function has the same effect. Thus, for a p-dimensional data set, there can be at most p discriminant functions. However, it can be shown that when there are G groups, at most $G - 1$ discriminant functions will improve the separation between groups. For any further discriminant functions (assuming that there are sufficient variables for these to exist), the between-groups variance will be zero, and hence the separation will be zero. Hence any further discriminant functions will make no contribution to separating the groups.

Example 12.3 Number of discriminant functions for the Swiss banknote data

Six measurements were taken on each Swiss 1000-franc note, so a maximum of six discriminant functions can be obtained for these data. However, there are only two types of note, counterfeit and genuine, so at most one of these discriminant functions will help to separate the two types of note. For the other five discriminant functions the separation, as measured by the ratio of the between-groups variance to the within-groups variance, will be zero. ♦

See Example 10.1.

In practice, when a multivariate data set consists of p variables and G groups, the maximum number of useful discriminant functions is the minimum of $G - 1$ and p. Thus, when the number of variables is at least as large as the number of groups, the number of discriminant functions is limited by the number of groups minus 1. Conversely, when there are more groups than variables, the number of variables is the limiting factor, though such data sets seldom arise in practice.

Activity 12.2 How many discriminant functions?

For each of the studies described below, write down the values of G and p, and hence state the maximum number of (potentially useful) discriminant functions that can be found.

(a) Nine morphological characteristics, such as plant height, average length of leaf blade and average blade, were measured on 55 plants in the genus *Tripsacum* (a plant related to maize). In this sample of plants, four species were represented (*T. floridanum*, *T. australe*, *T. maizar* and *T. zopilotense*). One aim of the study was to discover the extent to which the species have different characteristics.

(b) Seismograms from 28 earthquakes and 25 explosions in quarries were collected. The aim of the study was to see if the earthquakes and explosions could be distinguished using the seismograms. To this end, each seismogram was summarized by eighteen features (variables).

(c) In a study of Canadian youths, twelve variables were recorded that detailed the youths' self-reported delinquency (such as whether they had frequently got drunk or had ever stolen money), and eighteen variables that represented individual and family characteristics (such as whether they were still at school or were living in a one-parent family). The investigators were interested in whether the distribution of these variables differed for youths who had appeared in court in 1995 compared with those who had not.

(d) In a study of electrocardiograms (ECGs), tracings from 61 people were taken. Of these people, 35 were healthy volunteers, but the other 26 people had suffered a heart attack, and sixteen of those now had a condition called sustained ventricular tachycardia (SVT). One aim of this study was to investigate the extent to which it is possible to distinguish between these three groups on the basis of sixteen variables, each of which summarizes an ECG tracing in a different way.

(e) The satellite image data introduced in Example 10.7 are part of a larger data set in which soil types are classified in six groups: red soil, cotton crop, grey soil, damp grey soil, vegetation stubble and very damp grey soil. There are four measurements, corresponding to spectral bands A to D.

12.3 *How many discriminant functions are useful?*

In Subsection 12.2, you saw that when there are p variables and G groups in the data, it is possible to obtain p discriminant functions, of which $G-1$ may help in separating the groups. However, when the number of groups is not small, $G-1$ is a large number. Some way of measuring the extent to which each discriminant function helps in separating the groups is required.

One way of doing this is to look at the separation for each discriminant function. For each j, the separation for D_j, $\mathrm{Sep}(D_j)$, is non-negative. Moreover,

$$\mathrm{Sep}(D_1) \geq \mathrm{Sep}(D_2) \geq \cdots \geq \mathrm{Sep}(D_j) \geq \cdots \geq 0.$$

A discriminant function that has a relatively small separation does not contribute very much, so perhaps it can be safely ignored.

The separations decline for the same reason that the variances of successive principal components decline. (See Subsection 8.2.)

Example 12.4 Linear combinations for the discrimination of quarries

Data from four quarries were introduced in Example 12.1. Concentrations of six chemical elements were measured on rock samples from each of these quarries. Since there are four quarries, three discriminant functions may help to distinguish the samples. The separations for the three discriminant functions, D_1, D_2 and D_3, are 3.237, 1.460 and 0.314, respectively. Therefore D_3 is considerably less effective at separating the groups than D_1 and D_2. However, the separation achieved by D_2, though smaller than that for D_1, is still quite large. ♦

The **total separation** is defined to be the sum of the separations achieved by all the possible discriminant functions; that is,

$$\text{total separation} = \mathrm{Sep}(D_1) + \mathrm{Sep}(D_2) + \cdots + \mathrm{Sep}(D_p).$$

The total separation plays a similar role to the total variance in principal component analysis.

Notice that this expression contains p terms. It does not matter if some of the discriminant functions have zero separation, since they do not contribute to the value of the total separation.

The total separation measures the extent to which the groups in a data set can be separated by the variables available. For each discriminant function D_j, the **percentage separation achieved**, denoted PSA_j, is defined as follows:

$$\mathrm{PSA}_j = \frac{\mathrm{Sep}(D_j)}{\text{total separation}} \times 100\%.$$

The **cumulative percentage separation achieved** by discriminant functions $D_1, \ldots, D_j$, denoted CPSA_j, is as follows:

$$\mathrm{CPSA}_j = \mathrm{PSA}_1 + \mathrm{PSA}_2 + \cdots + \mathrm{PSA}_j.$$

The cumulative percentage separation achieved CPSA_j takes values between 0% and 100%. It measures the overall separation achieved by the combination of the first j discriminant functions.

The cumulative percentage separation achieved is analogous to the CPVE in principal component analysis.

Example 12.5 Linear combinations for the discrimination of quarries, continued

For the quarries data, D_1, D_2 and D_3 achieve separations of 3.237, 1.460 and 0.314, respectively. So

$$\begin{aligned}\text{total separation} &= \text{Sep}(D_1) + \text{Sep}(D_2) + \text{Sep}(D_3)\\ &= 3.237 + 1.460 + 0.314 = 5.011.\end{aligned}$$

Hence the percentage separation achieved by D_1 is

$$\text{PSA}_1 = \frac{3.237}{5.011} \times 100\% \simeq 64.6\%.$$

The percentage separation achieved by each discriminant function and the corresponding cumulative percentage separation achieved are given in Table 12.1.

Table 12.1 PSA and CPSA for the quarry data

Discriminant function	PSA	CPSA
D_1	64.6	64.6
D_2	29.1	93.7
D_3	6.3	100.0

Together, the first two discriminant functions achieve 93.7% of the maximum possible separation. Thus there is little to be gained by adding a third discriminant function. However, using two discriminant functions results in a marked improvement on the 64.6% of the total separation achieved using only one discriminant function. ♦

Activity 12.3 Comparing discriminations

Table 12.2 shows the separations achieved by the first three discriminant functions for three different data sets. In each data set, there are four groups and five variables, so the number of discriminant functions is effectively limited by the number of groups.

Table 12.2 Separations achieved by discriminant functions found for three data sets

Discriminant function	Data set A	B	C
D_1	10	5	20
D_2	9	4	1
D_3	1	3	0.5

(a) Calculate the total separation achieved for each data set.

(b) For each data set, calculate the percentage separation achieved by the first discriminant function.

(c) For each data set, calculate the cumulative percentage separation achieved by the first and second discriminant functions together.

(d) Use your answers to parts (a) to (c) to answer the following questions. Justify your answers.

(i) For which data set are the groups most effectively separated, using all three discriminant functions?

(ii) For which data set is the separation of the groups most improved by the use of a second discriminant function?

Summary of Section 12

In this section, the second and subsequent discriminant functions have been defined. You have seen that the number of useful discriminant functions that can be found is limited: for a data set with G groups and p variables, the maximum number of (useful) discriminant functions is the minimum of $G - 1$ and p. The percentage separation achieved and the cumulative percentage separation achieved have been introduced to assess how well the discriminant functions separate the groups.

Exercise on Section 12

Exercise 12.1 *Tracing opium*

The first discriminant function relating to 50 samples of legally grown opium in three divisions of India, which was given in Exercise 11.2, is

$$D_1 = 0.968Z_1 - 0.233Z_2 + 0.169Z_3 - 0.508Z_4,$$

where Z_1, Z_2, Z_3 and Z_4 are the group-standardized concentrations of the amino acids glycine, phenylalanine, isoleucine and aspartic acid, respectively.

(a) For these data, the second discriminant function is

$$D_2 = 0.429Z_1 + 1.253Z_2 + 0.518Z_3 - 1.092Z_4.$$

Interpret this function.

(b) Can a third discriminant function for these data be found? Is it likely to be useful? Explain your answer.

(c) For discriminant functions D_1 and D_2, $\text{Sep}(D_1) = 2.231$ and $\text{Sep}(D_2) = 1.006$. Calculate the percentage separation achieved by D_1 and by D_2. What do you conclude about the contribution made by D_2 to the separation of the groups?

(d) A scatterplot of the values of D_1 and D_2 is shown in Figure 12.4.

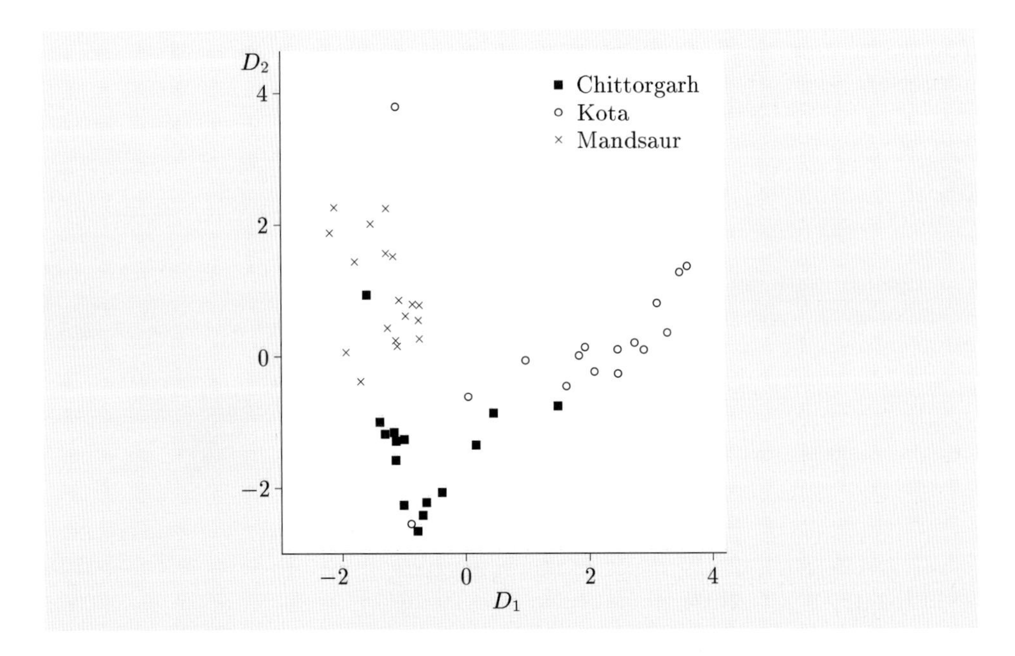

Figure 12.4 The first two discriminant functions for the opium data

Does this plot confirm your conclusion in part (c)? Explain your answer.

13 Allocation and prediction

In Sections 10 to 12, discriminant functions have been used to emphasize group structure in data. In this section, a major application of discriminant functions is discussed — the allocation of observations to groups based on the values of the variables. This provides a method of predicting to which group an observation belongs if this is not known. Example 13.1 illustrates the method.

Example 13.1 Counterfeit or genuine?

A data set consisting of measurements on 200 Swiss 1000-franc banknotes has been used to illustrate the ideas introduced in Sections 10 to 12. In this data set, whether or not each banknote is genuine or counterfeit is known. But suppose you are given another Swiss 1000-franc note dating back to the same period. Is this new note counterfeit or genuine?

Taking measurements of the length, width, borders and diagonal of this note would be quick and easy to do. Hence the value of D_1, the first discriminant function, for this new note can be obtained easily. If the value of D_1 for the new note matches the values of D_1 for the genuine notes more closely than it matches the values of D_1 for the counterfeit notes, then this would suggest that the new note is genuine. Conversely, if the value of D_1 for the new note matches the values of D_1 for the counterfeit notes more closely, then this would suggest that the new note is counterfeit. ♦

Measuring the note is almost certainly far quicker and easier than finding an expert in Swiss 1000-franc notes!

Rules for allocating observations to groups based on the first discriminant function are considered in this section. In Subsection 13.1, allocation rules are introduced, and some specific rules are derived in Subsection 13.2. A method for evaluating an allocation rule is described in Subsection 13.3.

Allocation rules can be developed for use with two or more discriminant functions, but these will not be considered in this book.

13.1 Allocation rules

When there is only one discriminant function, D, the task of allocating observations to groups reduces to splitting the range of possible values of D so that each possible value is associated with one of the groups. Then given a new observation, the value of D for the observation is calculated and the observation is allocated to the group corresponding to the observed value of D.

Suppose that the observations in a multivariate data set may be divided into two groups. Three examples of how the range of a discriminant function D (which takes values between 0 and 100) might be split are shown in Figure 13.1.

In Figure 13.1(a), values of D between 0 and 35 are allocated to group 1, and values above 35 are allocated to group 2. Every value between 0 and 100 is allocated to one of the groups.

The main difference between the three cases is the number of regions associated with each group. In Figure 13.1(a), all the values associated with group 1 are contiguous, so that there is one region associated with group 1. There is also one region associated with group 2. In Figure 13.1(b), there is one region associated with group 2, but there are two regions, corresponding to low and high values of D, associated with group 1. In Figure 13.1(c), there are several regions associated with each group. In this section, rules are considered for which the range of values is split so that each group is associated with one, and only one, region.

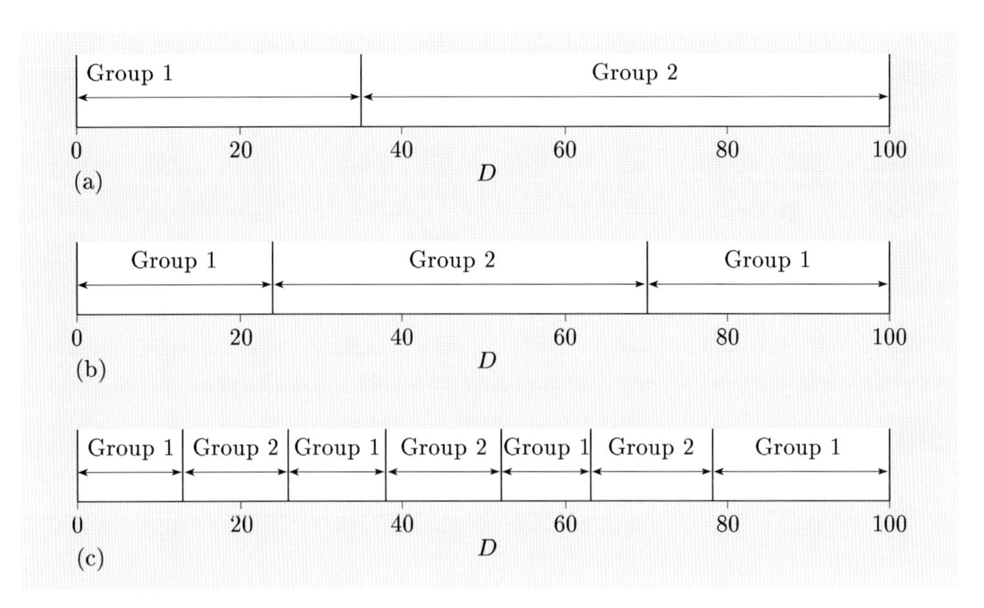

Figure 13.1 Types of region

Example 13.2 Splitting the range

The discriminant function for the Swiss 1000-franc banknotes based on all six measurements is

$$D = -0.005X_1 - 0.832X_2 + 0.849X_3 + 1.117X_4 + 1.179X_5 - 1.557X_6 + 194.649.$$

The constant term differs slightly from the value you obtained in Activity 11.2. This is due to rounding error.

The frequency distributions of the values of D for counterfeit notes and genuine notes are shown in Figure 13.2.

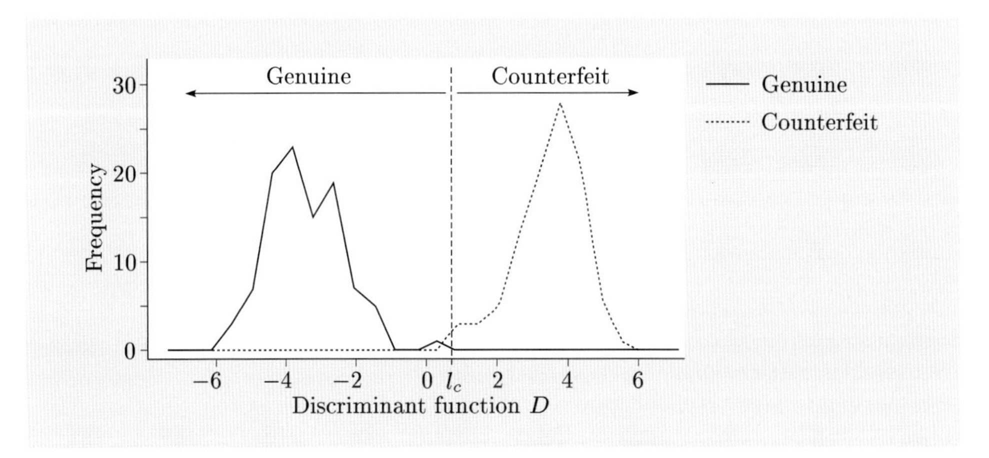

Figure 13.2 Frequency distributions of values of D for genuine notes and counterfeit notes

Notice that the values of D in Figure 13.2 tend to be larger for the counterfeit banknotes than for the genuine banknotes. Thus it is reasonable to split the range of D into two regions. Notes with a value of D less than or equal to some cut-off value l_c would be taken to be genuine, whilst banknotes with a value of D larger than l_c would be taken to be counterfeit. ♦

Suppose that d is the value of the discriminant function D for an observation being allocated to a group. Then, when there are two groups, the task of allocation can be reduced to a mathematical rule of the following form:

$$\begin{cases} \text{if } d \leq l_c & \text{allocate to group 1,} \\ \text{otherwise} & \text{allocate to group 2.} \end{cases}$$

Such a mathematical rule is known as an **allocation rule**.

In general, when there are G groups, the range of possible values for the discriminant function is split into G regions, one for each group, defined by $G-1$ cut-off values $l_1, l_2, \ldots, l_{G-1}$. These cut-off values are called **cut-off points** or **cutpoints**, and satisfy $l_1 < l_2 < \cdots < l_{G-1}$. The corresponding allocation rule is of the following form:

$$\begin{cases} \text{if } d \leq l_1 & \text{allocate to group 1,} \\ \text{if } l_1 < d \leq l_2 & \text{allocate to group 2,} \\ \quad \vdots & \quad \vdots \\ \text{if } l_{G-2} < d \leq l_{G-1} & \text{allocate to group } G-1, \\ \text{otherwise} & \text{allocate to group } G. \end{cases}$$

Example 13.3 Processing satellite images

Data from a satellite image were introduced in Example 10.7. These data comprise measurements using four spectral bands, over a set of 2414 pixels. Each pixel represents grey soil, damp grey soil or very damp grey soil. The first discriminant function D, based on the measurements in all four spectral bands, is

$$D = -0.054X_1 - 0.059X_2 - 0.024X_3 - 0.023X_4 + 13.606,$$

where X_1, X_2, X_3 and X_4 are the measurements in spectral bands A, B, C and D, respectively. The relative frequencies of the values of D for each of the soil types are represented in Figure 13.3.

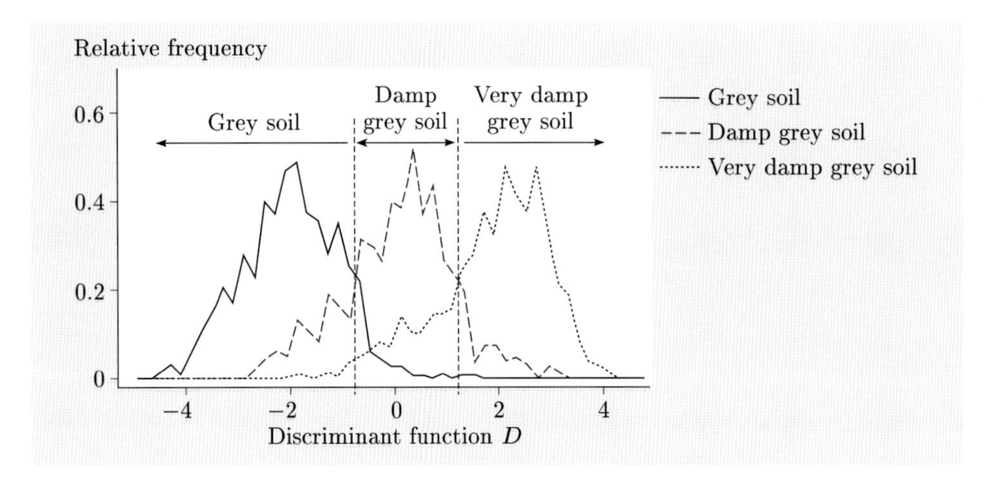

Figure 13.3 Relative frequencies of values of D for three soil types

Notice that the distributions of values of the discriminant function for the three groups overlap. Nevertheless, the values tend to be lower for grey soil and higher for very damp grey soil. Thus values of the discriminant function below a certain point l_1, say about -0.8, could reasonably be associated with grey soil. Similarly, values of the discriminant function above another point l_2, equal to about 1.2, could reasonably be associated with very damp grey soil. Intermediate values of the discriminant function would be associated with damp grey soil.

This rule could be written formally as follows:

$$\begin{cases} \text{if } d \leq -0.8 & \text{allocate to grey soil,} \\ \text{if } -0.8 < d \leq 1.2 & \text{allocate to damp grey soil,} \\ \text{otherwise} & \text{allocate to very damp grey soil.} \end{cases} \quad \blacklozenge$$

Activity 13.1 Types of rule

Figure 13.4 shows four pairs of histograms of observations on a variable X. Each pair represents observations from two groups. For each pair, explain whether or not it would be appropriate to allocate observations to groups using a rule in which the range of X is split into two regions, one region being associated with each group.

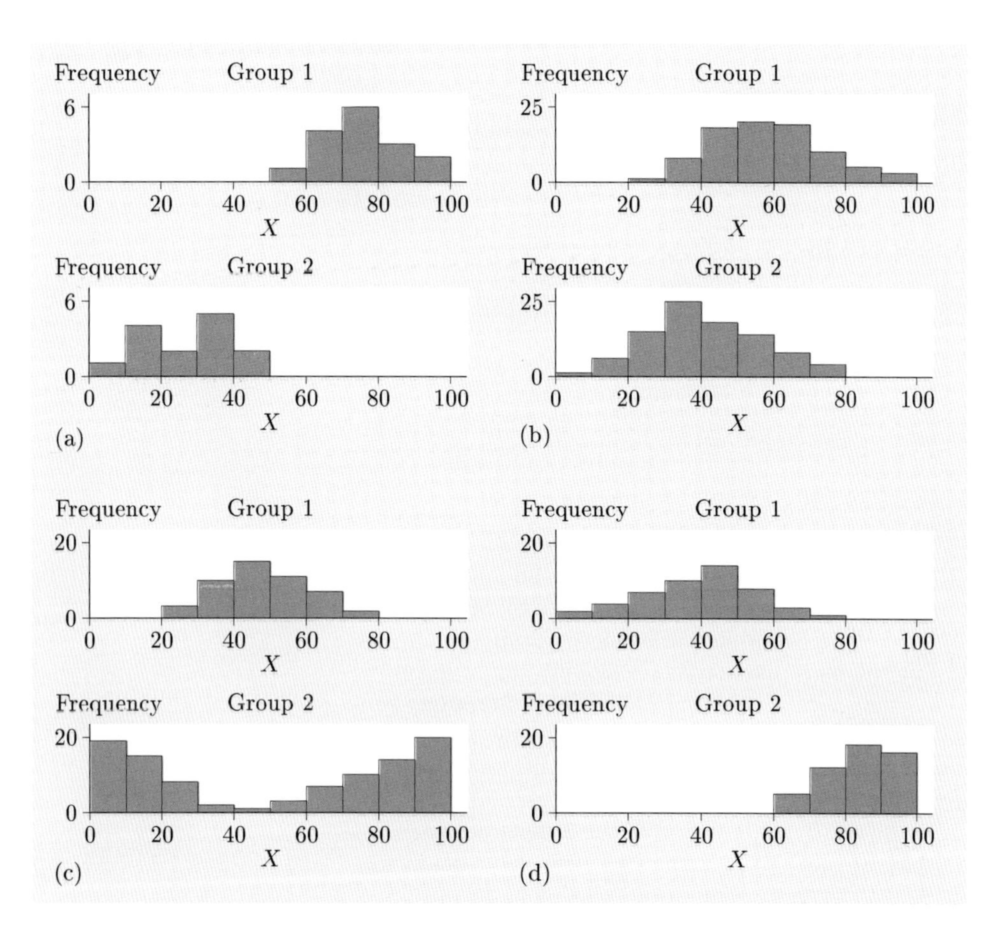

Figure 13.4 Four pairs of distributions of a variable X in two groups

13.2 Determining cut-off points

When one discriminant function D is used to allocate observations to groups, all that is required is to choose the values of $G - 1$ cutpoints appropriately.

In choosing the cutpoints, the following three factors must be considered.

- For each group g, the **probability density function** (p.d.f.) of the values of the discriminant function for an observation randomly selected from all those known to be in group g.
- For each group g, the **prior probability** that an observation chosen at random belongs to group g. This is the probability that the observation belongs to group g when nothing is known about the observation.
- For each pair of groups g_1 and g_2, the **cost** of wrongly allocating an observation to group g_1 when it actually belongs to group g_2.

The p.d.f.s can be estimated from the frequency distributions of D for a sample of observations for which the correct group allocation is known. For example, Figures 13.2 and 13.3 give estimates of the densities for each of the groups in the Swiss 1000-franc banknote data and in the satellite image data, respectively. The p.d.f.s may suggest roughly where the cutpoints should be located. However, the prior probabilities and the costs must also be taken in account when fixing the cutpoints. For example, if a particular group g is known to be very rare, then the prior probability for group g will be very small, and it might therefore be presumed that what looks like an observation from this rare group is more likely to be an atypical observation from a more common group. Also, if it is very important that observations belonging to a particular group are not missed because missing them might incur a large cost, then it is wise to allocate observations to that group, unless the value of the discriminant function clearly indicates that this is inappropriate.

Example 13.4 Identifying counterfeit notes

An allocation rule for Swiss 1000-franc banknotes depends on setting a cut-off value l_c for the discriminant function D.

The most appropriate value for l_c depends on the following two probability density functions:

◇ the p.d.f. of values of the discriminant function for genuine notes, denoted $f(d|\text{genuine})$;

◇ the p.d.f. of values of the discriminant function for counterfeit notes, denoted $f(d|\text{counterfeit})$.

The frequency distributions given in Figure 13.2 provide estimates of these two p.d.f.s. Typically, negative values of D are obtained for genuine notes, and positive values for counterfeit notes.

The value of l_c also depends on $P(\text{genuine})$, the probability that a randomly chosen note is genuine. It is reasonable to assume that the vast majority of notes in circulation are genuine. So if the rule is to be applied to all notes in circulation, then a small positive value of D would be more likely to correspond to an atypical genuine note than to a typical counterfeit note. So setting l_c high would ensure that atypical genuine notes would be correctly assigned. Thus in this case it would be appropriate to set the value of l_c high. On the other hand, if the rule is to be applied to notes which have been found in the possession of a known counterfeiter, then $P(\text{genuine})$ might be relatively low, and hence a much lower value of l_c would be appropriate because a note with a small positive value of D would then be more likely to be a counterfeit note than an atypical genuine one.

$P(\text{counterfeit})$ is equal to $1 - P(\text{genuine})$.

In this example, there are two groups, so two costs are relevant in selecting the best value for l_c. One of these is the cost of wrongly deciding that a genuine note is counterfeit. The other cost is the cost of wrongly deciding that a counterfeit note is genuine. These costs depend on the context. If the aim is simply to remove counterfeit notes from circulation, it may be worse to classify counterfeit notes as genuine (and hence leave them in circulation) than to classify genuine notes as counterfeit (and hence destroy them). On the other hand, if the aim is to find and prosecute anyone handling counterfeit notes, it may be far worse (thus incurring a high cost) to falsely accuse people of handling counterfeit notes when they do not have them, than to allow a few people to escape prosecution for handling counterfeit notes. ♦

Activity 13.2 will give you some practice at exploring the issues relating to allocation rules.

Activity 13.2 Diagnosing heart disease

Data relating to 120 patients with heart disease and 150 patients without heart disease were introduced in Activity 10.2. The data consist of four variables: age, resting blood pressure, serum cholesterol and maximum heart rate. Suppose that the discriminant function D based on these four variables has been determined. Based on D, an appropriate value of l_c, the cut-off value between having heart disease and not having heart disease, is to be chosen. You should assume that the value of D tends to be higher for patients with heart disease than for patients without heart disease.

(a) Which two distributions would the value of l_c depend on?

(b) Suppose that an allocation rule has been defined for use with patients who are suspected of suffering from heart disease, and that a value of l_c has been determined. Would the same value of l_c be appropriate if the rule was used to screen seemingly healthy people for heart disease? If not, should the value of l_c be higher or lower?

(c) Suppose that it is more costly to miss a case of heart disease than to indicate incorrectly that heart disease is present. How should this affect the value of l_c, compared to a situation in which the costs associated with each of these two misclassification errors are the same?

As has already been noted, for each group, the p.d.f. of the distribution of values of D can be estimated from samples of observations in each of the groups. In practice, it is often assumed (and will be assumed in this course) that these distributions are normal with common standard deviation σ, and that the mean for group g is μ_g. One consequence is that the distributions for the groups differ only in terms of their mean values $\mu_1, \ldots, \mu_G$.

Unfortunately, the prior probabilities and the costs are usually much more difficult to quantify and often rely on subjective judgements. So, for the rest of this section, the following two simplifying assumptions will be made. First, in the absence of any other knowledge, an observation is equally likely to have come from any of the groups. Secondly, the cost of allocating an observation to the wrong group is the same, whichever group the observation is allocated to and whichever group it actually belongs to.

It can be shown that, after making these assumptions, the best choice for the cutpoint l_c when there are only two groups is $(\mu_1 + \mu_2)/2$. Thus an observation for which the value of the discriminant function is d should be allocated to the group whose mean value μ_g is closest to d.

Example 13.5 Best choice for l_c

The distributions of the discriminant function D for the Swiss 1000-franc banknote data are shown in Figure 13.2. The mean value of D for genuine notes is -3.47, whereas the mean value of D for counterfeit notes is 3.47. Thus the best choice for l_c is

$$l_c = \tfrac{1}{2}(-3.47 + 3.47) = 0.$$

Thus any note with a negative value of D should be classified as a genuine note, and any note with a positive value of D should be classified as a counterfeit note. (Note that the cutpoint l_c is 0 because the numbers of genuine notes and counterfeit notes were the same in the sample used to formulate the rule: the fact that $l_c = 0$ is not a coincidence.) ♦

Activity 13.3 Counterfeit or genuine?

The discriminant function for the Swiss 1000-franc banknotes based on all six measurements is

$$D = -0.005X_1 - 0.832X_2 + 0.849X_3 + 1.117X_4 + 1.179X_5 - 1.557X_6 + 194.649.$$

A Swiss 1000-franc note of the same type as those used to determine the discriminant function was found to have the following dimensions: length 215.2, width at left edge 130.4, width at right edge 130.1, bottom border 10.1, top border 11.6 and diagonal 139.8. Calculate the value of D for this new note. Hence classify this note as either genuine or counterfeit.

The method of choosing the cutpoints when there are two groups can be extended to choose the cutpoints when there are more than two groups, as follows. When there are G groups, if the value of D for an observation is d, then the observation should be allocated to the group whose mean value μ_g is closest to d. Suppose that the groups are numbered so that $\mu_1 < \mu_2 < \cdots < \mu_G$. Then the $G - 1$ cutpoints are as follows:

The groups can always be numbered so that this is the case.

$$l_g = \tfrac{1}{2}(\mu_g + \mu_{g+1}), \quad g = 1, \ldots, G-1.$$

Example 13.6 illustrates how the discriminant function is used to construct an allocation rule.

Example 13.6 An allocation rule for soil dampness

In Example 13.3, you saw that the distribution of the discriminant function for the satellite image data varies according to whether the pixel corresponds to grey, damp grey or very damp grey soil. The mean of the discriminant function for each of the soil types is given in Table 13.1.

Table 13.1 Discriminant function means for different types of grey soil

Soil type	Mean
Grey soil	−2.024
Damp grey soil	0.019
Very damp grey soil	1.866

There are three soil types, so two cut-points, l_1 and l_2, are needed. Grey soil pixels have the lowest mean, and very damp grey soil pixels have the highest mean, so the groups should be numbered in the following way:

group 1: grey soil,
group 2: damp grey soil,
group 3: very damp grey soil.

Then the cutpoints between the groups are calculated as follows:

$$l_1 = \tfrac{1}{2}(\mu_1 + \mu_2) = \tfrac{1}{2}(-2.024 + 0.019) \simeq -1.002,$$
$$l_2 = \tfrac{1}{2}(\mu_2 + \mu_3) = \tfrac{1}{2}(0.019 + 1.866) \simeq 0.943.$$

Thus if the discriminant function for a pixel is less than or equal to −1.002, the pixel should be allocated to the grey soil group. If the discriminant function is between −1.002 and 0.943, the pixel should be allocated to the damp grey soil group. And if the discriminant function is greater than 0.943, the pixel should be allocated to the very damp grey soil group. The rule can be written formally as follows:

$$\begin{cases} \text{if } d \leq -1.002 & \text{allocate to grey soil,} \\ \text{if } -1.002 < d \leq 0.943 & \text{allocate to damp grey soil,} \\ \text{otherwise} & \text{allocate to very damp grey soil.} \end{cases}$$ ♦

Activity 13.4 How damp is the soil?

For the satellite image data, the discriminant function D based on measurements in all four spectral bands is

$$D = -0.054X_1 - 0.059X_2 - 0.024X_3 - 0.023X_4 + 13.606.$$

The variables X_1, X_2, X_3 and X_4 relate to measurements in bands labelled A, B, C and D. Suppose that the measurements given in Table 13.2 were recorded for ten pixels.

Table 13.2 Measurements taken on ten pixels

	Spectral band				Discriminant
Pixel	A	B	C	D	function
1	76	79	87	63	
2	93	111	118	92	
3	82	102	105	87	−1.36
4	71	79	81	67	1.63
5	80	94	98	76	−0.36
6	95	109	117	89	−2.81
7	63	77	79	64	2.29
8	84	99	104	83	−1.18
9	92	107	118	88	−2.53
10	66	79	80	70	1.85

(a) Calculate the values of the discriminant function for pixel 1 and pixel 2.

(b) Use the discriminant function and the allocation rule given in Example 13.6 to allocate each pixel to a soil type.

13.3 Misclassification rates and confusion matrices

The discriminant function with appropriately chosen cutpoints can be used to specify an allocation rule. Using this allocation rule, measurements taken on a new observation can be used to predict which group the observation belongs to. However, with any such prediction, an indication of the likely accuracy of the prediction should also be given.

Estimation of prediction accuracy requires a set of observations for which the correct group is known. Then, for this set of data, the allocated group can be compared with the actual group. The most obvious data set to use for this purpose is the original sample on which the discriminant function was determined and the allocation rule based. For this sample, which is known as the **training set**, the group indicated by the allocation rule is compared with the actual group an observation belongs to. However, the accuracy of the allocation rule is usually overestimated, since the same data are used to establish the rule and to evaluate it. To obtain a better idea of the accuracy of an allocation rule, the rule should be applied to a second set of data for which the group that each observation belongs to is also known; this set is called a **test set**. The accuracy of the rule can then be determined by comparing the true group membership with the membership predicted by the allocation rule for observations in the test set.

Example 13.7 Classification of Swiss 1000-franc banknotes

In Example 13.5, an allocation rule based on a sample of 100 genuine and 100 counterfeit Swiss 1000-franc banknotes was obtained. The allocation rule based on these notes is as follows: for a note whose value of D is d,

$$\begin{cases} \text{if } d \leq 0 & \text{classify as genuine,} \\ \text{otherwise} & \text{classify as counterfeit.} \end{cases}$$

Since the values of the discriminant function for the 100 counterfeit notes in the training set of 200 notes are all positive, using this rule, all the counterfeit notes are classified as counterfeit. However, the discriminant function is positive for one of the genuine notes. So, using this rule, 99 genuine notes are correctly classified as genuine, but one genuine note is not.

Note that the allocation rule was developed specifically to do well on the training set of 200 notes. It might not do so well on a different set of 200 notes. In particular, it is unlikely that every counterfeit note would be correctly classified. ♦

When an observation is allocated to the wrong group, it is said to be **misclassified**. The **misclassification rate** (or **error rate**) is the percentage of observations that are misclassified.

Example 13.8 Misclassification rate for the Swiss banknotes

In Example 13.7, none of the 100 counterfeit notes was misclassified and only one of the 100 genuine notes was misclassified. Thus for the Swiss 1000-franc banknote data,

$$\begin{aligned} \text{misclassification rate} = \frac{\text{number misclassified}}{\text{number in sample}} \times 100\% &= \frac{1}{200} \times 100\% \\ &= 0.5\%. \end{aligned}$$ ♦

Note that the misclassification rate depends only on the number of observations that are misclassified, not on the way in which they are misclassified. However, this extra information can be conveyed in a **confusion matrix**. When there are G groups, a confusion matrix has G rows and G columns. Element (i, j) of the matrix is the percentage of observations which are actually in group i but were allocated to group j. Thus the elements down the main diagonal correspond to the percentages of observations that have been classified correctly in each group. So it is to be hoped that the percentages on the main diagonal are close to 100%, whilst the off-diagonal percentages should ideally be zero.

Example 13.9 A confusion matrix for the Swiss banknotes

For the Swiss 1000-franc banknotes data, there are two groups, counterfeit and genuine. So the corresponding confusion matrix has two rows and two columns. Labelling the counterfeit notes as group 1 and the genuine notes as group 2 (as in Example 10.6), the first row of the matrix corresponds to the 100 counterfeit notes, and the second row of the matrix corresponds to the 100 genuine notes. Similarly, the first and second columns of the matrix correspond to the notes classified as counterfeit and genuine, respectively. Using the misclassifications described in Example 13.7, the confusion matrix is as follows.

	Allocated group	
Actual group	Counterfeit	Genuine
Counterfeit	100%	0%
Genuine	1%	99%

Notice that, unlike the other matrices you have met in this book, this matrix is not symmetric. There is no reason why the percentage of counterfeit notes misclassified as genuine should be equal to the percentage of genuine notes classified as counterfeit. ♦

Activity 13.5 Interpreting a confusion matrix

The allocation rule given in Example 13.6 for classifying the type of soil that a pixel represents was used to classify all 2414 pixels in the training set. Based on this classification, the confusion matrix is as follows.

	Allocated soil type		
Actual soil type	Grey soil	Damp grey soil	Very damp grey soil
Grey soil	86.9%	12.9%	0.2%
Damp grey soil	16.9%	66.0%	17.1%
Very damp grey soil	0.7%	17.8%	81.5%

(a) What percentage of pixels representing grey soil were correctly classified?

(b) What percentage of pixels representing damp grey soil were classified as representing very damp grey soil?

(c) If a pixel representing damp grey soil was misclassified, what type of soil was it more likely to have been misclassified as?

(d) A test set of 1078 pixels was also available. For this test set, the confusion matrix is as follows.

	Allocated soil type		
Actual soil type	Grey soil	Damp grey soil	Very damp grey soil
Grey soil	86.1%	13.4%	0.5%
Damp grey soil	11.4%	67.8%	20.9%
Very damp grey soil	0.9%	19.1%	80.0%

The sum of the entries in the middle row is not exactly 100%. This is due to rounding error.

Compare the two confusion matrices. Do they support the assertion that the rate of misclassification is underestimated in the training set?

Summary of Section 13

In this section, rules for allocating observations to groups on the basis of the values of a discriminant function D have been considered. Allocation rules based on dividing the range of D into G regions, one for each group, have been described. You have seen that formulating such a rule involves choosing a sequence of $G-1$ cutpoints, $l_1, \ldots, l_{G-1}$. Some of the factors that must be taken into account when choosing the cutpoints have been discussed. A special case has been considered in which the best choice for the cutpoints depends only on the mean value of D in each of the groups. The accuracy of an allocation rule can be assessed by comparing the allocated group with the actual group for each observation in a set of data for which the group each observation belongs to is known. The misclassification rate and the confusion matrix have been defined. You have seen that a misclassification rate or confusion matrix estimated using the training set — that is, the data set used to formulate the rule — will tend to overestimate the accuracy of the allocation rule.

Exercise on Section 13

Exercise 13.1 Tracing opium

In Example 10.2 and Exercise 10.1, a data set was described which relates to the identification of sources of opium, based on 50 samples of legally grown opium from three divisions in India: Chittorgarh (15 samples), Kota (17 samples) and Mandsaur (18 samples). Concentrations of four amino acids were measured: X_1, concentration of glycine; X_2, concentration of phenylalanine; X_3, concentration of isoleucine; and X_4, concentration of aspartic acid. In terms of these unstandardized variables, the first discriminant function is

$$D = 6.333X_1 - 0.864X_2 - 2.480X_3 + 4.920X_4 - 1.154.$$

The mean values of D in each of the three groups are given in Table 13.3.

Table 13.3 Discriminant function means

Division	Mean of D
Chittorgarh	−0.670
Kota	1.984
Mandsaur	−1.316

(a) Assuming equal prior probabilities and equal costs of misclassification, write down the allocation rule.

(b) Use the allocation rule to predict which division a sample of opium came from if the concentrations of amino acids were as follows: $X_1 = 0.060$, $X_2 = 0.183$, $X_3 = 0.080$ and $X_4 = 0.230$.

(c) The following confusion matrix was obtained using the training set.

	Allocated division		
Actual division	Chittorgarh	Kota	Mandsaur
Chittorgarh	47%	7%	47%
Kota	12%	82%	6%
Mandsaur	28%	0%	72%

The sum of the entries in the top row is 101%, not 100%. This is the result of rounding error.

(i) Samples originating from which location are most likely to be correctly classified?

(ii) Comment on the accuracy of the classification of samples from Chittorgarh.

14 Discrimination in practice

In this section, you will learn how to obtain discriminant functions in SPSS, and how to construct and evaluate allocation rules.

Refer to Chapters 5 and 6 of Computer Book 3 for the work in this section.

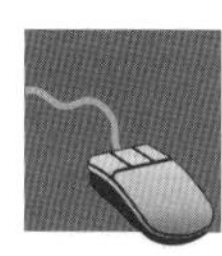

Summary of Section 14

In this section, you have used SPSS to obtain discriminant functions, based on both group-standardized and unstandardized variables. You have also learned how to construct and apply allocation rules to multivariate data. You have obtained misclassification rates and confusion matrices, and used these to assess the performance of allocation rules.

15 Exercises on Book 3

Exercise 15.1 *Measuring contamination in the Swedish environment*

Copper (Cu) and molybdenum (Mo) are essential elements for life, especially for ruminants such as the moose. In a survey of the bio-availability of these elements in Sweden, concentrations of copper and molybdenum were measured (in mg per kg) in samples of roots of certain plants and mosses (referred to as BGS, which stands for Bio-Geochemical Samples), and of moose liver. In addition, copper concentrations were measured in soil samples. Samples of all three types of material were collected from counties across Sweden. The investigators grouped the counties into three regions: Southwest, East and North.

Frank, A., Danielsson, R. and Selinus, O. (2004) Comparison of two monitoring systems for Cu and Mo in the Swedish environment. *Science of the Total Environment*, **330**, 131–143.

(a) A matrix scatterplot of the data is shown in Figure 15.1, with different plotting symbols for counties in the Southwest, East and North.

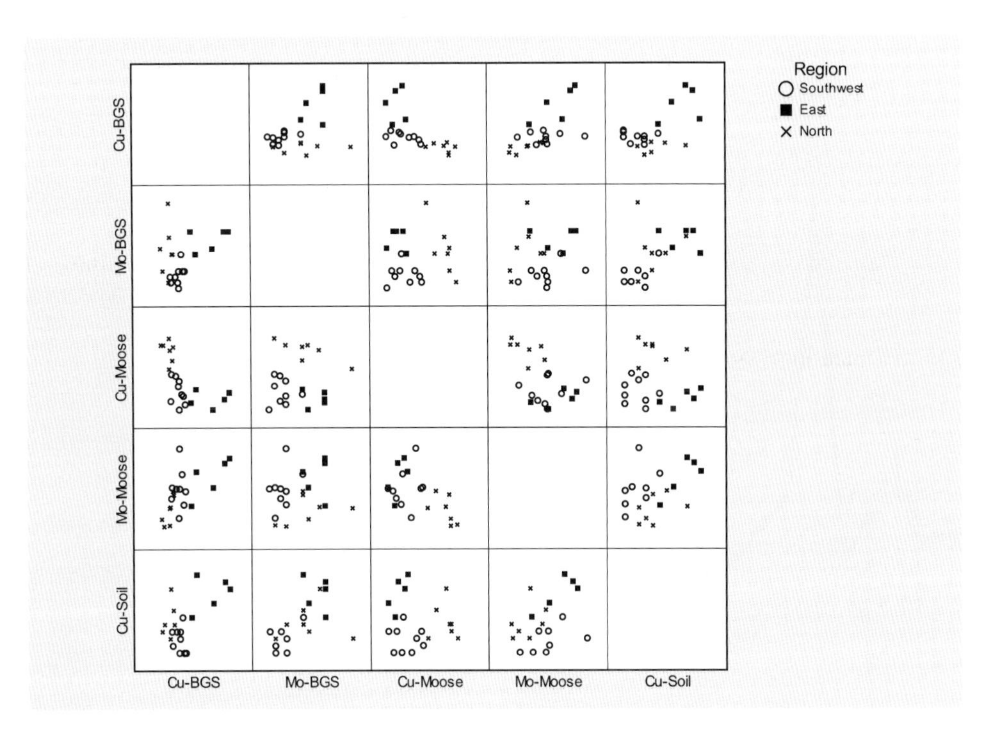

Figure 15.1 Matrix scatterplot of copper and molybdenum concentrations in counties of Sweden

(i) Do there appear to be any unusual points? If so, in what way are they unusual? (Ignore the three regions for this part of the question.)

(ii) Describe two ways in which the regions appear to differ.

(b) The correlation matrix for the five variables Cu-BGS (X_1), Mo-BGS (X_2), Cu-Moose (X_3), Mo-Moose (X_4) and Cu-Soil (X_5) is

$$\begin{pmatrix} 1 & -0.109 & -0.517 & 0.569 & 0.369 \\ -0.109 & 1 & -0.167 & 0.180 & 0.617 \\ -0.517 & -0.167 & 1 & -0.514 & -0.150 \\ 0.567 & 0.180 & -0.514 & 1 & 0.437 \\ 0.369 & 0.617 & -0.150 & 0.437 & 1 \end{pmatrix}.$$

(i) Between which pair of measurements is there the strongest (linear) relationship?

(ii) Between which pair of measurements is there the weakest relationship?

(iii) The measurements in BGS and Moose are meant to be measuring the same thing. What aspects of the correlation matrix suggest that this is not the case?

Exercise 15.2 *Describing subspecies*

Francisella tularensis is the bacterium that causes tularemia, a potentially serious disease transmitted by ticks and mosquitoes. There are four subspecies of *Francisella tularensis*, and it is important to identify to which subspecies a particular bacterium belongs. A study was undertaken to identify the subspecies of the bacterium using a technique called mass spectroscopy. This exercise is based on data from ten samples of the *novicida* subspecies. The composition of these samples was compared by measuring the concentrations (represented by a signal-to-noise ratio) of 37 distinct proteins, identified by their molecular mass (in kiloDaltons, kDa).

Lundquist, M., Caspersen, M.B., Wikström, P. and Forsman, M. (2005) Discrimination of *Francisella tularensis* subspecies using surface enhanced laser desorption ionization mass spectrometry and multivariate data analysis. *FEMS Microbiology Letters*, **243**, 303–310.

(a) (i) State the dimension of this data set.

(ii) State how many observations there are in this data set.

(b) A profile plot for the molecular masses (each corresponding to a different protein) is shown in Figure 15.2.

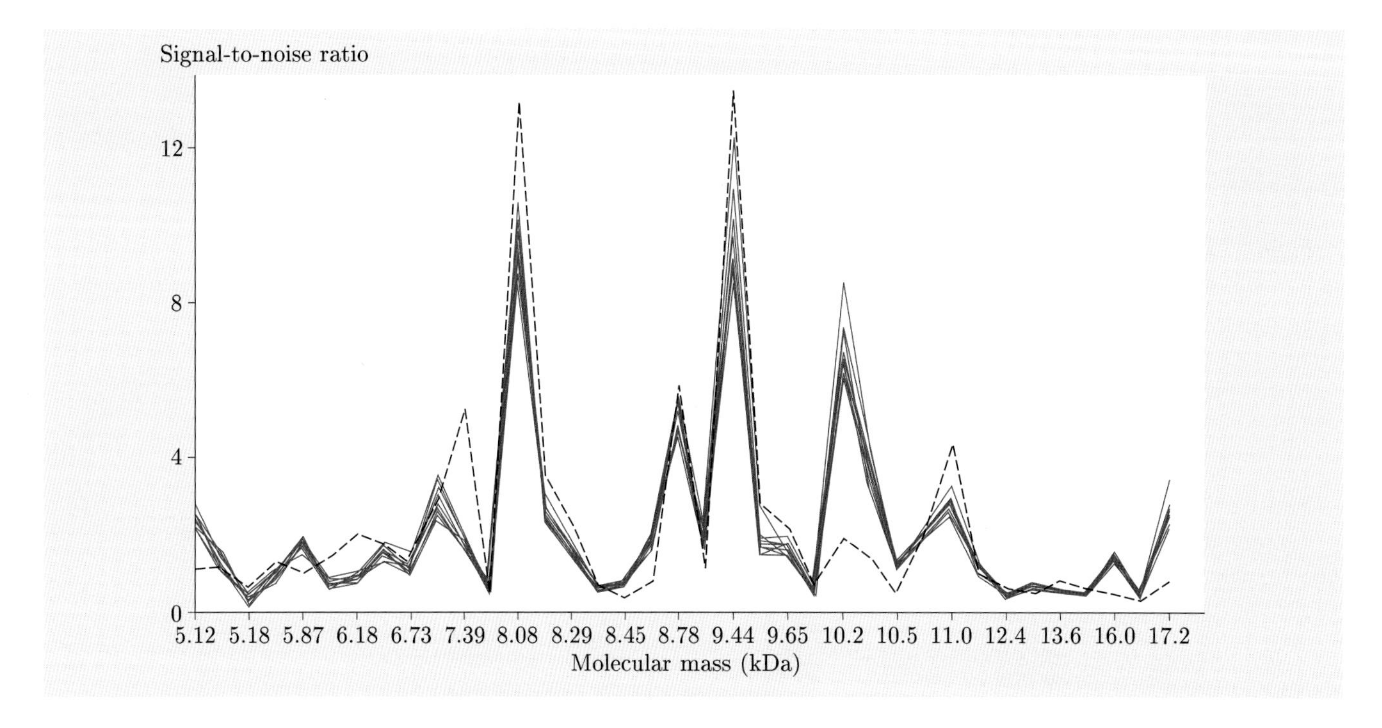

Figure 15.2 Profile plot of signal-to-noise ratios measured at different molecular masses

(i) Nineteen of the masses are labelled along the x-axis. Do the spacings between the positions at which the points are plotted reflect the differences in molecular masses? Explain your answer.

(ii) Nine of the samples (represented by solid blue lines) correspond to exactly the same strain of *novicida*. Briefly describe the patterns in signal-to-noise levels at different masses for these samples.

(iii) The tenth sample (represented by the broken black line) corresponds to a different strain of *novicida*. Compare and contrast the pattern in signal-to-noise levels for this strain with the strain represented by the other nine samples.

Exercise 15.3 *Melanoma mortality rates*

This exercise is based on mortality rates for melanoma (a cancer of the skin) among men and women in 45 countries. The mortality rates are measured per million population per year.

Shanmugam, R. and Johnson, C. (2005) At a crossroad of data envelopment and principal component analyses. *Omega*, doi: 10.1016/j.omega.2005.007.005.

(a) A scatterplot of the mortality rates is shown in Figure 15.3.

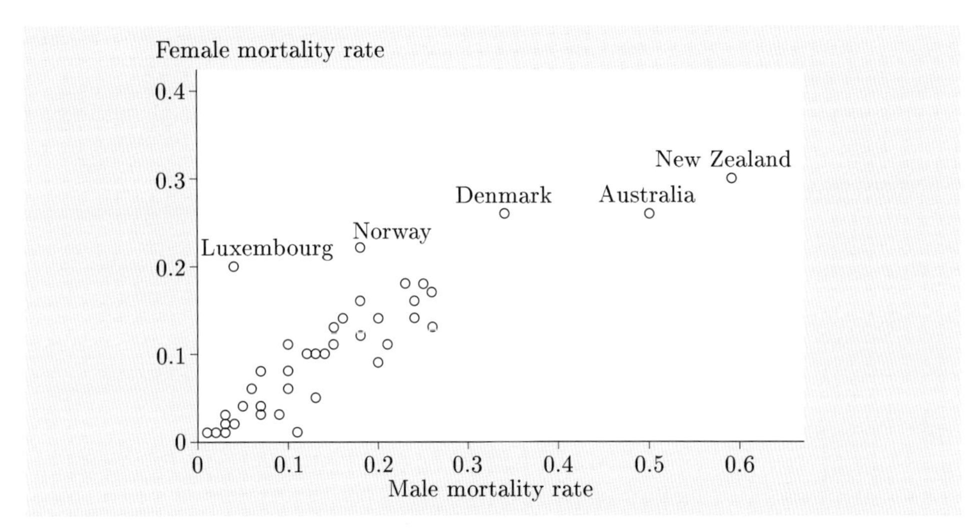

Figure 15.3 Male and female mortality rates for melanoma in 45 countries

(i) Describe the relationship between the male and female mortality rates for melanoma for the countries that are not labelled in the scatterplot.

(ii) Describe how the relationship between male and female mortality rates for melanoma differs for the labelled points compared with the unlabelled points.

(iii) It could be argued that the point representing Denmark should not have been labelled. Explain why.

(b) A single measure of mortality was required. For this it was decided to use principal component analysis (PCA).

(i) Give a reason why it might make sense to analyse the raw (unstandardized) data.

(ii) Give a reason why it could be argued that it is better to analyse the standardized data.

(c) PCA was done on the raw data. The loadings for the first principal component Y_1 are $\alpha_1 = 0.863$ and $\alpha_2 = 0.505$ (where X_1 and X_2 are the male and female mortality rates, respectively).

(i) For these data, the mean male mortality rate is 0.1469 and the mean female mortality rate is 0.1011. Write down the linear combination Y_1 that corresponds to the first principal component.

(ii) Calculate the value of Y_1 for Northern Ireland, which had a mortality rate of 0.20 for men and a mortality rate of 0.14 for women (per million per year).

(iii) Interpret the first principal component.

(d) The variance of X_1 is 0.014, the variance of X_2 is 0.006, and the variance of the first principal component is 0.019. Calculate the percentage variance explained by the first principal component. Hence comment on the quality of the approximation provided by the first principal component.

Exercise 15.4 Identifying subspecies

This exercise is based on data from the study described in Exercise 15.2. The investigators collected data on sixteen samples from four subspecies of *Francisella tularensis*: subspecies *tularensis*, *mediasiatica*, *holarctica* and *novicida*. These four subspecies differ in their virulence, and hence it is important to distinguish between them. However, laborious and time-consuming biochemical tests are required to do this. Thus it is of interest to find out whether the subspecies can be classified more rapidly by mass spectrometry. (Mass spectrometry measures the concentrations of different proteins. The concentrations are measured by a signal-to-noise ratio. Each protein is identified by its molecular mass.)

The investigators found that readings of the signal-to-noise ratios at six different molecular masses seemed to help distinguish the subspecies. These six variables are labelled $X_1, X_2, \ldots, X_6$.

(a) The between-groups and within-groups covariance matrices of $X_1, X_2, \ldots, X_6$ are

$$\mathbf{B} = \begin{pmatrix} 0.739 & -0.366 & 0.387 & 0.014 & 0.037 & 0.156 \\ -0.366 & 0.799 & -0.751 & 0.076 & -0.080 & 0.267 \\ 0.387 & -0.751 & 3.237 & 0.201 & 0.297 & 0.073 \\ 0.014 & 0.076 & 0.201 & 0.040 & 0.016 & 0.081 \\ 0.037 & -0.080 & 0.297 & 0.016 & 0.027 & 0.001 \\ 0.156 & 0.267 & 0.073 & 0.081 & 0.001 & 0.261 \end{pmatrix},$$

$$\mathbf{W} = \begin{pmatrix} 0.285 & -0.010 & -0.021 & -0.050 & -0.007 & 0.014 \\ -0.010 & 0.308 & 0.007 & 0.073 & 0.001 & -0.002 \\ -0.021 & 0.007 & 0.016 & 0.004 & 0.005 & -0.027 \\ -0.050 & 0.073 & 0.004 & 0.353 & 0.003 & 0.200 \\ -0.007 & 0.001 & 0.005 & 0.003 & 0.002 & -0.015 \\ 0.014 & -0.002 & -0.027 & 0.200 & -0.015 & 0.653 \end{pmatrix}.$$

(i) Calculate the separation achieved by each of the six variables. If only one variable were to be used, which would be best?

(ii) From the values of the elements of **B** and **W**, is there evidence that a linear combination of the variables will improve the separation of the groups? Justify your answer.

(b) The first discriminant function, using group-standardized variables, is

$$D_1 = 0.142Z_1 - 0.249Z_2 + 2.086Z_3 + 0.278Z_4 - 1.743Z_5 - 0.311Z_6.$$

Interpret this discriminant function. Which variables appear to be the most important? Do any appear not to be important? Explain your answers.

(c) For the first discriminant function D_1,

$$V_b(D_1)/V_w(D_1) = 665.220.$$

Comment on how well the first discriminant function separates the subspecies, compared to the separation achieved by the original variables $X_1, X_2, \ldots, X_6$ on their own.

(d) (i) The group means for D_1 are given in Table 15.1. Obtain the allocation rule based on the first discriminant function. (You may assume equal prior probabilities and equal costs of misclassification.)

Table 15.1 Discriminant function means

Subspecies	Mean of D_1
tularensis	−8.779
mediasiatica	−7.942
holarctica	−8.398
novicida	59.093

(ii) The first discriminant function based on the unstandardized data is

$$D_1 = 0.265X_1 - 0.448X_2 + 16.388X_3 + 0.468X_4 - 40.547X_5 - 0.385X_6 - 9.701.$$

Use the allocation rule you obtained in part (d)(i) to classify the two samples whose characteristics are given below.

X_1	X_2	X_3	X_4	X_5	X_6
1.35	0.48	5.28	1.98	0.42	2.10
0.17	1.41	0.16	0.51	0.03	0.19

(iii) The confusion matrix for the training set based on the first discriminant function is as follows.

	Allocated group			
Actual group	*tularensis*	*mediasiatica*	*holarctica*	*novicida*
tularensis	50%	25%	25%	0%
mediasiatica	0%	100%	0%	0%
holarctica	50%	37.5%	12.5%	0%
novicida	0%	0%	0%	100%

Comment on the accuracy of the classification of subspecies based on this allocation rule. Are the misclassification rates surprising, in the light of the group means given in part (d)(i)?

(e) One way the misclassification rates can be reduced is by considering a second discriminant function. Figure 15.4 shows a scatterplot of the samples according to the values of the first two discriminant functions.

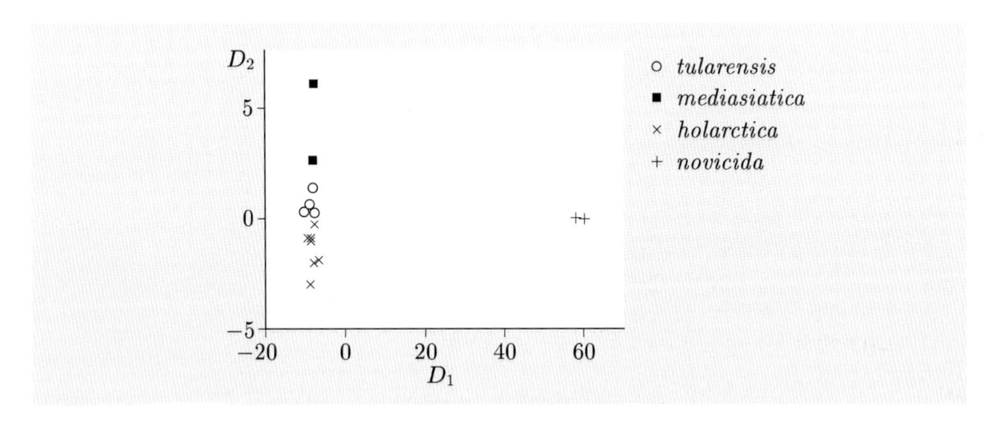

Figure 15.4 Scatterplot of the first two discriminant functions

Does the second discriminant function appear to help separate the groups? If so, in what way?

(f) State how many further discriminant functions could be used to separate the groups. Explain your answer.

Summary of Book 3

Part I

Multivariate analysis techniques are required when two or more variables need to be considered together. As in other areas of statistics, a multivariate analysis usually begins with a graphical inspection of the data. Several graphical techniques for use with multivariate data are available, including matrix scatterplots, three-dimensional scatterplots and profile plots. Numerical summaries for multivariate data include the mean vector and the covariance matrix. Multivariate data are commonly standardized to describe and quantify the relationship between variables measured in different units or on different scales. The covariance matrix of the standardized data is the correlation matrix of the original unstandardized data.

Part II

When the dimension of a multivariate data set is moderate or large, standard graphical techniques such as the matrix scatterplot become unwieldy. In such circumstances, a lower-dimensional approximation to the original data is required, chosen so as to distort the data as little as possible. In principal component analysis, the data are approximated by linear combinations of the original variables. These linear combinations, called principal components, are chosen with maximum variance subject to some constraints on the loadings. In some cases, for example when variables are measured in different units, the variables should be standardized prior to analysis. The total variance provides a benchmark against which the quality of the approximation provided by using one or more principal components may be assessed, using the percentage variance explained and the cumulative percentage variance explained. Several methods are available for choosing an appropriate number of principal components, including numerical cut-offs, Kaiser's criterion and the scree plot.

Part III

Observations in a multivariate data set may fall into several known groups. The separation of the groups can be assessed visually using scatterplots and frequency diagrams. The extent to which a variable separates groups can be quantified using a measure based on the ratio of the between-groups variance to the within-groups variance. Better separation may be achieved by using linear combinations of several variables, rather than a single variable. In canonical discrimination, the linear combination achieving the largest possible separation is selected; this linear combination is called the first discriminant function. To aid the interpretation of the loadings, the discriminant function is often based on group-standardized variables. Further discriminant functions may be used to improve the separation of groups, up to a maximum determined by the number of groups and the dimension of the data. In some circumstances, a discriminant function can be used to define an allocation rule to classify new observations. The performance of an allocation rule can be assessed using confusion matrices.

Learning outcomes

You have been working to develop the following skills.

Part I

- ◇ Display and interpret multivariate data using two-dimensional scatterplots and matrix scatterplots.
- ◇ Interpret multivariate data using profile plots.
- ◇ Obtain and interpret the mean vector of a multivariate data set.
- ◇ Obtain and interpret covariance and correlation matrices.
- ◇ Describe the dimension of a multivariate data set.
- ◇ Standardize variables in a multivariate data set.
- ◇ Obtain graphical and numerical summaries in SPSS.

Part II

- ◇ Identify when dimension reduction of a multivariate data set may be advisable.
- ◇ Identify when two linear combinations result in equivalent approximations.
- ◇ Calculate the variance of a linear combination of up to three variables, given the variances and covariances of the variables.
- ◇ Explain how the first and subsequent principal components of a multivariate data set are calculated.
- ◇ Interpret the loadings of a principal component.
- ◇ Decide whether or not data should be standardized prior to analysis by principal components.
- ◇ Determine the maximum number of principal components that can be used to represent a data set.
- ◇ Calculate and interpret the total variance, the percentage variance explained, and the cumulative percentage variance explained.
- ◇ Choose the number of principal components to include based on numerical cut-offs, Kaiser's criterion or a scree plot.
- ◇ Carry out a principal component analysis in SPSS.

Part III

- ◇ Interpret a scatterplot representing different groups in a multivariate data set.
- ◇ Calculate the between-groups variance and the within-groups variance of a variable, given the means and variances for the groups.
- ◇ Interpret the between-groups and within-groups covariance matrices of a multivariate data set.
- ◇ Calculate the separation achieved by a linear combination of up to three variables from the between-groups and within-groups covariance matrices.
- ◇ Interpret the separation achieved by a linear combination of variables.
- ◇ Explain how the first and subsequent discriminant functions of a multivariate data set are calculated.
- ◇ Obtain the loadings of a discriminant function based on group-standardized variables from the loadings based on standardized variables, and interpret them.
- ◇ Determine the maximum number of useful discriminant functions that can be found.
- ◇ Calculate and interpret the total separation, the percentage separation achieved, and the cumulative percentage separation achieved.

- ◇ Describe the factors that must be considered in designing an allocation rule.
- ◇ Obtain and use an allocation rule based on cut-off values of the discriminant function.
- ◇ Obtain and interpret a confusion matrix for an allocation rule.
- ◇ Use SPSS to undertake a discriminant analysis and allocation.

Solutions to Activities

Solution 1.1

(a) The two variables are antibody level to diphtheria toxoid, and antibody level to tetanus toxoid.

(b) The combined antibody scores range from 0.05 to 0.6. The scores tend to be either low or high, with relatively few scores in the middle of the range.

(c) Although the tetanus antibody level is more heavily weighted than the diphtheria antibody level in the calculation of the combined score, most of the variation in the combined scores might be due to differences in the diphtheria antibody levels. For example, if all the tetanus antibody levels were low, then a high combined score would result only when the diphtheria antibody level was high.

Solution 1.2

(a) The data in the first data column of Table 1.5 are for copper (Cu), so X_1 represents the data for copper.

(b) The sixth variable in Table 1.5 is lithium (Li), so X_6 represents the data for lithium.

(c) Observation 3 is the third row in Table 1.5, so it corresponds to observations for the leaf of the plant.

(d) The value of x_{48} is the number in the fourth row and eighth column of Table 1.5, so $x_{48} = 8.16$.

(e) Data for the measurement of log concentrations in the stem of the plant are given in the second row of Table 1.5, so $i = 2$. The logarithms of the manganese concentrations are given in the third column, so $j = 3$.

Solution 2.1

(a) House price and household income appear to be positively related. Authorities where the average household income is high also appear to have high average house prices.

(b) The authorities in London tend to have higher average house prices and higher average household incomes than in other regions. Differences between regions other than London are rather difficult to spot on this plot.

(c) Arguably a couple of the points relating to local authority areas in London are out of line with the others. In particular, in one London local authority, the average house price of under £200 000 seems to be quite low compared with the average household income in that area (just under £80 000).

Solution 2.2

(a) The Isles of Scilly did better than the City of London in Mathematics, but less well in English.

(b) The symbol for the point representing the City of London is relatively large, compared to the others in the plot, suggesting that it is supposed to be relatively close to the eye of the observer. This would perhaps suggest a high score in Science, perhaps closer to 100% than 50%, since the z-axis rises out of the page.

(c) It is not really possible to tell which of the City of London and the Isles of Scilly obtained the better score in Science. (In fact, the City of London obtained the better score.)

Solution 2.3

(a) There are strong positive relationships between the three mathematics variables. Thus, in general, a boy who scored highly in one of the subjects also did well in the other two. The strongest relationship is between the scores in arithmetic and algebra, as the points lie closest to a straight line.

(b) There does not appear to be a relationship between the age of a boy and the scores of the boy in geometry, arithmetic and algebra.

Solution 2.4

(a) Overall, the subscores seem to be positively related to one another (or at least they are not negatively related).

(b) There is a strong positive relationship between two variables if the points in the scatterplot of the variables are fairly close to a line with positive slope. Thus there appear to be strong positive relationships between the following pairs of subscores: H and I, E and F, C and D, A and C.

(c) Subscore variable B seems to be only weakly related to most of the others.

Solution 2.5

(a) Generally, the gene expression is relatively low initially, and increases over the next time period. At the 6-hour point, the relative expression of most of the genes is fairly close to 1. There are two genes for which the gene expression is relatively low around the 12-hour point.

(b) The first group consists of genes whose relative expression rose sharply in the first two hours and then declined. The second group (Figure 2.9(b)) consists of genes whose relative expression remained raised during the period from 2 to 12 hours. For the genes in the third group (Figure 2.9(c)), the relative expression seems to increase steadily over the time period. The fourth and smallest group consists of genes whose relative expression declined over the period from 2 to 12 hours.

Solution 3.1

(a) The variable X_1 represents the log concentration of copper (Cu). Thus the mean log concentration of copper is the first entry in the mean vector — that is, 2.31.

(b) The mean log concentration of nickel (Ni) is the fifth entry in the mean vector — that is, 1.52.

(c) The largest element of the mean vector is the ninth: 9.48. Thus the largest mean log concentration is for variable X_9. Hence the chemical element with the greatest mean log concentration is calcium (Ca).

Solution 3.2

(a) The mean performance in English (as a percentage) is

$$\overline{x}_1 = \frac{96.6 + 86.9 + \cdots + 80.5}{10} = \frac{845.7}{10} = 84.57.$$

(b) The score for English is the first variable, Mathematics is the second and Science is the third. Thus the mean vector is $(84.57, 79.42, 92.01)$. All three elements are percentages.

Solution 3.3

In data set A, there is a clear negative relationship between the variables. In data set C, there is a clear positive relationship. In data set B, the two variables do not seem to be related.

Solution 3.4

(a) The variance of the performance in English, s_1^2, is found using Formula (3.1):

$$\begin{aligned} s_1^2 &= \frac{(96.6 - 84.57)^2 + \cdots + (80.5 - 84.57)^2}{9} \\ &= \frac{144.7209 + \cdots + 16.5649}{9} \\ &= \frac{189.6410}{9} \simeq 21.071. \end{aligned}$$

(b) The covariance of the performances in Mathematics and Science, s_{23}, is given by

$$\begin{aligned} s_{23} &= \tfrac{1}{9}\big((79.3 - 79.42)(93.1 - 92.01) + \cdots \\ &\qquad + (78.0 - 79.42)(90.1 - 92.01)\big) \\ &= \frac{-0.12 \times 1.09 + \cdots + -1.42 \times -1.91}{9} \\ &= \frac{-0.1308 + \cdots + 2.7122}{9} \\ &= \frac{11.0680}{9} \simeq 1.230. \end{aligned}$$

Solution 3.5

The covariance matrix $\mathbf{S}$ is

$$\mathbf{S} = \begin{pmatrix} 21.071 & 2.095 & 3.028 \\ 2.095 & 3.155 & 1.230 \\ 3.028 & 1.230 & 1.345 \end{pmatrix}.$$

Solution 3.6

(a) The variable X_3 is the log concentration of manganese (Mn). Thus the variance of the log concentration of manganese is the element $(3, 3)$ in the covariance matrix, that is, 1.129.

(b) The variance of the log concentration of strontium (Sr) is element $(7, 7)$ of the covariance matrix, that is, 0.283.

(c) The variable X_1 is the log concentration of copper (Cu), and the variable X_6 is the log concentration of lithium (Li). Thus the covariance between these two variables is element $(1, 6)$ of the covariance matrix (or equivalently element $(6, 1)$), that is, 0.202.

(d) The covariance between the log concentration of zinc (Zn) and the log concentration of iron (Fe) is element $(4, 2)$ (or equivalently element $(2, 4)$) of the covariance matrix, that is, -0.336.

(e) The covariance between the log concentration of nickel (Ni) and the log concentration of calcium (Ca) is element $(5, 9)$, that is, 0.466. This is positive, suggesting that the log concentrations of these elements are positively related.

(f) The upper triangle is just a mirror image of the lower triangle. Element (j, k) in the lower triangle is identical to element (k, j) in the upper triangle. In a covariance matrix, element (j, k) corresponds to the covariance s_{jk} and element (k, j) to the covariance s_{kj}. From the definition of the covariance in Formula (3.2), it follows that $s_{jk} = s_{kj}$, so element (j, k) must be equal to element (k, j).

Solution 4.1

(a) The variables are all weights (of the same order of magnitude), and hence it would be sensible to measure them using the same units (kg for example). So the covariance matrix would be interpretable.

(b) It would make sense to measure age and length of education using the same units (such as years), but the weekly income would necessarily be in different units (such as pounds). Thus a covariance matrix would not be interpretable.

(c) The number of trips to the cinema has no units, whereas the distance to the nearest cinema and the amount spent would necessarily be measured in different units (such as miles and pounds, respectively). Therefore a covariance matrix based on these variables would not be interpretable.

Solution 4.2

(a) The mean standardized house price is

$$\overline{z}_1 = \frac{2.14 + 0.79 + \cdots + (-0.87)}{9} = \frac{0}{9} = 0.$$

(b) The variance of the standardized house prices is

$$\frac{(2.14 - 0)^2 + \cdots + (-0.87 - 0)^2}{9 - 1} = \frac{8.0028}{8} = 1.000\,35.$$

Thus the sample variance of Z_1 is 1.00 to two decimal places.

Solution 4.3

Since $\overline{x}_2 = 32.587$ and $s_2^2 = 38.6$, the standardized household income is calculated using the formula

$$z_{i2} = \frac{x_{i2} - 32.587}{\sqrt{38.6}}.$$

For example, for the first observation,

$$z_{12} = \frac{46.288 - 32.587}{\sqrt{38.6}} \simeq 2.21.$$

For the second observation,

$$z_{22} = \frac{38.478 - 32.587}{\sqrt{38.6}} \simeq 0.95.$$

The values of the standardized household income are given in Table S.1.

Table S.1 Standardized household income in nine English regions

Region	Standardized household income
London	2.21
South East	0.95
South West	−0.48
Eastern	0.20
West Midlands	−0.12
East Midlands	−0.52
North East	−0.83
North West	−0.64
Yorkshire & Humber	−0.77

Solution 4.4

(a) One of the elements on the main diagonal, element $(2, 2)$, is not equal to 1.

(b) One of the elements in the lower triangle, element $(3, 2)$, is greater than 1 and hence is too large to be a correlation.

(c) The upper triangle is not the mirror image of the lower triangle. For example, element $(1, 2)$ is 0.7 but element $(2, 1)$ is 0.2.

(d) The matrix is not square.

Solution 4.5

(a) The highest correlation is 0.879. From the position of this coefficient in the matrix, this correlation is between the second and third variables, that is, between Mathematics and Science. Thus the strongest linear relationship is between the scores achieved in Mathematics and in Science.

(b) All the off-diagonal correlation coefficients in the correlation matrix are quite close to one, so there seems to be a positive linear relationship between each pair of variables.

Solution 4.6

(a) All the correlation coefficients are positive. This indicates that better than average ability in any one aspect is associated with better than average ability in all the others.

(b) The four largest correlations are as follows: 0.91 between H and I, followed by 0.84 between E and F, 0.80 between A and C, and 0.79 between C and D.

(c) Subscore B has rather low correlations with subscores D to I (less than 0.5).

(d) The findings in parts (a) to (c) are similar to those obtained in Activity 2.4.

Solution 6.1

(a) The two variables are multiplied together rather than added, so this approximation is not equivalent to the average.

(b) In the average, the two variables are multiplied by the same constant (0.5). However, two different constants are used in this approximation, so it is not equivalent to the average.

(c) Although the variables are multiplied by the same constant, the difference is then taken, not the sum, so this approximation is not equivalent to the average.

(d) All the averages have been shifted by -1, so $c_1 = 1$ and $c_2 = -1$. So this approximation is equivalent to the average.

(e) Although the variables are multiplied by the same constant, the difference is then taken, not the sum. So this approximation is not equivalent to the average.

(f) This approximation may be obtained by multiplying the average $(X_1 + X_2)/2$ by the constant $c_1 = \sqrt{2}$ and adding the constant $c_2 = -8/\sqrt{3}$, so it is equivalent to the average.

Solution 6.2

(a) When $\alpha_1 = 1$ and $\alpha_2 = 0$, the value of y_1 is simply the value of x_{11}, so $y_1 = 2.31$.

(b) When $\alpha_1 = 0$ and $\alpha_2 = 1$, the value of y_1 is simply the value of x_{12}, so $y_1 = 4.58$.

(c) When $\alpha_1 = 0.8$ and $\alpha_2 = 0.6$,

$$\begin{aligned} y_1 &= 0.8x_{11} + 0.6x_{12} \\ &= 0.8 \times 2.31 + 0.6 \times 4.58 \\ &= 1.848 + 2.748 \\ &= 4.596. \end{aligned}$$

(d) When $\alpha_1 = 1/\sqrt{2}$ and $\alpha_2 = -1/\sqrt{2}$,

$$\begin{aligned} y_1 &\simeq 0.707x_{11} - 0.707x_{12} \\ &= 0.707 \times 2.31 - 0.707 \times 4.58 \\ &\simeq 1.633 - 3.238 \\ &\simeq -1.605. \end{aligned}$$

(e) When $\alpha_1 = 0.6$ and $\alpha_2 = -0.8$,

$$\begin{aligned} y_1 &= 0.6x_{11} - 0.8x_{12} \\ &= 0.6 \times 2.31 - 0.8 \times 4.58 \\ &= 1.386 - 3.664 \\ &= -2.278. \end{aligned}$$

Solution 6.3

Since $V(X_1) = 3.615$, $V(X_2) = 1.452$ and $\text{Cov}(X_1, X_2) = 1.959$, using (6.3) gives

$$V(Y) = 3.615\alpha_1^2 + 1.452\alpha_2^2 + 2 \times 1.959 \times \alpha_1\alpha_2.$$

(a) When $\alpha_1 = 0.8$ and $\alpha_2 = 0.6$,

$$\begin{aligned} V(Y) &= 3.615 \times 0.64 + 1.452 \times 0.36 + 2 \times 1.959 \times 0.48 \\ &\simeq 4.717. \end{aligned}$$

(b) When $\alpha_1 = 1/\sqrt{2}$ and $\alpha_2 = -1/\sqrt{2}$,

$$\begin{aligned} V(Y) &= 3.615 \times 0.5 + 1.452 \times 0.5 + 2 \times 1.959 \times (-0.5) \\ &\simeq 0.575. \end{aligned}$$

(c) When $\alpha_1 = 0.6$ and $\alpha_2 = -0.8$,

$$\begin{aligned} V(Y) &= 3.615 \times 0.36 + 1.452 \times 0.64 \\ &\quad + 2 \times 1.959 \times (-0.48) \\ &\simeq 0.350. \end{aligned}$$

In each case, the value matches that in Table 6.5.

Solution 6.4

(a) In the scatterplot, regions with a large percentage of grassland tend to have a low percentage of arable land, and vice versa. So in a good one-dimensional approximation, we would expect the regions to be roughly in the order of the percentage of arable land (or, equivalently, the percentage of grassland). We would expect the points representing the North and the North West to be close together at one end of the scale, and we would expect the points representing Yorkshire & Humber and the West Midlands to be close together. At the other end of the scale, we would expect the points representing the South East, East Midlands and East Anglia to be well spaced out.

(b) Using Formula (6.3), the variance of Y is given by

$$\begin{aligned} V(Y) &= \alpha_1^2\, V(X_1) + \alpha_2^2\, V(X_2) + 2\alpha_1\alpha_2\, \text{Cov}(X_1, X_2) \\ &= \alpha_1^2 \times 230.12 + \alpha_2^2 \times 98.93 - 2\alpha_1\alpha_2 \times 149.39. \end{aligned}$$

(i) When $\alpha_1 = 0.6$ and $\alpha_2 = 0.8$,

$$\begin{aligned} V(Y) &= 0.36 \times 230.12 + 0.64 \times 98.93 - 0.96 \times 149.39 \\ &\simeq 2.74. \end{aligned}$$

(ii) When $\alpha_1 = 0.8$ and $\alpha_2 = 0.6$,

$$\begin{aligned} V(Y) &= 0.64 \times 230.12 + 0.36 \times 98.93 - 0.96 \times 149.39 \\ &\simeq 39.48. \end{aligned}$$

(iii) When $\alpha_1 = 0.6$ and $\alpha_2 = -0.8$,

$$\begin{aligned} V(Y) &= 0.36 \times 230.12 + 0.64 \times 98.93 + 0.96 \times 149.39 \\ &\simeq 289.57. \end{aligned}$$

(iv) When $\alpha_1 = 0.8$ and $\alpha_2 = -0.6$,

$$\begin{aligned} V(Y) &= 0.64 \times 230.12 + 0.36 \times 98.93 + 0.96 \times 149.39 \\ &\simeq 326.31. \end{aligned}$$

(c) The given maximum variance is larger than all of the variances calculated in part (b). Also, in part (b) the largest variances were associated with choices for which α_1 is positive and α_2 is negative. Indeed, of the choices for α_1 and α_2 which were investigated in part (b), the choice which had the highest variance ($\alpha_1 = 0.8$ and $\alpha_2 = -0.6$) is the closest to the pair of values $\alpha_1 = 0.84$ and $\alpha_2 = -0.54$. So it is plausible that the variance is a maximum for these values of α_1 and α_2.

(d) For the North West region (region 2), the value of the first principal component is

$$\begin{aligned} y_2 &= 0.84x_{21} - 0.54x_{22} - (0.84\overline{x}_1 - 0.54\overline{x}_2) \\ &\simeq 0.84 \times 15.9 - 0.54 \times 45.2 \\ &\quad - (0.84 \times 32.5 - 0.54 \times 35.8) \\ &\simeq -19.0. \end{aligned}$$

(e) The choice of $\alpha_1 = 0.84$ and $\alpha_2 = -0.54$ seems to provide a good one-dimensional approximation to the data. Low values are given to regions with a high percentage of grassland and a low percentage of arable land. Similarly, high values are given to regions with a high percentage of arable land and a low percentage of grassland. Also, the approximation seems to have picked up both the similarity between the North and North West regions, and that between the West Midlands and Yorkshire & Humber. The approximation also reflects the differences between the South East, East Midlands and East Anglia regions.

Solution 7.1

(a) When $\alpha_1 = \alpha_2 = \alpha_3 = 1/\sqrt{3}$, the variance of Y is given by

$$\begin{aligned} V(Y) &= 26.22\alpha_1^2 + 19.78\alpha_2^2 + 11.81\alpha_3^2 \\ &\quad + 2 \times 17.06 \times \alpha_1\alpha_2 + 2 \times 13.69 \times \alpha_1\alpha_3 \\ &\quad + 2 \times 13.44 \times \alpha_2\alpha_3 \\ &= 26.22/3 + 19.78/3 + 11.81/3 \\ &\quad + 2 \times 17.06/3 + 2 \times 13.69/3 + 2 \times 13.44/3 \\ &\simeq 48.7. \end{aligned}$$

(b) When $\alpha_1 = \alpha_2 = \alpha_3 = 1/\sqrt{3}$, the variance of Y is 48.7. This is a little smaller than the variance obtained for the principal component, which is 50.0. This indicates that the first principal component provides a slightly better approximation to the data than that used in *The Times*.

Solution 7.2

For a bivariate data set, the percentage variance explained is given by

$$\text{PVE} = \frac{V(Y)}{\text{TV}} \times 100\% = \frac{V(Y)}{V(X_1)+V(X_2)} \times 100\%.$$

(a) For the interest rate data,

$$\text{PVE} = \frac{4.771}{3.615+1.452} \times 100\% \simeq 94.2\%.$$

Thus the principal component accounts for 94.2% of the total variance. This is a very high proportion, so the principal component gives an excellent approximation to the bivariate data.

(b) For the land cover data,

$$\text{PVE} = \frac{327.68}{230.12+98.93} \times 100\% \simeq 99.6\%.$$

Thus the principal component accounts for 99.6% of the total variance. This is a very high proportion, so the principal component is an excellent approximation to the bivariate data.

Solution 7.3

(a) The variable with the largest loading will be the marathon, because when the times are all measured in seconds, the variance of the marathon times is very much greater than that of any other variable.

(b) An improvement of one second in the 100 m produces an increase in the value of the principal component of 0.000 33. On the other hand, an improvement of one second in the marathon increases the value of the principal component by 0.98, which is $0.98/0.000\,33 \simeq 2992$ times as large. However, an improvement of one second for the 100 m record for a country would generally have a large effect on the ranking of that country for the 100 m, whereas an improvement of one second in the marathon would generally have a marginal effect on the ranking for the marathon. Thus the principal component does not provide a useful overall ranking of countries: it effectively ignores all events other than the marathon.

(c) The PVE is very high, suggesting that the principal component provides an excellent approximation to the data. This does not contradict part (b), where the emphasis was on using the principal component to rank the countries, making use of information from all components.

Solution 7.4

(a) Despite being measured in the same units, the concentrations are far more variable for some of the chemicals than for the others. In particular, the variance of the carbon monoxide concentrations is 100 times larger than the next largest variance. At the other end of the scale, the variance of the benzene concentrations is more than 200 times smaller than the next smallest variance.

(b) The total variance for the unstandardized data set is the sum of the variances. That is,

$$\text{TV} = 0.118 + 38\,788 + 384 + 80.7 + 24.3 = 39\,277.118.$$

Thus the percentage variance explained by CO is

$$\frac{\text{variance of CO}}{\text{TV}} \times 100\% = \frac{38\,788}{39\,277.118} \times 100\% \simeq 98.8\%.$$

(c) In the standardized data set, every variable has a variance of 1. So the total variance is equal to the number of variables, 5.

Thus, for the standardized data set, the percentage variance explained by CO is

$$\frac{\text{variance of CO}}{\text{TV}} \times 100\% = \frac{1}{5} \times 100\% = 20\%.$$

(d) The variance of the first principal component is 3.52. Thus, for this linear combination, the percentage variance explained is

$$\text{PVE} = \frac{V(Y)}{\text{TV}} \times 100\% = \frac{3.52}{5} \times 100\% = 70.4\%.$$

(e) The approximation given in part (d) is likely to be the more useful. Although it captures proportionately much less variance than that in part (b), it is not dominated by a single chemical, carbon monoxide.

Solution 7.5

(a) In this study, the seven variables all represent percentages. Thus, as they are all measured in the same units, it may make sense to consider linear combinations of the unstandardized data.

(b) In this study, eight of the variables relate to numbers of reports, and two of the variables relate to a length of time (for installation). As the variables are necessarily measured in different units, it only makes sense to use linear combinations of the standardized data.

(c) In this study, the variables are measured in a mixture of units, relating to areas, energy and weights. Thus for these data it only makes sense to use linear combinations of the standardized data.

(d) In this study, the answers to each question were given on the same three-point scale. So, here it may make sense to use linear combinations of the unstandardized data.

Solution 8.1

(a) As the data set has been standardized, each standardized variable has variance 1, and hence the total variance is equal to the number of variables. In this data set there are 14 variables, so the total variance TV is 14. The percentage variances explained by the first and second components are

$$\text{PVE by } Y_1 = \frac{4.672}{14} \times 100\% \simeq 33.37\%,$$

$$\text{PVE by } Y_2 = \frac{3.394}{14} \times 100\% \simeq 24.24\%.$$

(b) The cumulative variance captured by the two components is

$$V(Y_1) + V(Y_2) = 4.672 + 3.394 = 8.066.$$

Hence the cumulative percentage variance explained by Y_1 and Y_2 is

$$\text{CPVE} = \frac{V(Y_1) + V(Y_2)}{\text{TV}} \times 100\% = \frac{8.066}{14} \times 100\% \simeq 57.61\%.$$

(c) The first principal component accounts for only 33.37% of the total variance, so it was necessary to obtain the second principal component. However, the first and second components together still account for only 57.61% of the total variance. Hence they do not provide a very good approximation to the original 14-dimensional data set.

Solution 8.2

(a) The two races with the smallest loadings (in absolute value) for the second principal component are the two middle-distance events, the 800 m and the 1500 m races. Of the remaining variables, the sprints (100 m to 400 m) have positive loadings, whereas the long-distance races (5000 m to marathon) have negative loadings. Hence the second component represents a contrast between performance in sprint and long-distance events.

(b) The four largest loadings (in absolute value) are for the 100 m and 200 m races (both loadings positive) and the 400 m and 800 m races (both loadings negative). This principal component could perhaps be interpreted as contrasting performance in the 100 m and 200 m events with performance over 400 m and 800 m. (However, this interpretation is slightly marred by the loading for the marathon (0.263) which is not much smaller than the loadings for the 100 m and 200 m races.)

(c) There is one outlier, in the upper right-hand corner of the scatterplot. This is a country that scored unusually highly on the first principal component, and thus performed less well in the events than the other countries. The remaining countries split into two groups: a main group in the upper left-hand part of the scatterplot, and below it a group of six countries. These countries scored low values on the second principal component, and thus did comparatively better in the sprint events than in the long-distance events.

Solution 8.3

(a) For each data set, the maximum number of principal components is equal to the dimension of the data. The dimensions of the data sets in the four studies are as follows: 7 for study (a), 10 for study (b), 14 for study (c), and 12 for study (d).

(b) The flaw in the argument is that the CPVE is always at least as large with five principal components as it is with four. To decide whether the improvement in the CPVE provided by the fifth component justifies including it, the percentage variance explained by each individual component is required.

Solution 8.4

The variance of each of the principal components and the cumulative percentage variance explained by the four principal components of the standardized mathematical ability data set are given in Table S.2.

Table S.2 Variance and CPVE

Principal component	Variance	CPVE
1	2.193	54.8
2	1.001	79.9
3	0.495	92.2
4	0.311	100.0

(a) To meet the 90% CPVE criterion, three components should be used.

(b) The variance of the second principal component is slightly greater than 1, whereas the variance of the third principal component is much less than 1. So, using Kaiser's criterion, the most appropriate number of components is two.

Solution 8.5

In Figure 8.5(a), there is a dramatic change in the slope after component 3. Thus the scree plot indicates that two components should be retained.

In Figure 8.5(b), the variance falls steeply up to the fifth component. After that, there is little change in the variance. So this plot indicates that four components should be retained.

In Figure 8.5(c), there appears to be a change in slope at component 10. This indicates that nine components should be retained.

In Figure 8.5(d), there appear to be two changes in slope. The first, and more striking, change occurs at component 3. The second, more subtle, change occurs at component 11. In this situation, the appropriate number of components is not entirely clear. It could be argued on the basis of the scree plot either that two components should be retained or that ten components should be retained.

In such situations, using other approaches to deciding how many components to retain might help to resolve the issue. For example, in this case the first two components account for less than 50% of the variance. So in order to provide a good approximation to the data, it may be better to retain the first ten components.

Solution 10.1

Samples from Mandsaur tend to have higher concentrations of phenylalanine than samples from the other two locations, so the cloud of points for Mandsaur lies to the right (along the x-axis) of the clouds for the other locations. Thus phenylalanine concentration separates observations in Mandsaur from observations in the other two locations quite well.

However, phenylalanine concentration does not separate samples from Kota and Chittorgarh, as the clouds of points corresponding to Kota and Chittorgarh lie at similar distances along the x-axis: the concentrations from these two locations span roughly the same range of values.

Solution 10.2

(a) If the group of patients with heart disease is labelled as group 1 and the group of patients without heart disease as group 2, then $n_1 = 120$, $n_2 = 150$ and $N = 270$.

The grand mean for age is obtained using (10.4):

$$\overline{\overline{x}} = \frac{n_1\overline{x}_1 + n_2\overline{x}_2}{N} = \frac{120 \times 56.6 + 150 \times 52.7}{270} \simeq 54.4333.$$

The between-groups variance for age is calculated using (10.2):

$$V_b = \frac{n_1(\overline{x}_1 - \overline{\overline{x}})^2 + n_2(\overline{x}_2 - \overline{\overline{x}})^2}{N-2} = \frac{120(56.6 - 54.4333)^2 + 150(52.7 - 54.4333)^2}{270-2} \simeq 3.7836.$$

The within-groups variance for age is found using (10.1):

$$V_w = \frac{(n_1 - 1)s_1^2 + (n_2 - 1)s_2^2}{N-2} = \frac{(120-1) \times 8.12^2 + (150-1) \times 9.51^2}{270-2} \simeq 79.5588.$$

Hence the separation for age is given by

$$\text{separation} = \frac{V_b}{V_w} \simeq \frac{3.7836}{79.5588} \simeq 0.048.$$

The separations for the other three variables are given in Table S.3.

Table S.3 Separations

Variable	Separation
Blood pressure	0.024
Cholesterol	0.014
Maximum heart rate	0.211

(b) Maximum heart rate achieves the best separation of the two groups of patients, because the value of the separation is greatest for this variable. Cholesterol separates the groups the least well, because the value of the separation is lowest for this variable.

Solution 10.3

(a) There are three groups and $N = 2414$ (as in Example 10.8). The grand mean $\overline{\overline{x}}$ is given by

$$\overline{\overline{x}} = \frac{n_1\overline{x}_1 + n_2\overline{x}_2 + n_3\overline{x}_3}{N} = \frac{961 \times 105.50 + 415 \times 90.94 + 1038 \times 77.42}{2414} \simeq 90.9228.$$

The between-groups variance V_b is calculated using (10.6):

$$\begin{aligned} V_b &= \frac{n_1(\overline{x}_1 - \overline{\overline{x}})^2 + n_2(\overline{x}_2 - \overline{\overline{x}})^2 + n_3(\overline{x}_3 - \overline{\overline{x}})^2}{N-3} \\ &= \frac{1}{2411}\big(961 \times (105.50 - 90.9228)^2 \\ &\qquad + 415 \times (90.94 - 90.9228)^2 \\ &\qquad + 1038 \times (77.42 - 90.9228)^2\big) \\ &\simeq 163.19. \end{aligned}$$

The within-groups variance V_w is found using (10.7):

$$V_w = \frac{(n_1 - 1)s_1^2 + (n_2 - 1)s_2^2 + (n_3 - 1)s_3^2}{N-3} = \frac{960 \times 47.138 + 414 \times 66.565 + 1037 \times 59.091}{2411} \simeq 55.61.$$

Hence the separation achieved by the Band B measurements is

$$\text{separation} = \frac{V_b}{V_w} \simeq \frac{163.19}{55.61} \simeq 2.93.$$

(b) The measurements from Band B separate the types of soil best, because the separation for Band B is higher than the separations for the other bands. Bands A, C and D achieve similar degrees of separation between the three types of soil.

Solution 10.4

(a) The variable with the smallest within-groups variance is age ($V_w(X_1) = 79.53$). The variable with the largest between-groups variance is maximum heart rate ($V_b(X_4) = 92.93$).

(b) The separations are obtained from the ratios of the variances. So for age, the separation is $3.76/79.53 \simeq 0.047$. For blood pressure, the separation is $7.47/312.50 \simeq 0.024$; for cholesterol, it is $37.97/2644.09 \simeq 0.014$; and for maximum heart rate, it is $92.93/444.31 \simeq 0.209$. These values are the same (up to rounding error) as those obtained in Activity 10.2.

(c) There are two pairs of variables for which the between-groups covariance and the within-groups covariance have different signs: blood pressure and maximum heart rate, and cholesterol and maximum heart rate. In both cases, the within-groups covariance is positive, and the between-groups covariance is negative. Thus, in each case, the two variables are positively related within groups, but negatively related between groups.

(d) A combination of maximum heart rate and blood pressure and/or cholesterol is likely to achieve better separation than maximum heart rate on its own.

Solution 11.1

(a) For each linear combination D, the within-groups variance $V_w(D)$ and the between-groups variance $V_b(D)$ are given by (11.5) and (11.6). Using the required variances and covariances, whose values are given in Example 11.1, these formulas may be written as follows:

$$V_w(D) = 0.137\alpha_1^2 + 0.099\alpha_2^2 + 0.090\alpha_1\alpha_2,$$
$$V_b(D) = 0.006\alpha_1^2 + 0.033\alpha_2^2 - 0.028\alpha_1\alpha_2.$$

(i) When $\alpha_1 = 0.8$ and $\alpha_2 = -0.6$,

$$\begin{aligned} V_w(D) &= 0.137 \times (0.8)^2 + 0.099 \times (-0.6)^2 \\ &\quad + 0.090 \times 0.8 \times (-0.6) \\ &= 0.080\,12, \end{aligned}$$

$$\begin{aligned} V_b(D) &= 0.006 \times (0.8)^2 + 0.033 \times (-0.6)^2 \\ &\quad - 0.028 \times 0.8 \times (-0.6) \\ &= 0.029\,16. \end{aligned}$$

(ii) When $\alpha_1 = 1$ and $\alpha_2 = 0$,

$$V_w(D) = 0.137(1)^2 + 0.099(0)^2 + 0.090(1)(0) = 0.137,$$
$$V_b(D) = 0.006(1)^2 + 0.033(0)^2 - 0.028(1)(0) = 0.006.$$

(iii) When $\alpha_1 = 0$ and $\alpha_2 = 1$,

$$V_w(D) = 0.137(0)^2 + 0.099(1)^2 + 0.090(0)(1) = 0.099,$$
$$V_b(D) = 0.006(0)^2 + 0.033(1)^2 - 0.028(0)(1) = 0.033.$$

(iv) When $\alpha_1 = 0.6$ and $\alpha_2 = 0.8$,

$$\begin{aligned} V_w(D) &= 0.137 \times (0.6)^2 + 0.099 \times (0.8)^2 \\ &\quad + 0.090 \times 0.6 \times 0.8 \\ &= 0.155\,88, \end{aligned}$$

$$\begin{aligned} V_b(D) &= 0.006 \times (0.6)^2 + 0.033 \times (0.8)^2 \\ &\quad - 0.028 \times 0.6 \times 0.8 \\ &= 0.009\,84. \end{aligned}$$

(b) Using the variances calculated in part (a)(i) and Formula (11.4),

$$\text{separation} = \frac{V_b(D)}{V_w(D)} = \frac{0.029\,16}{0.080\,12} \simeq 0.36.$$

The other separations are calculated similarly. The results are shown in Table S.4.

Table S.4 Between-groups variances, within-groups variances and separations

α_1	α_2	$V_b(D)$	$V_w(D)$	$V_b(D)/V_w(D)$
1	0	0.006	0.137	0.04
0.8	0.6	0.002 28	0.166 52	0.01
$1/\sqrt{2}$	$1/\sqrt{2}$	0.005 50	0.163 00	0.03
0.6	0.8	0.009 84	0.155 88	0.06
0	1	0.033	0.099	0.33
0.8	−0.6	0.029 16	0.080 12	0.36
$1/\sqrt{2}$	$-1/\sqrt{2}$	0.033 50	0.073 00	0.46
0.6	−0.8	0.036 72	0.069 48	0.53

(c) The separation is largest when $\alpha_1 = 0.6$ and $\alpha_2 = -0.8$, so choosing these values of α_1 and α_2 separates the genuine notes and the counterfeit notes best.

Solution 11.2

(a) For this discriminant function,

$$\begin{aligned} c &= -0.005 \times 214.895 - 0.832 \times 130.120 \\ &\quad + 0.849 \times 129.955 + 1.117 \times 9.415 \\ &\quad + 1.179 \times 10.650 - 1.557 \times 140.485 \\ &\simeq -194.665. \end{aligned}$$

So an alternative way of writing the discriminant function D is as follows:

$$\begin{aligned} D &= -0.005X_1 - 0.832X_2 + 0.849X_3 + 1.117X_4 \\ &\quad + 1.179X_5 - 1.557X_6 + 194.665. \end{aligned}$$

(b) The loadings used in D_2 are double those used in D in absolute value. However, the signs of the loadings in D and D_2 do not match: for D, three loadings are negative and three are positive, but for D_2, all the loadings are positive. So D_2 cannot be obtained by multiplying D by one constant and adding another, and hence it is not equivalent to D.

Solution 11.3

(a) For $j = 1, 2, \ldots, 6$, $a_j = \alpha_j\sqrt{V_w(X_j)}$. Since $V_w(X_1) = 0.137$,

$$a_1 = \alpha_1\sqrt{V_w(X_1)} = -0.005\sqrt{0.137} \simeq -0.002.$$

Similar calculations give $a_2 \simeq -0.262$, $a_3 \simeq +0.279$, $a_4 \simeq +1.028$, $a_5 \simeq +0.758$ and $a_6 \simeq -0.788$. Thus

$$\begin{aligned} D &= -0.002Z_1 - 0.262Z_2 + 0.279Z_3 + 1.028Z_4 \\ &\quad + 0.758Z_5 - 0.788Z_6. \end{aligned}$$

This discriminant function was quoted in Example 10.4; the differences in some of the coefficients are due to rounding error.

(b) The largest loadings (in absolute value) are those for Z_4 (the width of the bottom border), Z_5 (the width of the top border), and Z_6 (the length of the diagonal of the central motif). These all relate to the design on the notes. Since a_4 and a_5 are positive and a_6 is negative, the shape of the design is important in distinguishing between genuine notes and counterfeit notes. The value of a_1 is close to zero, suggesting that the length of the notes is not very important.

The term $-0.262Z_2 + 0.279Z_3$ measures the discrepancy between the widths at the left and right edges of the notes. So this discrepancy also plays a role in discriminating between the notes. However, it is not as important as the shape of the design, because the loadings a_2 and a_3 are much smaller in absolute value than those relating to the design.

(c) The loading for Z_1 is -0.002, which is very much smaller in absolute value than the value 0.673 obtained in Example 11.5. However, in Example 11.5, the discriminant function was based solely on the length and the width at the left edge. When only these two variables are considered, length becomes more important (but the separation achieved is less than that achieved when all six variables are used).

Solution 12.1

(a) All the loadings for D_1 are positive, so the first discriminant function is broadly equivalent to a weighted average of the four variables. The measurements taken using spectral band B are given the greatest weight, and those using spectral band A the next largest weight. The measurements taken using spectral bands C and D are given similar, lower, weights.

(b) Two of the loadings in D_2 are positive, and two are negative. So D_2 represents a difference between the measurements in the various spectral bands. The loading relating to Z_4 is very small, indicating that spectral band D barely contributes to D_2.

(c) **(i)** The cloud of points corresponding to very damp grey soil is located furthest to the left, and the cloud of points corresponding to grey soil is located furthest to the right. The cloud of points corresponding to damp grey soil is in the centre.

(ii) There is some separation horizontally, based on the values of the first discriminant function D_1, though the separation is not very good. However, there is little difference between the vertical positions of the three clouds of points. This indicates that the distributions of values of D_2 for the three groups overlap greatly. Thus the second discriminant function does not seem to add very much to the separation of the soil types.

Solution 12.2

(a) In this study, each of the morphological characteristics represents a variable, so $p = 9$. The different species of the plants divide the data into four groups, so $G = 4$. The maximum number of useful discriminant functions is the minimum of $G - 1$ and p, that is, 3.

(b) In this study, there are eighteen variables, so $p = 18$. There are two groups (earthquakes and explosions), so $G = 2$. Thus the minimum of $G - 1$ and p is 1. In this study, there is at most one useful discriminant function.

(c) In this study, there are 30 variables, but only two groups (whether the youth appeared in court in 1995 or not). So the minimum of $G - 1$ and p is 1, and hence there is at most one useful discriminant function.

(d) In this study, there are three groups (healthy, heart attack but not SVT, heart attack and SVT) and sixteen variables. So the minimum of $G - 1$ and p is 2, and hence there are at most two useful discriminant functions.

(e) In this study, there are six groups and four variables. So the minimum of $G - 1$ and p is 4, and hence there are at most four useful discriminant functions.

Solution 12.3

(a) The total separation is the sum of the separations achieved by the three discriminant functions. For data set A, the total separation is 20. For data set B it is 12, and for data set C it is 21.5.

(b) For any data set, the percentage separation achieved by the first discriminant function is given by

$$\text{PSA}_1 = \frac{\text{Sep}(D_1)}{\text{total separation}} \times 100\%.$$

For data set A,

$$\text{PSA}_1 = \frac{10}{20} \times 100\% = 50\%.$$

For data set B,

$$\text{PSA}_1 = \frac{5}{12} \times 100\% \simeq 42\%.$$

For data set C,

$$\text{PSA}_1 = \frac{20}{21.5} \times 100\% \simeq 93\%.$$

(c) The percentage separation achieved by the first two discriminant functions is

$$\text{CPSA}_2 = \frac{\text{Sep}(D_1) + \text{Sep}(D_2)}{\text{total separation}} \times 100\%.$$

For data set A,

$$\text{CPSA}_2 = \frac{19}{20} \times 100\% = 95\%.$$

For data set B,

$$\text{CPSA}_2 = \frac{9}{12} \times 100\% = 75\%.$$

For data set C,

$$\text{CPSA}_2 = \frac{21}{21.5} \times 100\% \simeq 98\%.$$

(d) **(i)** The total separation is greatest for data set C. So the groups can be separated most effectively in this data set.

(ii) The increase in the cumulative percentage separation achieved when a second discriminant function is used is greatest for data set A. So in data set A the separation of the groups is most improved by the use of a second discriminant function.

Solution 13.1

In Figure 13.4(a), all the values associated with group 1 are above 50, and all the group 2 values are below 50. So it would be appropriate to use a rule based on two regions.

Although there is a lot of overlap in the histograms for the two groups in Figure 13.4(b), the group 1 values are generally a bit higher than the group 2 values. Therefore it would be appropriate to use a rule based on two regions.

In Figure 13.4(c), there are two regions of values of X that should ideally be associated with group 2 values (very high values and very low values). Hence it would not be appropriate to use a rule based on only two regions.

The group 1 values in Figure 13.4(d) are more spread out than the group 2 values. Nevertheless, group 2 values tend to be higher than group 1 values, so it would be appropriate to use a rule based on two regions.

Solution 13.2

(a) The value of l_c depends on the distribution of the discriminant function D for patients with heart disease and on the distribution of the discriminant function D for patients without heart disease.

(b) Using the same value of l_c for screening apparently healthy people would not be appropriate because it would lead to too many healthy people being suspected of having heart disease. It would probably be more appropriate to raise the value of l_c, so that a value of D above the threshold is more likely to be representative of those who have heart disease than to be atypical for someone who does not have heart disease.

(c) The value of l_c should be lowered, so that more cases are classified as having heart disease than would otherwise be the case.

Solution 13.3

Substituting the values $X_1 = 215.2$, $X_2 = 130.4$, $X_3 = 130.1$, $X_4 = 10.1$, $X_5 = 11.6$ and $X_6 = 139.8$ in D gives

$$\begin{aligned} d &= -0.005 \times 215.2 - 0.832 \times 130.4 + 0.849 \times 130.1 \\ &\quad + 1.117 \times 10.1 + 1.179 \times 11.6 - 1.557 \times 139.8 \\ &\quad + 194.649 \\ &\simeq 2.825. \end{aligned}$$

For this note, d is positive so the note should be classified as a counterfeit note. (In fact, this note was counterfeit.)

Solution 13.4

(a) For pixel 1, $X_1 = 76$, $X_2 = 79$, $X_3 = 87$ and $X_4 = 63$, so the value of the discriminant function is

$$\begin{aligned} d_1 &= -0.054 \times 76 - 0.059 \times 79 - 0.024 \times 87 \\ &\quad - 0.023 \times 63 + 13.606 \\ &= 1.304 \simeq 1.30. \end{aligned}$$

Similarly, for pixel 2,

$$\begin{aligned} d_2 &= -0.054 \times 93 - 0.059 \times 111 - 0.024 \times 118 \\ &\quad - 0.023 \times 92 + 13.606 \\ &= -2.913 \simeq -2.91. \end{aligned}$$

(b) Any pixel whose value of D is -1.002 or less should be allocated to the grey soil group. Thus pixels 2, 3, 6, 8 and 9 should be allocated to the grey soil group. Pixels 1, 4, 7 and 10 should be allocated to the very damp grey soil group because their values of the discriminant function are all above 0.943. Pixel 5 should be allocated to the damp grey soil group because d_5 lies between -1.002 and 0.943.

Solution 13.5

(a) 86.9% of grey soil pixels were correctly classified as grey soil.

(b) 17.1% of damp grey soil pixels were classified as very damp grey soil.

(c) A greater percentage of damp grey soil pixels were classified as very damp grey soil than were classified as grey soil. So if a damp grey soil pixel was misclassified, it was more likely to be classified as a very damp grey soil pixel.

(d) Notice that two of the three percentages on the main diagonal of the second confusion matrix are lower than the corresponding percentages on the main diagonal of the first confusion matrix. Also, most of the percentages in off-diagonal positions are higher in the second confusion matrix. Thus pixels in the training set were slightly less likely to be misclassified compared with pixels in the test set.

Solutions to Exercises

Solution 1.1

(a) There are two variables, one corresponding to the average three-month interest rate and the other to the average interest rate of ten-year government bonds, so the dimension of this data set is 2. There are ten observations.

(b) Each variable corresponds to the level of one of the proteins, so there are five variables, and hence the dimension of this data set is 5. There are thirteen observations.

(c) Each type of measurement taken on a note corresponds to a variable, so there are six variables. Thus the dimension of this data set is 6. There are 200 observations.

(d) The concentration of each trace element corresponds to a variable. Thus there are 25 variables, and the dimension of this data set is 25. There are 41 observations.

Solution 2.1

(a) There is a positive linear relationship between the cost of property crime and the cost of crimes against the person: areas with high property crime costs also tend to have high costs of crimes against the person.

(b) There does not seem to be a relationship between local and state expenditure on policing. There is little difference between the level of local expenditure in areas which have high state expenditure and areas which have low state expenditure.

(c) The data do not appear to support the statement that higher spending on policing is associated with lower losses from crime. On the contrary, areas with high losses from property crime and personal crime tend to have greater local expenditure on policing.

(d) There is one clear outlier. This corresponds to an area with very high local expenditure on policing but also the lowest state expenditure on policing. In addition, this area has by far the highest losses from property and personal crime. In fact, this area is the District of Columbia — the only area which is purely urban and is not a state. Arguably there are also a further four outliers, which stand out largely as a result of their high state expenditure on policing. (These points correspond to the states of Alaska, Delaware, Pennsylvania and Massachusetts.)

Solution 2.2

(a) The highest concentrations were recorded for calcium (Ca) and magnesium (Mg), and the lowest concentrations were recorded for lithium (Li). The lowest concentration of each element except nickel was found in the stems of the plant, and the highest concentration was generally found in the leaves.

(b) The relative concentrations of copper (Cu), zinc (Zn) and nickel (Ni) do not fit the general pattern. For each of these three chemical elements, the concentration found in the flowers was higher than that found in the leaves. Also, the concentration of nickel in the herbs was lower than that in the stems.

Solution 3.1

(a) The mean tetanus antibody level, $\overline{x}_1$, is

$$\overline{x}_1 = \frac{2.8 + 3.4 + 3.4}{3} = \frac{9.6}{3} = 3.2.$$

Similarly, the mean diphtheria antibody level, $\overline{x}_2$, is

$$\overline{x}_2 = \frac{1.3 + 1.1 + 2.5}{3} = \frac{4.9}{3} \simeq 1.63.$$

So, for participants who had both a systemic and a local reaction to the injection, the mean vector of antibody levels is $(3.2, 1.63)$.

(b) There is evidence of a relationship between antibody levels and the strength of adverse reaction to the injection. The mean tetanus antibody levels increase from 1.52 for those who had no reaction to 3.2 for those who had both systemic and local reactions. The evidence provided by the mean diphtheria levels indicates a relationship less clearly. The highest mean diphtheria antibody levels were obtained for the group who had the worst reactions. However, the mean diphtheria antibody levels for those who had a systemic reaction and for those who had no reaction are approximately equal.

Solution 3.2

(a) The largest element on the main diagonal is 30 204, for element $(2, 2)$. So the variable with the largest variance is X_2, the cost of crimes against the person.

(b) The off-diagonal elements with the greatest absolute value are elements $(2, 4)$ and $(4, 2)$, with common value 3441. So the greatest covariance (in absolute value) is between X_2 and X_4, the cost of crimes against the person and local expenditure on policing.

(c) The covariance between the cost of property crime and the cost of crimes against the person (elements $(1, 2)$ and $(2, 1)$) is 1803, which is positive and relatively large (compared to the other values in the matrix). The covariance between state expenditure on policing and local expenditure on policing (elements $(3, 4)$ and $(4, 3)$) is -10, which is fairly small in absolute value compared to the other values in the matrix. So the covariance matrix supports both the assertions in the question.

Solution 4.1

(a) The mean of the tetanus antibody levels is 1.986 and the variance is 0.919, so the standardization transformation is

$$z_{i1} = \frac{x_{i1} - 1.986}{\sqrt{0.919}}.$$

The mean of the diphtheria antibody levels is 0.826 and the variance is 0.649, so the standardization transformation is

$$z_{i2} = \frac{x_{i2} - 0.826}{\sqrt{0.649}}.$$

The values of the standardized variables for the three participants who had both systemic and local reactions to the injection are given in Table S.5.

Table S.5 Raw and standardized antibody levels in three participants

Tetanus		Diphtheria	
Raw	Standardized	Raw	Standardized
2.8	0.85	1.3	0.59
3.4	1.47	1.1	0.34
3.4	1.47	2.5	2.08

(b) The correlation matrix is

$$\begin{pmatrix} 1 & 0.276 \\ 0.276 & 1 \end{pmatrix}.$$

The correlation coefficient between the two antibody levels is positive, indicating that there is a positive association between the two antibody levels. However, the coefficient is quite small so the association is weak.

Solution 4.2

(a) The strongest association corresponds to the pair of personality traits with the largest correlation in absolute value. So, for these data, the strongest association is between neuroticism (X_1) and agreeableness (X_4) with a correlation coefficient of -0.57. This association is negative, which means that the more a student identified with being neurotic, the less they tended to identify with being agreeable.

(b) The correlation coefficients between neuroticism and the other personality traits are all between -0.38 and -0.57. As these coefficients are all negative, this means that the more a student identified with being neurotic, the less they identified with the other personality traits.

(c) The correlation coefficients between the course grade and the personality traits are all less than 0.20 in absolute value. So there does not appear to be an association between the course grade and any of the personality traits.

Solution 4.3

(a) All the correlations are positive. This means that when a location strongly stimulated a particular positive emotion, the location also tended to stimulate the other positive emotions strongly.

(b) The largest correlation, 0.80, was between Pleasing and Exciting. The next largest, 0.65, was between Pleasing and Enjoying.

(c) The correlations between the variable Challenging and the other seven variables are all less than 0.3.

(d) All the positive emotions appear to be positively correlated. Pleasing and Exciting, and Pleasing and Enjoying, are the most highly correlated. Challenging, on the other hand, appears to describe a rather different emotion from the other seven positive emotions.

Solution 6.1

(a) The variance of Y can be calculated using Formula (6.3):

$$\begin{aligned} V(Y) &= \alpha_1^2\,V(X_1) + \alpha_2^2\,V(X_2) + 2\alpha_1\alpha_2\,\mathrm{Cov}(X_1, X_2) \\ &= (1/\sqrt{2})^2 \times 0.919 + (1/\sqrt{2})^2 \times 0.649 \\ &\quad + 2 \times (1/\sqrt{2}) \times (1/\sqrt{2}) \times 0.213 \\ &= 0.997. \end{aligned}$$

(b) Choosing $\alpha_1 = 2/\sqrt{5}$ and $\alpha_2 = 1/\sqrt{5}$ leads to the best approximation to the two-dimensional data among those listed, because the variance of Y is the largest for this choice of α_1 and α_2.

Solution 6.2

(a) There is no clear relationship between the two variables. Low tetanus antibody levels are perhaps weakly associated with low diphtheria antibody levels. However, quite a few young adults had high tetanus antibody levels and low diphtheria antibody levels, or low tetanus antibody levels and high diphtheria antibody levels.

(b) There is no clear pattern to be summarized by a single variable, so this suggests that it is not possible to choose a good one-dimensional approximation to these data.

Solution 7.1

In Figure 7.4(a), the observed values of X_1 lie between 25 and 35. In contrast, the observed values of X_2 lie between 0 and 60, and hence are far more spread out. So X_2 has a much larger variance than X_1. Thus the principal component would be dominated by X_2.

In Figure 7.4(b), the values of X_1 and X_2 both lie between 0 and 60. Since the values of X_1 and X_2 seem to have similar spread, the principal component is not likely to be dominated by one of the variables.

In Figure 7.4(c), the range of observed X_1 values is much larger than the range of observed X_2 values. So the variance of X_1 is much greater than that of X_2. Hence the principal component is likely to be dominated by X_1.

In Figure 7.4(d), the range of observed values of X_1 is similar to that of X_2: for both variables the points generally lie between 0 and 50. Hence the principal component would not be dominated by either of the variables.

Solution 7.2

(a) The loadings are all very similar. This suggests that the first principal component can be interpreted as being equivalent to the average of the standardized national records.

(b) In this data set, there are eight variables, so the total variance of the standardized variables is 8. Thus the percentage variance explained by the first principal component is

$$\begin{aligned}\text{PVE} &= \frac{V(Y)}{\text{TV}} \times 100\% \\ &= \frac{6.622}{8} \times 100\% \simeq 82.8\%.\end{aligned}$$

This percentage is high, which suggests that the first principal component represents a good approximation to the full eight-dimensional data set.

Solution 8.1

(a) The dimension of the data set is eight, so the maximum number of principal components is eight.

(b) **(i)** The principal components relate to standardized data. So the total variance is equal to the dimension of the data set, in this case 8. The cumulative percentage variance explained by the first two principal components is

$$\begin{aligned}&\frac{\text{cumulative variance for } Y_1 \text{ and } Y_2}{\text{total variance}} \times 100\% \\ &= \frac{V(Y_1) + V(Y_2)}{8} \times 100\% \\ &= \frac{3.664 + 0.979}{8} \times 100\% \\ &\simeq 58.0\%.\end{aligned}$$

So the missing entry is 58.0.

(ii) If at least 85% of the variance is to be explained, then five principal components should be retained, because the cumulative percentage variance explained is less than 85% for component 4 and greater than 85% for component 5.

(iii) Strictly speaking, using Kaiser's criterion, only one principal component should be retained because the variance is greater than 1 only for the first principal component. However, in practice, three components might be retained using this criterion, because the variances for components 2 and 3 are only just less than 1.

(c) The scree plot drops quite sharply between components 1 and 2 and then flattens out, so one principal component should be retained.

Solution 10.1

(a) If the samples from Chittorgarh are labelled as group 1, the samples from Kota as group 2, and the samples from Mandsaur as group 3, then $n_1 = 15$, $n_2 = 17$ and $n_3 = 18$. When the variable X represents the measurements of glycine, $\overline{x}_1 = 0.185$, $\overline{x}_2 = 0.597$ and $\overline{x}_3 = 0.203$. So, using Formula (10.5) for the grand mean,

$$\overline{\overline{x}} = \frac{15 \times 0.185 + 17 \times 0.597 + 18 \times 0.203}{50} \simeq 0.3316.$$

Thus, using Formula (10.6), the between-groups variance for glycine is

$$\begin{aligned}V_b = \tfrac{1}{47}\big(&15(0.185 - 0.3316)^2 + 17(0.597 - 0.3316)^2 \\ &+ 18(0.203 - 0.3316)^2\big) \\ \simeq\ & 0.0387.\end{aligned}$$

(b) The variances of the phenylalanine concentrations in groups 1, 2 and 3 are 0.0622, 0.0724 and 0.0813, respectively. So

$$\begin{aligned}V_w &= \frac{14 \times 0.0622 + 16 \times 0.0724 + 17 \times 0.0813}{47} \\ &\simeq 0.0726.\end{aligned}$$

(c) The separation for glycine is obtained using Formula (10.3):

$$\text{separation} = \frac{0.0387}{0.0233} \simeq 1.66.$$

For phenylalanine,

$$\text{separation} = \frac{0.0789}{0.0726} \simeq 1.09.$$

(d) The amino acid with the highest separation is glycine, so glycine is the amino acid that would be most helpful for indicating the origin of a sample.

Solution 11.1

(a) The first two loadings have been multiplied by 10, but not the third, so this is not an equivalent linear combination, and hence it is not a discriminant function.

(b) The loadings and the constant term (2.5) of the original discriminant function have all been multiplied by the same value, 3, so this linear combination is equivalent to the original discriminant function. Therefore it is a discriminant function.

(c) The original discriminant function may be written as

$$D = a_1 Z_1 + a_2 Z_2 + a_3 Z_3,$$

where

$$\begin{aligned}a_1 &= 0.3\sqrt{0.09} = 0.09, \\ a_2 &= 0.4\sqrt{0.16} = 0.16, \\ a_3 &= -0.5\sqrt{0.25} = -0.25.\end{aligned}$$

Since $Z_1 + Z_2 - Z_3$ is not equivalent to this linear combination, it is not a discriminant function.

(d) After group-standardization, the loadings should be $0.3\sqrt{11.1} \simeq 1$, $0.4\sqrt{6.25} = 1$ and $-0.5\sqrt{4} = -1$. Since this is the case, this linear combination is a discriminant function.

Solution 11.2

The loadings for Z_1 and Z_3 are positive, whereas the loadings for Z_2 and Z_4 are negative, so the discriminant function represents a contrast in amino acid levels. The glycine levels are the most important indicator of which division a sample came from. The phenylalanine and isoleucine levels are the least important.

Solution 12.1

(a) The largest loadings (in absolute value) of the second discriminant function D_2 are for phenylalanine and aspartic acid, and these have opposite signs. Thus D_2 largely corresponds to the difference between phenylalanine and aspartic acid concentrations. The other loadings are smaller, so D_2 depends on the glycine and isoleucine levels to a lesser extent.

(b) There are three groups (and four variables), so the maximum number of useful discriminant functions (the minimum of $G-1$ and p) is 2. Hence, although a third discriminant function could be obtained, its separation would be zero, so it would not be useful.

(c) For these data, there is a maximum of two useful discriminant functions. So

$$\begin{aligned}\text{total separation} &= \text{Sep}(D_1) + \text{Sep}(D_2)\\ &= 2.231 + 1.006\\ &= 3.237.\end{aligned}$$

Thus the percentage separation achieved by D_1 is

$$\begin{aligned}\text{PSA}_1 &= \frac{\text{Sep}(D_1)}{\text{total separation}} \times 100\%\\ &= \frac{2.231}{3.237} \times 100\%\\ &\simeq 68.9\%.\end{aligned}$$

Similarly, the percentage separation achieved by D_2 is $1.006/3.237 \times 100\% \simeq 31.1\%$. The second discriminant function accounts for a fairly large percentage of separation, so D_2 contributes substantially to the separation of the groups.

(d) The clouds of points representing samples from Chittorgarh and Mandsaur are separated vertically but not horizontally. So the first discriminant function alone does not separate the samples from Chittorgarh and Mandsaur. However, the two discriminant functions together achieve a good separation of the three groups. Thus the plot confirms the conclusion given in part (c).

Solution 13.1

(a) Samples from Mandsaur have the lowest mean value of D, and samples from Kota have the highest mean. So label Mandsaur as group 1, Chittorgarh as group 2, and Kota as group 3. Then

$$l_1 = \tfrac{1}{2}(-1.316 - 0.670) = -0.993,$$

$$l_2 = \tfrac{1}{2}(-0.670 + 1.984) = 0.657.$$

The allocation rule is as follows:

$$\begin{cases}\text{if } d \leq -0.993 & \text{allocate to Mandsaur,}\\ \text{if } -0.993 < d \leq 0.657 & \text{allocate to Chittorgarh,}\\ \text{otherwise} & \text{allocate to Kota.}\end{cases}$$

(b) When $X_1 = 0.060$, $X_2 = 0.183$, $X_3 = 0.080$ and $X_4 = 0.230$,

$$\begin{aligned}d &= 6.333 \times 0.060 - 0.864 \times 0.183\\ &\quad - 2.480 \times 0.080 + 4.920 \times 0.230 - 1.154\\ &\simeq 0.001.\end{aligned}$$

So this sample should be classified as having come from Chittorgarh.

(c) **(i)** A sample classified as having come from Kota is most likely to be correctly classified, since the corresponding diagonal value (82%) is the largest.

(ii) Over half of samples from Chittorgarh (54%) are misclassified as coming from Kota or Mandsaur. Thus the allocation rule is not accurate for classifying samples from Chittorgarh.

Solution 15.1

This exercise covers some of the ideas and techniques discussed in Sections 2 and 4.

(a) **(i)** There appear to be (at least) two unusual points. The first is the county with the largest value of Mo-BGS, and is apparent by looking across the second row of the scatterplot. This point does not appear to follow the pattern suggested by the positive relationships between Mo-BGS and Cu-BGS, and between Mo-BGS and Cu-Soil.

The second unusual point is the county with the largest value of the variable Mo-Moose, and is apparent by looking across the fourth row of the scatterplot. This point does not appear to follow the pattern suggested by the positive relationships between Mo-Moose and Cu-BGS, and between Mo-Moose and Cu-Soil.

(ii) The Eastern counties appear to have higher values of Cu-BGS than counties in the Southwest or North. The Northern counties appear to have higher values of Cu-Moose than counties in the Southwest or East.

(b) **(i)** The strongest linear relationship is between Mo-BGS and Cu-Soil: the correlation is 0.617, which is the largest in absolute value.

(ii) The weakest linear relationship is between Cu-BGS and Mo-BGS: the correlation is -0.109, which is the smallest in absolute value.

(iii) If BGS and Moose were measuring the same thing, one would expect that the correlations between Cu-BGS and Cu-Moose, and between Mo-BGS and Mo-Moose, would both be positive and relatively large in absolute value. However, the correlation between Cu-BGS and Cu-Moose is -0.517, which is relatively large but negative, whereas that between Mo-BGS and Mo-Moose is 0.180, which is rather small in absolute value.

Solution 15.2

This exercise covers some of the ideas and techniques discussed in Section 2.

(a) (i) The variables in this data set are the molecular masses. There are 37 masses so p, the dimension of the data set, is 37.

(ii) The observations are strains of the *novicida* subspecies. There are ten strains, so the number of observations n is 10.

(b) (i) The labels on the x-axis represent nineteen of the molecular masses. These are equally spaced: the scale on the axis does not reflect the differences in molecular mass.

(ii) The nine observations are very similar, since their profiles are indistinguishable. The highest signal-to-noise ratios are obtained at masses 8.08, 8.78, 9.44 and 10.2 kDa.

(iii) This strain also registers strong signal-to-noise ratios at masses 8.08, 8.78 and 9.44 kDa, but not at 10.2 kDa. There is also a strong signal-to noise ratio at 7.39 kDa, which is not present for the other strains. Other more minor differences were registered at 5.12, 6.18, 11.0, 16.0 and 17.2 kDa.

Solution 15.3

This exercise covers some of the ideas and techniques discussed in Sections 2, 6 and 7.

(a) (i) There is an increasing, roughly linear relationship between male and female mortality rates for melanoma in the countries that have not been labelled on the scatterplot.

(ii) Several of the labelled countries do not appear to conform to the linear relationship described in part (a)(i). In New Zealand and Australia, the male mortality rate is higher than expected, given the female mortality rate. In Luxembourg and Norway, the female mortality rate is higher than expected, given the male mortality rate.

(iii) Denmark conforms to the linear relationship described in part (a)(i), and hence should perhaps not have been singled out. However, the melanoma mortality rates for both males and females are higher in Denmark than in the unlabelled countries; so Denmark is unusual in this respect.

(b) (i) It makes sense to analyse the unstandardized data since the two variables — male and female mortality rates — are measured in the same units.

(ii) It might be better to analyse the standardized data because the variability in male mortality rates is greater than the variability in female rates.

(c) (i) The first principal component is the following linear combination:

$$Y_1 = 0.863(X_1 - 0.1469) + 0.505(X_2 - 0.1011),$$

where X_1 is the male melanoma mortality rate and X_2 is the female melanoma mortality rate.

(ii) For Northern Ireland, the value of Y_1 is

$$0.863(0.20 - 0.1469) + 0.505(0.14 - 0.1011) \simeq 0.0655.$$

(iii) Both loadings are positive, so the first principal component is equivalent to a weighted average of the male and female rates. As expected in view of its higher variance, the male mortality rate has the larger loading.

(d) Since there are only two variables, the total variance is

$$\text{TV} = V(X_1) + V(X_2) = 0.014 + 0.006 = 0.020.$$

Therefore the percentage variance explained by the first principal component is

$$\text{PVE} = \frac{0.019}{0.020} \times 100\% = 95\%.$$

The first principal component thus accounts for 95% of the variance in these data. This is more than is accounted for by either the male mortality rate or the female mortality rate separately. The first principal component gives a good approximation to this bivariate data set.

Solution 15.4

This exercise covers some of the ideas and techniques discussed in Part III.

(a) (i) The separation achieved by variable X_j is given by

$$\text{Sep}(X_j) = \frac{V_b(X_j)}{V_w(X_j)},$$

where $V_b(X_j)$ is element (j, j) of $\mathbf{B}$, and $V_w(X_j)$ is element (j, j) of $\mathbf{W}$, $j = 1, 2, \ldots, 6$. Hence, for example,

$$\text{Sep}(X_1) = \frac{0.739}{0.285} \simeq 2.593.$$

Similarly, $\text{Sep}(X_2) \simeq 2.594$, $\text{Sep}(X_3) \simeq 202.313$, $\text{Sep}(X_4) \simeq 0.113$, $\text{Sep}(X_5) = 13.500$ and $\text{Sep}(X_6) \simeq 0.400$. Thus, if only one variable were used, the best separation would be achieved by X_3.

(ii) If the between-groups and within-groups covariances for an element (i, j) have opposite signs, this suggests that combining these variables would improve the separation. There are some such elements — for example, element $(3, 1)$ is 0.387 for $\mathbf{B}$ and -0.021 for $\mathbf{W}$, and element $(3, 6)$ is 0.073 for $\mathbf{B}$ and -0.027 for $\mathbf{W}$. Thus it is possible that combining variables will improve the separation.

(b) The largest loadings (in absolute value) are those for Z_3 and Z_5. They are of opposite sign, indicating that the difference in signal-to-noise ratios at the corresponding molecular masses is important in separating the subspecies. The other variables have loadings that are much smaller in absolute value, and hence are much less important.

(c) The separation achieved by the first discriminant function is 665.220, which is much greater than that achieved by any variable on its own. In particular, combining variables achieves much better separation than using X_3 on its own, which achieved a separation of 202.313.

(d) (i) The groups should be labelled in increasing order of the means. Thus group 1 is *tularensis*, group 2 is *holarctica*, group 3 is *mediasiatica*, and group 4 is *novicida*. (Note how similar the means are for groups 1, 2 and 3.) The cut-off point between groups 1 and 2 is the average of the means for groups 1 and 2, so

$$l_1 = \tfrac{1}{2}(-8.779 - 8.398) \simeq -8.588.$$

Similarly,

$$l_2 = \tfrac{1}{2}(-8.398 - 7.942) = -8.170$$

and

$$l_3 = \tfrac{1}{2}(-7.942 + 59.093) \simeq 25.576.$$

If d is the value of the first discriminant function for an observation, the allocation rule is as follows:

$$\begin{cases} \text{if } d \leq -8.588 & \text{allocate to group 1, } \textit{tularensis}, \\ \text{if } -8.588 < d \leq -8.170 & \text{allocate to group 2, } \textit{holarctica}, \\ \text{if } -8.170 < d \leq 25.576 & \text{allocate to group 3, } \textit{mediasiatica}, \\ \text{otherwise} & \text{allocate to group 4, } \textit{novicida}. \end{cases}$$

(ii) For the first sample, the value of D_1 is

$$\begin{aligned} d = {} & 0.265 \times 1.35 - 0.448 \times 0.48 + 16.388 \times 5.28 \\ & + 0.468 \times 1.98 - 40.547 \times 0.42 \\ & - 0.385 \times 2.10 - 9.701 \\ \simeq {} & 60.06. \end{aligned}$$

Since $d > 25.576$, this sample is allocated to the *novicida* subspecies.

Similarly, the value of D for the second sample is -8.72. Since $-8.72 \leq -8.588$, the second sample is allocated to the *tularensis* subspecies.

(iii) The confusion matrix shows that samples from the *mediasiatica* and *novicida* subspecies are classified without error. However, only 50% of samples from the *tularensis* subspecies and 12.5% of samples from the *holarctica* subspecies are correctly classified. This is not surprising. Since the means of D for *tularensis*, *holarctica* and *mediasiatica* are very close together, slight variation in the value of D can result in misclassification. In particular, with *holarctica* being the middle group of these three, it is not unexpected that samples from this subspecies are so frequently misallocated to the two adjoining groups.

(e) The second discriminant function D_2 helps to separate the three subspecies *tularensis*, *holarctica* and *mediasiatica*, which are spread out vertically in the scatterplot. Samples from the *holarctica* subspecies correspond to low values of D_2, and samples from the *mediasiatica* subspecies score highest, while samples from the *tularensis* subspecies lie in between.

(f) Since there are four groups and sixteen observations, the maximum number of potentially useful discriminant functions is three. So at most one more discriminant function might be used to separate the groups.

Index